8085A
Cookbook

by
**Christopher A. Titus, Jonathan A. Titus,
and David G. Larsen**

Howard W. Sams & Co., Inc.
4300 WEST 62ND ST. INDIANAPOLIS, INDIANA 46268 USA

FIRST EDITION
THIRD PRINTING—1982

International Standard Book Number: 0-672-21697-3
Library of Congress Catalog Card Number: 80-50053

Printed in the United States of America.

Preface

Ever since the first microprocessor integrated circuit, the Intel 4004, was introduced, thousands of engineers have been engaged in designing microcomputer systems using these types of "chips." With the first microprocessors, such as the Intel 4004 and 8008, the designs were very complex. In fact, Intel routinely provided complete schematic diagrams for 4004- and 8008-based microcomputers in user's manuals. This was done in order to get engineers "over the hump" of designing microcomputers. There were no college or industrial courses or even books that taught how microcomputers were designed.

The 4004 is a 4-bit microprocessor and, as such, it did not have much "computing power." This limitation, combined with the complexity of a "simple" microcomputer, prevented the 4004 from attaining general acceptance. The 8008, which was the first 8-bit microprocessor, was also difficult to design into a microcomputer. It requires a precisely timed two-phase nonoverlapping clock and a considerable number of standard TTL integrated circuits to make it work. The 8008 was used by both industry and hobbyists, but because of its complexity few people designed their own 8008-based microcomputers. One of the most popular, general-purpose 8008-based microcomputers was the Mark-8, which was designed by Dr. Jonathan Titus. The construction details and printed-circuit board layouts were published by *Radio-Electronics* magazine in 1974. Because of the complexity of even simple 4004- and 8008-based microcomputers it would have been almost impossible for someone to write a book about microcomputer design based on either of these two chips.

The first widely accepted microprocessor was the Intel 8080. A greatly improved version of the 8008, it is high-speed, general-purpose and requires only a few additional integrated circuits to make it work. Hobbyists once again played a major role in the initial popularity of this chip. Many of the original microcomputer users and programmers started on the Altair 8800, which was manufactured by MITS (now a division of the Pertec Computer Corporation). Although the first 8080 chips cost $360 each, many people recognized the potential of the chip and designed it into a number of products.

The 8085A (which is really a slightly improved version of the 8080), along with the 8080, took microcomputer design out of the hands of electronics engineers and gave it to mechanical and chemical engineers, physiologists, chemists, physicists, and workers in a number of other disciplines. By using the 8085A, almost anyone can design a microcomputer. In fact, by using an 8085A we will design a three-chip microcomputer no larger than 4½ × 3½ × ½ inches (11.4 × 8.9 × 1.3 cm)! Intel even provides a schematic diagram and printed-circuit board layout for this type of microcomputer. Unfortunately, not all problems can be solved with this small microcomputer. You may need more memory in one application and additional peripheral devices in another application. Of course, you could go to a microcomputer manufacturer and purchase additional memory or peripheral interface boards, but in many situations this may not be practical. The boards from the manufacturer may be too expensive, may take 20 or 30 weeks to be delivered, or may not even help you solve your problem. Therefore, in this book you will actually learn how an 8085A-based microcomputer is designed. At many points you will have the opportunity to design part or all of a complete microcomputer system. To do this, however, the authors will assume that you have some knowledge of basic logic (gates, flip-flops, decoders, etc.). We will use the 8085A exclusively in our designs because it is low-cost and because a tremendous amount of software is already available that can be executed on an 8085A-based microcomputer.

We will discuss the electrical design of an 8085A-based microcomputer. We will not discuss the managerial decision-making processes required to determine whether or not a microcomputer should be used in a particular product, nor will we discuss thermal, mechanical, or electromagnetic interference design points. We will only be concerned with the electrical interconnections required to create a microcomputer from a handful of integrated circuits.

To better understand how the 8085A is used with other integrated circuits we will discuss the internal organization and timing of the 8085A in the first chapter. Included in this chapter are discussions about buses, control signals, memory, and peripheral addressing and information interchange.

In the second chapter we actually begin the design process by generating control signals and demultiplexing one of the 8085A buses with external logic. The next three chapters deal with microcomputer memory design. The techniques of address decoding, along with chip selects and the different types of memories available for your use, are also covered.

Chapter 6 contains information about electrically wiring peripheral (I/O) devices to the microcomputer. In general, input/output (I/O) devices are either input or output devices, and both types of devices are discussed in detail. In Chapter 7 a number of the 8085A-family integrated circuits are described along with their advantages and disadvantages. These "family" devices are the integrated circuits that were designed specifically for use in 8085A-based microcomputer systems. However, because they are so sophisticated, they can be used with a number of other microprocessors.

In the last chapter the design methods and techniques discussed in the previous chapters are brought together so that a number of *completely operational* 8085A-based microcomputers are actually designed by you.

Of course, it would be impossible to include, in one book, all of the design methods and techniques required to "start from scratch" to the point of building and programming a microcomputer system. In this book we will be concerned only with the electrical design. We will not discuss 8085A software design, data acquisition software, data processing, disk operating systems, or the subtle points of using analog-to-digital and digital-to-analog converters. A number of these topics have been discussed at great length in other books by the authors (see the inside of the front cover).

DAVID G. LARSEN, JONATHAN A. TITUS,
AND CHRISTOPHER A. TITUS

"The Blacksburg Group"

Contents

Memory and Peripheral Decoding—Input/Output Capabilities—
Mounting the Microcomputer Components—System Expansion—Power
Supply Requirements—A Small, Low-Cost, 8085A-Based Microcom-
puter—Conclusion—Bibliography—Problems

APPENDIX A

APPENDIX B

APPENDIX C

APPENDIX D

CHAPTER 1

Basic Microprocessor/ Microcomputer Concepts

The 8085A is one of many popular commercially available micro-processors (Fig. 1-1). Within this ½-inch × 2-inch (1.27- × 5-cm) package are the electronics that give the 8085A all of its capabilities (Fig. 1-2). For instance, the 8085A can add two numbers between zero and 255 in 1.28 μs (less than two millionths of a second). The 8085A can also store numbers in memory or read numbers from memory in only 2.24 μs. However, for the microprocessor to be used in many applications, it must be electrically wired to memory, control, and peripheral integrated circuits. Once this is done, a *microcomputer* is created. Therefore we have an 8085A *microprocessor* integrated circuit which is used in an 8085A-based *microcomputer*. The pin configuration for the 8085A, that is, the signals that the 8085A outputs and inputs on specific pins, is shown in Fig. 1-3.

Even though the 8085A and most of the other microprocessors are incredibly fast, they still solve problems and perform operations using many of the same techniques that humans use. For instance, if you are told to add 100 sets of two two-digit numbers, you would probably write (store) the results on paper. There are very few people who could remember all 100 results. The microprocessor stores the results of additions and other operations in *semiconductor memory* configured from standard memory "chips" (Fig. 1-4).

When we write our results on paper we do not write them down in a haphazard order. Instead, each result might be written on a separate line or with a "label" such as "Result number 3 is . . . ." The micro-processor has the same problem, that is, where to store each individual

Fig. 1-1. The 8085A microprocessor.

**Fig. 1-2. The 8085 microprocessor silicon "chip" contained within the
integrated circuit.**

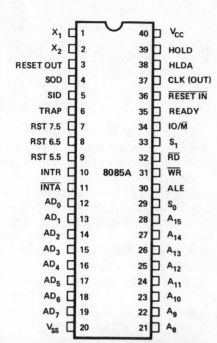

Fig. 1-3. The pin configuration (pin-out) of the 8085A microprocessor.

X₁	1	40	Vcc

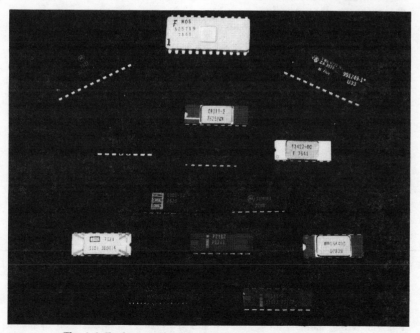

Fig. 1-4. Typical semiconductor memory integrated circuits.

result (number) in memory. The microprocessor selects one out of many possible memory locations by specifying the *address* of a particular memory location. The result is then stored in this memory location by the microprocessor.

EXECUTING PROGRAMS

If we are baking a cake or fixing a car for the first time, how do we know what to do? We are not born with the recipes of 50 different cakes in our head, nor do we intuitively know how to fix a car. We have to see someone else do it first or read how it is done. That is, we must be programmed to bake a cake or fix an automobile; we have to *read* and *perform* a *specific sequence of instructions*.

We read these instructions from a piece of paper, while the 8085A microprocessor reads its instructions from memory. This specific sequence of instructions for the microprocessor is called a *program*. To read a program from memory and execute it the microprocessor must (1) address or specify a specific memory location, (2) read the instruction, and (3) based on the instruction read, perform one or many operations. Once the instruction has been executed, the microprocessor has to read the next instruction and execute it, too. To perform these operations, microprocessors usually communicate with memory using *16 address lines* and *8 data lines* (Fig. 1-5).

Microprocessors operate with *binary* numbers only. Therefore each one of the address or data lines can have the binary value of zero (0) or one (1). In the 8085A, as in most other microprocessors, a "zero,"

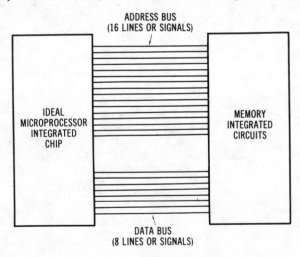

Fig. 1-5. Wiring memory integrated circuits to an ideal microprocessor by means of an address bus and a data bus.

or *logic zero,* is represented by a voltage near *ground* (*0 volts*) and a "one," or *logic one,* is represented by a voltage near *+3 volts.* Since each address line can be either a logic one or zero, regardless of the states of the other address lines, the 8085A can address 2^{16} or 65,536 (64K) memory locations.

To transfer information (instructions or data values) between a memory location and the 8085A, the information must flow over the 8 data lines. These data lines are also binary, so there are 2^8 or 256 different values that can flow over these 8 data lines. Because the 8085A can add and subtract 8-bit numbers and can read or write 8-bit numbers from or to memory and I/O devices, the 8085A is considered to be an *8-bit microprocessor.*

Quite often, the term *bus* is used to describe a group of related signals. This means that the *data bus* is composed of the 8 data lines and that the *address bus* is composed of the 16 address lines. In Fig. 1-6 note the slash (/) that is drawn through the address and data buses, and the numbers near each slash that represent the number of signals in each bus. For the data bus this is 8; for the address bus, 16.

The data and address buses have also been drawn with "arrowheads." These arrowheads indicate the direction of information flow. The address bus has an arrowhead at one end, and this indicates that the microprocessor always generates the 16-bit memory address and sends it to memory. The integrated circuits that make up the microcomputer memory never generate an address. The data bus, on the other hand, has arrows at both ends; therefore, information can "flow" from the microprocessor to memory, or from memory to the microprocessor. Information flows in only one direction at any one time, however. Therefore the information flow on the data bus is *bidirectional,* while the address bus is *uni-*

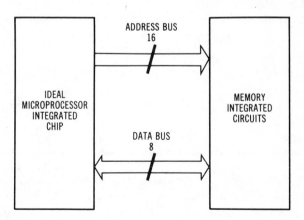

Fig. 1-6. A microprocessor connected to memory integrated circuits using an address bus and a data bus.

directional, because addresses always flow in one direction (microprocessor to memory).

As we have seen, the 8085A can either read information from memory or write information into memory, but not both at the same time. The 8085A *knows* that it is to read or write data, but the memory integrated circuits *do not inherently know* what the 8085A is doing (reading, writing, or neither). Therefore, if the 8085A must write information into memory, it must tell the memory integrated circuits that a write operation is being performed. By doing this the memory integrated circuits can accept the information from the data bus and write the information into the memory location specified by the 16-bit address on the address bus. If the 8085A needs to read information from memory, not only must it place a 16-bit address on the address bus, but it must also inform the specified memory location to place its contents on the data bus.

The microprocessor informs the memory that it needs to write to or read from it, by generating one of two possible signals. One signal is used to indicate that a *memory-read* operation is taking place and the other signal is used to indicate that a *memory-write* operation is taking place. These two signals, which are generated by the microprocessor perhaps in combination with some external logic, are called $\overline{\text{MEMW}}$ ($\overline{\text{MEMORY WRITE}}$) and $\overline{\text{MEMR}}$ ($\overline{\text{MEMORY READ}}$). These signals are pronounced "memory write bar" and "memory read bar." In this case a "bar" over a signal means that it is "active" in the logic zero or ground state. Therefore, if the microprocessor is writing to memory, it must place a 16-bit address on the address bus (to specify a memory location), an 8-bit data value on the data bus and then it must generate the negative-going pulse, $\overline{\text{MEMW}}$. To read from a memory location the microprocessor must place a 16-bit address on the address bus, and then pulse the $\overline{\text{MEMR}}$ line. This will cause the specified memory location to place its data on the data bus, and this data will be gated into the 8085A microprocessor. Unfortunately, the 8085A chip does not have signals labeled $\overline{\text{MEMR}}$ and $\overline{\text{MEMW}}$. As you will see in another section of this chapter, however, the 8085A does have signals that can be combined with external logic integrated circuits, so that the $\overline{\text{MEMW}}$ and $\overline{\text{MEMR}}$ signals can be readily generated. The addition of the $\overline{\text{MEMR}}$ and $\overline{\text{MEMW}}$ signals can be seen in the "ideal" microcomputer system (Fig. 1-7).

Of course, there is the possibility, and it occurs many times while a program is being executed, that the 8085A and its external logic will not be reading from memory or writing to memory. For example, this will occur when the 8085A is processing data internally, since the 8085A does not have to communicate with memory. Once the internal data processing has been completed (2 to 5 μs), the 8085A may have been programmed to save the result in memory, or to read a value from memory, and then continue processing.

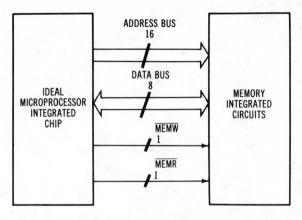

Fig. 1-7. A microcomputer with memory and appropriate control signals.

BASIC BINARY DATA AND ADDRESS VALUES

The decimal values 2039 and 3290 are not equal. Do you know why? Of course, the reason is that each digit position in the 4-digit number has a different significance. The number 2039 is equal to $2 \times 1000 + 0 \times 100 + 3 \times 10 + 9 \times 1$ and the number 3290 is equal to $3 \times 1000 + 2 \times 100 + 9 \times 10 + 0 \times 1$. The same is true of binary numbers—the type of numbers that the 8085A works with. That is, a different significance is assigned to each bit in an 8- or 16-bit binary number. The binary addresses 1011010111111010 and 0000011111111111 are not equal, nor are the data values 11011011 and 11110110, even though they contain the same number of zeros and ones.

In decimal numbers each digit to the left of the decimal point increases by powers of ten ($\ldots$, 10^3, 10^2, 10^1, and 10^0). In binary the digits to the left of the "decimal point" (really the "binary point") increase by powers of two ($\ldots$, 2^3, 2^2, 2^1, and 2^0). This means that an 8-bit binary number contains digits that have a significance of 2^7, 2^6, 2^5, 2^4, 2^3, 2^2, 2^1, and 2^0. The decimal equivalence of each binary bit in an 8-bit word is listed in Fig. 1-8.

Quite often, when discussing or describing microprocessor/microcomputer operations, the terms *byte* and *word* are used. In general, for 8-bit microprocessors, such as the 8085A, a byte is an 8-bit value (data or instruction). Therefore the 8085A can read a *byte* from memory by placing an address on the 16-bit address bus and by generating the MEMR signal. The term *word* is often used interchangeably with byte. If a microprocessor with a 16-bit data bus is used, then a single 16-bit word may contain two 8-bit bytes. Since the 8085A is "an 8-bit" microprocessor, however, the terms are often used interchangeably.

$$
\begin{aligned}
2^7 &= 2\times2\times2\times2\times2\times2\times2 &= 128 \\
2^6 &= 2\times2\times2\times2\times2\times2 &= 64 \\
2^5 &= 2\times2\times2\times2\times2 &= 32 \\
2^4 &= 2\times2\times2\times2 &= 16 \\
2^3 &= 2\times2\times2 &= 8 \\
2^2 &= 2\times2 &= 4 \\
2^1 &= 2 &= 2 \\
2^0 &= 1 &= 1
\end{aligned}
$$

Fig. 1-8. The decimal significance of position bits in an 8-bit number.

From Fig. 1-8 we can see that the largest 8-bit binary number is 11111111 or $128 + 64 + 32 + 16 + 8 + 4 + 2 + 1$, or decimal 255. Of course, the smallest 8-bit word is 00000000, or zero. Using Fig. 1-8, what is the decimal equivalent of 11000001? This value is equal to decimal $128 + 64 + 1$, or 193. Not only is a different significance assigned to each bit in an 8-bit binary byte, but a different significance is also assigned to each bit in a 16-bit binary word (Fig. 1-9).

The decimal value for the largest 16-bit binary value, 1111111111111111, can be calculated from Figs. 1-8 and 1-9. This value is equal to decimal 65,535. The smallest 16-bit value is 0000000000000000, or zero. What is the value of 0010011100010000? The decimal value for this binary number is 10,000. Based on Figs. 1-8 and 1-9 you should

$$
\begin{aligned}
2^{15} &= 2\times2\times2\times2\times2\times2\times2\times2\times2\times2\times2\times2\times2\times2\times2 &= 32.768 \\
2^{14} &= 2\times2\times2\times2\times2\times2\times2\times2\times2\times2\times2\times2\times2\times2 &= 16.384 \\
2^{13} &= 2\times2\times2\times2\times2\times2\times2\times2\times2\times2\times2\times2\times2 &= 8192 \\
2^{12} &= 2\times2\times2\times2\times2\times2\times2\times2\times2\times2\times2\times2 &= 4096 \\
2^{11} &= 2\times2\times2\times2\times2\times2\times2\times2\times2\times2\times2 &= 2048 \\
2^{10} &= 2\times2\times2\times2\times2\times2\times2\times2\times2\times2 &= 1024 \\
2^9 &= 2\times2\times2\times2\times2\times2\times2\times2\times2 &= 512 \\
2^8 &= 2\times2\times2\times2\times2\times2\times2\times2 &= 256
\end{aligned}
$$

Fig. 1-9. The decimal significance of the most significant 8 bits in a 16-bit number.

now be able to see why the 8085A can address 65,536 different 8-bit memory locations. It can address memory location zero (0000000000000000) up to memory location 1111111111111111, or 65,535, or a total of 65,536 different memory locations. Memory location zero is a valid memory location.

To distinguish each address line and data line in the "bus" from one another, a number is assigned to each one. Therefore the microprocessor has data lines D0 through D7 (8 data lines) in the data bus and address lines A0 through A5 in the address bus (16 address lines). The numbers assigned to each address and data line indicate its significance. Data line D7 is used by the most significant (2^7 or 128) data bit in an 8-bit word. As expected, data bit D0 has the least significance, or a value of one or zero. Table 1-1 contains the significance of each data line. Table 1-2 contains the significance of each address line in the address bus.

Table 1-1. The Significance of the 8 Data Lines

Data Line	Significance
D7	128
D6	64
D5	32
D4	16
D3	8
D2	4
D1	2
D0	1

Table 1-2. The Significance of the 16 Address Lines

Address Line	Significance
A15	32,768
A14	16,384
A13	8,192
A12	4,096
A11	2,048
A10	1,024
A9	512
A8	256
A7	128
A6	64
A5	32
A4	16
A3	8
A2	4
A1	2
A0	1

MICROCOMPUTER MEMORY INTEGRATED CIRCUITS

There are basically two different types of random-access memory that are most often used with microcomputers: read/write (R/W) memory and read-only memory (ROM). There are also a number of different R/W and ROM memory integrated circuits. Read/write memories are available that contain 256 words, each of which is 4 bits "wide" (256×4); 1024 words that are 1 bit wide (1K×1); 1024 words that are 4 bits wide (1K×4); and 4096 words that are 1 bit wide (4K×1). There are also a number of other "configurations." Regardless of the "width" of a particular memory integrated circuit (the number of bits in each word), we must use enough of the memory integrated circuits so that every memory location contains an 8-bit byte. To do this we could use two 256×4 memory integrated circuits, so that we had 256 eight-bit memory locations. Eight 1K×1, 4K×1, or two 1K×4 R/W memory integrated circuits could also be used to store programs composed of a sequence or sequences of instructions or data. Since R/W memory is used, the 8085A can actually read data values from memory, calculate results, and save the results back in memory. Unfortunately, if we turn the microcomputer power off, the information (data and/or instructions) will be lost. Read/write memories require power to retain information.

The read-only memories (ROMs) that are frequently used with microcomputers are usually 8 bits wide. These memories may contain 256, 1024, 2048, 4096, or 8192 words. Both data and instructions can be stored in read-only memories. However, the result of a calculation, or a number entered into the microcomputer by a keyboard, *cannot* be written into read-only memory. There are a number of different types of ROMs, some of which we can program "in the field," called PROMs and EPROMs. Even so, special programmers are required to store information in EPROM/PROM read-only memories. In addition, some read-only memories are "programmed" during the semiconductor manufacturing process. Some new types of memories are available that can be used to store data values or the results of calculations, and these values will remain in the microcomputer memory, even if the power to the microcomputer system is turned off. These devices, however, are expensive and are not easy to use.

INTERNAL 8085A REGISTERS

The 8085A has a number of internal "registers" that are very similar to R/W memory locations (Fig. 1-10). There are seven general-purpose registers. This means that the programmer can program the 8085A so that temporary data values, results from some microcomputer operation, or even memory addresses are saved in one or more of these registers. Each register can be used to store 8 bits of information—a single byte. To make programming the 8085A easier each register is assigned a single letter name: A, B, C, D, E, H, and L. The A register is also called the *accumulator,* since it can be used to "accumulate" the results of a mathematical or logical operation performed by the 8085A. If an 8-bit value is contained in the A register, it can be manipulated in special ways not possible when other registers are used. The A register is generally used to accept data from peripheral devices such as keyboards, sensors, switches, or analog-to-digital converters. The content of the A register can also be output or written out, under program control, to devices such as digital-to-analog converters, lamps, controllers, and printers.

There are five *flags* associated with the A register. These flags are set or cleared when one of the 8085A logical or mathematical instructions is executed. Three flags indicate the parity, sign of the result, and whether

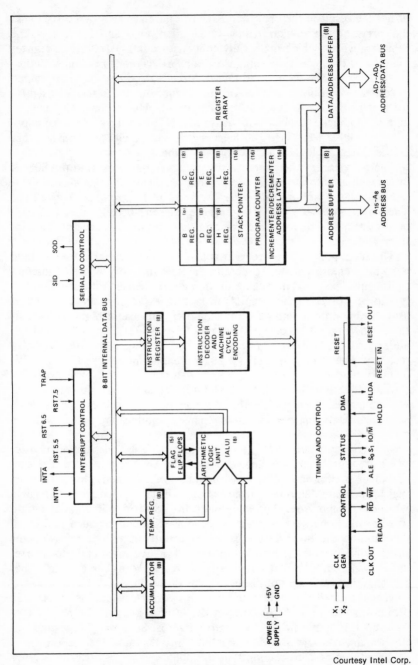

Courtesy Intel Corp.

Fig. 1-10. A block diagram of the 8085A microprocessor.

or not the result of the operation is zero. There are also two carry flags: the carry and the auxiliary carry. Quite often, programmers refer to the 8-bit flag word (which really only contains five flags) and the A register together as the *processor status word,* or *PSW.* Perhaps the most important feature of the flags is the fact that the 8085A can be programmed to test the condition, or state, of one or more of these flags. Based on the results of these tests the 8085A can decide whether or not to execute one or another sequence of instructions. This gives the 8085A the capability to make decisions. The flags remain set or cleared until another mathematical or logical instruction alters them.

There are three other important registers contained within the 8085A integrated circuit that deserve our attention. These are the *stack pointer (SP),* the *instruction register (IR),* and the *program counter (PC).* These registers are not general-purpose registers because they can only be used to perform specific tasks, and they cannot be used for the temporary storage of data.

The stack pointer (SP) register is a 16-bit register that is used to hold a 16-bit memory address, generally an R/W memory address. Instructions can be executed that cause the content of the general-purpose registers to be stored on the "stack," an area of R/W memory specially set aside during programming for the temporary storage of register information. When this is done the stack pointer provides the 8085A with an address so that the registers can be saved in a specific order in R/W memory. Therefore, the stack, or stack area, is simply a section of R/W memory that is set aside for temporary storage when stack instructions are executed. For the stack to be useful the stack pointer must be loaded with an address associated with R/W memory. The stack is also used to store *return,* or *linking,* addresses when subroutines are called within a program.

The 16-bit program counter (PC) and the 8-bit instruction register (IR) are closely related, since they actually control the sequential execution of a program. When instructions are executed, the instruction register actually determines what actions will take place and where data will flow to and from, both internally in the 8085A integrated circuit and externally between memory and the 8085A, and between peripheral devices and the 8085A. The program counter is used to provide the memory address of the location in which the *next* instruction to be executed is stored. All of the registers that we have discussed, and other registers that we have not discussed, are shown in Fig. 1-10.

When the 8085A integrated circuit is *reset,* which is caused by grounding the $\overline{\text{RESET IN}}$ input of the 8085A integrated circuit (Figs. 1-3 and 1-10), the PC is cleared to all zeros. Since the PC always addresses the memory location that contains the next instruction to be executed, the first instruction that the 8085A executes, after it is reset, must be in memory location zero. Therefore, after the 8085A has been reset, the 16-bit content of the PC is placed on the 16-bit address bus, and the instruction that is contained in this memory location is read (fetched) from memory and written into the IR. The logic associated with the IR then decodes the instruction and decides what actions are required for the instruction to be executed. When the instruction is decoded the 8085A may transfer data from one register to another, it may write a data value out to a peripheral device, or it may test the condition (state) of one of the flags contained in the flag word.

As instructions are fetched and executed, the PC is incremented so that it points to the memory location that contains the *next* instruction to be executed. Not only can the PC be reset to all zeros and incremented, but it can also be loaded with a nonsequential 16-bit address. This loading operation is generally performed when the 8085A branches, or jumps, to instructions stored in another section of memory.

THE 8085A INSTRUCTION SET

Just as we can *read* instructions from an automobile manual or cookbook, the 8085A *reads* instructions from memory. Once an instruction is read from memory, the required operations are performed. The next sequential instruction is then read from memory and executed. The 8085A, along with all other microprocessors, executes sequential instructions in exactly the same manner.

The 8085A has 246 distinct instructions that it can execute. Many of the instructions, however, cause very similar operations to be performed. For instance, there are 18 eight-bit-addition, 18 eight-bit-subtraction, and 4 sixteen-bit-addition instructions that the 8085A can execute. The 8085 does not have any multiply or divide instructions. Therefore all of these add and subtract instructions will be classified as *mathematical* instructions. The 8085A can also move an 8-bit data value contained in any one of the general-purpose registers to any of the other general-purpose registers; there are 49 of these register-oriented *data movement* instructions. In fact, there are five different classes of instructions:

Data movement instructions
Mathematical and logical instructions
Branch or transfer-of-control instructions
Input/output (I/O) instructions
Interrupt and miscellaneous instructions

The data movement instructions are used to move 8-bit bytes between any of the general-purpose registers or between any general-purpose registers and *any* of the 65,536 possible memory locations. Of course, it makes sense to write information only into an R/W memory location. The 8085A can also read any information from an R/W or ROM memory location into any of the general-purpose registers.

As mentioned before, the 8085A also has a number of add and subtract instructions. The add instructions can be used to add 8- or 16-bit numbers, while the subtract instructions can only be used to subtract 8-bit numbers. Although it may seem that the 8085A is limited to operating mathematically on numbers between 0 and 255 (8-bit) and 0 and 65,535 (16-bit), this is not so. Remember, most people can only add and subtract single-digit numbers between zero and nine. However, larger numbers can still be added or subtracted. For instance:

$$\begin{array}{r} 32,468 \\ + 18,956 \\ \hline \end{array} \qquad \begin{array}{r} 9503 \\ - 4977 \\ \hline \end{array}$$

In the addition or subtraction example, most people would start with the least significant digits first (8+6 or 3−7). The 8085A can be programmed to "tackle" mathematical problems in the same way. By breaking large numbers into 8-bit bytes and then performing either an addition or subtraction operation, the 8085A can add or subtract 500-, 700-, or even 1000-bit numbers. As a point of reference, $2^{512} \simeq 10^{150}$.

The logical instructions that the 8085A can execute include AND, OR, exclusive OR, compare, rotate, increment, and decrement. All of these operations can also be performed using standard transistor-transistor logic (TTL) or complementary metal-oxide semiconductor (CMOS) logic. The power of using a microcomputer to perform these operations lies in the fact that we can *easily* change the microcomputer program to perform new combinations of these functions. If we had to change hardwired TTL or CMOS logic so that it performed these functions, it could take hours or days.

The *branch* or *transfer-of-control* instructions give the 8085A its decision-making capabilities. If the result of a particular mathematical or logical operation is zero, or the temperature of a tank of liquid that the 8085A is monitoring exceeds a preset temperature, the 8085A could sound an alarm. The reason that the 8085A can do this is because the questions "Is the result equal to zero?" and "Is the result greater than . . . ?" can be asked by the 8085A. There are a total of eight different "questions" or *conditions* that the 8085A can test. In fact, the conditions that can be tested are the states of the four flags (not the auxiliary carry flag) contained in the processor status word (PSW).

The 8085A can also execute two different input/output (I/O) instructions, so that it can communicate with external or *peripheral* devices. Typical devices include seven-segment light-emitting diode (LED) displays, keyboards, cassettes, PROM programmers, teletypewriters, cathode-ray tube terminals (crt's), floppy disks, line printers, and even other microcomputers. Even though a peripheral may have 64 or 128 bits of information that need to be transferred to the microcomputer, the 8085A can only *input* 8 bits of information into the A register at any one time. Once in the A register the data value can be *output* to another peripheral or it can be saved in memory. To output information to a peripheral, the data must first be stored with the A register.

The 8085A also has what are called *interrupt instructions,* which are primarily used by high-speed peripherals that are *interfaced* (electrically wired) to the microcomputer. There are also other instructions that do not "fit" into any of the previous categories. These instructions operate primarily on the content of the A register or accumulator. For a detailed treatment of the 8085A instruction set, along with hundreds of software examples, refer to References 1 and 2 at the end of the chapter.

COMMUNICATING WITH I/O DEVICES

As mentioned in the previous section on the 8085A instruction set, there are two instructions that the 8085A can use to communicate with I/O devices. These instructions are IN and OUT. The IN instruction is used to input information into the 8085A A register from an external hardware device, and the OUT instruction is used to output the information in the A register to an external hardware device. When an IN or OUT instruction is executed in a program, there must be some method of specifying whether the 8085A is communicating with a high-speed paper-tape reader, a teletypewriter, or some other I/O device. In fact, the 8085A must specify one out of many possible peripheral devices.

When an IN or OUT instruction is stored in the microcomputer memory, *an 8-bit device address must also be stored immediately after the instruction.* When either the IN or OUT instruction is executed, the device address contained in the *two-byte instruction* is read from memory, and placed *on address lines A0 through A7 and also on lines A8 through A15.* External logic in the *peripheral* interface must be wired to one group of address lines or the other, so the peripheral can determine if the microprocessor wants to communicate with it. This is very similar to the actions that occur when the microprocessor addresses memory. The microprocessor has to generate a memory address and it also has to generate one of two possible control signals ($\overline{\text{MEMW}}$ or $\overline{\text{MEMR}}$), so that the addressed memory location knows whether to place information on the data bus, or whether it is to receive information from the data bus. Therefore, not only must the 8085A place the device address on the address bus, it also must generate one of two possible I/O control signals: $\overline{\text{IN}}$ or $\overline{\text{OUT}}$ when an I/O instruction is executed. These signals are similar to $\overline{\text{MEMR}}$ and $\overline{\text{MEMW}}$, but they are only used to control the flow of information between the 8085A and peripheral devices when IN or OUT instructions are executed.

If the 8085A is executing an IN instruction, the 8085A must read an 8-bit byte from a peripheral device into the A register. Therefore the 8085A places the 8-bit device address on the address bus, and brings the $\overline{I/O\ R}$ signal (*also called* $\overline{IN}$) to a logic zero. The specified peripheral device uses the combination of the device address and the $\overline{I/O\ R}$ ($\overline{IN}$) signal to gate information from the *input port* onto the data bus and into the A register. If an OUT instruction is being executed, the 8085A places the device address on the data bus, and brings the $\overline{I/O\ W}$ ($\overline{OUT}$) signal to a logic zero. At the same time the content of the A register is placed on the data bus. The peripheral device that is being addressed uses the $\overline{I/O\ W}$ or $\overline{OUT}$ signal to gate the content of the A register on the data bus, into the peripheral's interface logic.

The $\overline{I/O\ R}$ and $\overline{I/O\ W}$ signals have been added to the microcomputer system diagram in Fig. 1-11. Note that the data bus goes to the peripheral devices and that the peripheral devices can use either address lines A0 through A7 or A8 through A15, so that they can receive the device address generated by the microprocessor. *The address bus only contains a peripheral device address during the execution of either an IN or OUT instruction.*

ADDITIONAL 8085A FEATURES AND CONTROL SIGNALS

The 8085A must not only generate memory and peripheral control signals, such as $\overline{MEMR}$, $\overline{MEMW}$, $\overline{IN}$, and $\overline{OUT}$, but it also uses and generates other control signals that are absolutely necessary for proper microcomputer operation.

8085A Power Requirements

The 8085A requires only +5 volts (170 mA) for proper operation. This is a good feature, particularly if remote (battery powered) or low-cost microcomputer-based systems must be designed and built. The 8085A microprocessor design is based on the 8080A, which requires power supplies of +5, +12, and −5 volts.

X1 and X2 Clock Inputs

When the 8085A communicates with memory or peripheral devices, it generates memory and I/O control signals (pulses). The period (duration) of these pulses is determined by the frequency at which the 8085A is clocked. A crystal, resistor-capacitor (*RC*) or inductor-capacitor (*LC*) network or a TTL-compatible oscillator can be applied to the 8085A clock inputs. For the standard 8085A a maximum clock frequency of 6.25 MHz may be used. For the 8085A-2 a maximum clock frequency of 10 MHz may be used. Internal logic in the 8085A (either version) divides this clock frequency by two, before it is used by the rest of the 8085A microprocessor. Therefore, for the 8085A, the minimum clock cycle time is 320 ns (3.125 MHz); for the 8085A-2, it is 200 ns (5 MHz). The 8085A also outputs this clock frequency in TTL-compatible form at the CLOCK OUT pin, pin *37,* for use by memory or peripheral devices.

In the remainder of this book we will use the term "8085A." However, either the 8085A or 8085A-2 can be used. These two integrated circuits are electrically and functionally identical, except that the 8085A-2 can be clocked at a higher frequency than the 8085A. We should also note that when Intel first produced this microprocessor it was called the 8085. Due to a few problems with this version of the chip, however, Intel changed the design and began manufacturing the 8085A version. If you plan on building a microcomputer using this microprocessor, use the 8085A (or 8085A-2). In fact, it would probably be difficult for you to even *find* the 8085 version of the microprocessor.

RESET IN (Input), RESET OUT (Output)

When you want to begin executing a program, there has to be some way for the 8085A to begin executing the program at a specific memory location. By applying a logic zero to the 8085A RESET IN input, the 16-bit program counter is reset to zero. When the RESET IN input is brought back up to a logic one, the 8085A fetches (reads) the instruction stored in memory location zero and executes it. It then fetches and executes the next sequential instruction. This serves to start the computer, assuming that a useful program actually starts at location "zero."

Quite often a push button and an *RC* network are wired to the RESET IN input so that (1) when power is first applied to the microcomputer system the PC is automatically reset and program execution is begun and (2) the user can cause the 8085A to begin executing the same program, again.

The RESET OUT signal is often used to reset memory and peripheral integrated circuits. This signal is a logic one for as long as the RESET IN signal is a logic zero. When the RESET IN input is taken to a logic one, the RESET OUT output goes to a logic zero.

HOLD (Input), HLDA (Output)

The hold (HOLD) and hold acknowledge (HLDA) signals are both active as logic ones. These signals are generally used with direct-memory access (dma) devices and in multiprocessor environments. Neither of these topics will be discussed in this book. For additional information about dma devices, see Reference 3. *For proper microcomputer operation in simple microcomputer systems, the HOLD input of the 8085A microprocessor integrated circuit should be grounded.*

SID (Input), SOD (Output)

The SID input can be controlled by external devices simply by applying logic levels to it. The state of the SID pin can then be tested under software control. The SOD output pin can be set by a program to either a logic one or a logic zero. Simple microcomputer control systems could test the state of a float valve or switch by monitoring the SID input, and as a result of the state of the SID pin the state of the SOD pin could be changed by appropriate program steps to turn a light off or to turn a pump on.

The SID and SOD pins can also be used, *under software control,* by the 8085A to communicate with an asynchronous serial peripheral device, such as a teletypewriter or cathode-ray tube terminal (crt). The software required to perform these functions is complex and it will not be discussed. If you are interested in this topic, however, see Chapter 1 in Reference 2.

READY (Input)

Every memory integrated circuit and every integrated circuit in a peripheral interface requires a known amount of time to respond to an address, data or control signal ($\overline{\text{MEMR}}$, $\overline{\text{MEMW}}$, $\overline{\text{IN}}$, or $\overline{\text{OUT}}$). Some integrated circuits require only 20 or 30 ns to respond, while some devices require 200 to 300 ns to respond. In general, these devices are "fast enough" to operate with the 8085A. However, there are some devices that require 1 or 2 μs to respond to an 8085A request. If a memory integrated circuit or peripheral integrated circuit requires this much or more time to respond, the device can take the READY line to a logic zero (ground) when it is addressed. This will cause the 8085A to "mark time" or *wait,* for the addressed device to respond. Once the device is ready to respond to the requested action, it would take the READY line back up to a logic one. By doing this the 8085A will complete the memory read, memory write, I/O read, or I/O write instruction. The 8085A will then continue to execute the remainder of the program at "full speed," unless another selected device activates the READY input.

This signal and its use will be discussed in detail in another chapter. However, in general, most peripheral and memory devices are fast enough to keep up with the 8085A requests. If this is true, the READY input to the microprocessor should be wired directly to +5 volts through a 1-kilohm pull-up resistor.

INTR (Input), $\overline{\text{INTA}}$ (Ouput)

When used with most peripheral devices, you can program the 8085A to ask each peripheral device the question "Do you have data?" or "Do you want data?" This is generally done through the use of instructions that monitor or test a "ready" signal or flag that is supplied by each I/O device. If the I/O device signals that it is ready, the computer leaves the monitoring software routine to supply or accept the data, fulfilling the I/O device's request. An input (IN) instruction is generally used to monitor the "ready" *flag* supplied by the I/O device, and various combinations of logic and branching instructions allow the 8085A to perform the necessary actions.

In some cases, however, the 8085A may have to perform so many other tasks that it does not have the time to execute even a single IN instruction, in order to see if a peripheral has or requires any data. If such a case exists, the peripheral can be wired to the interrupt (INTR) pin of the 8085A, through some external logic. By taking the INTR input to a logic one, the peripheral tells the 8085A that it needs attention. In fact, the peripheral will *interrupt* the 8085A, regardless of what it is doing.

Of course, the peripheral may actually try to interrupt the 8085A while it is right in the middle of executing an instruction. If this occurs, the 8085A will finish executing that instruction. The interrupt acknowledge ($\overline{\text{INTA}}$) signal will then be generated (a logic zero pulse) by the 8085A *to acknowledge to the peripheral device that the interrupt has been accepted.* In most peripheral interface designs the INTA signal is actually used, with external logic, to tell the 8085A exactly what to do (what instruction to execute) or where to go in memory, in order to *service* the peripheral. To service the peripheral the 8085A may have to input data, output data, or pulse the peripheral device. In another chapter we will discuss I/O devices and interrupts in greater depth. Most small systems do not use interrupts, so the INTR input to the 8085A microprocessor should be grounded.

The 8085A integrated circuit also has four additional interrupt inputs: TRAP, RST5.5, RST6.5, and RST 7.5. Each of these inputs can be wired directly to a peripheral device that needs the capability of interrupting the 8085A. Like the INTR input, if these interrupts are not used, they should be grounded.

In another chapter you will learn that it is possible for us to program the 8085A with two or three instructions, so that the 8085A does not acknowledge interrupts. This is particularly important if the 8085A has to execute some time-dependent instructions.

THE "IDEAL MICROPROCESSOR INTEGRATED CIRCUIT" VS. THE 8085A

In Figs. 1-5, 1-6, 1-7, and 1-11 is shown an "ideal" microprocessor integrated circuit that has 16 address lines, 8 data lines, and the control signals $\overline{\text{MEMR}}$, $\overline{\text{MEMW}}$, $\overline{\text{I/O R}}$ ($\overline{\text{IN}}$), and $\overline{\text{I/O W}}$ ($\overline{\text{OUT}}$). Unfortunately, the 8085A does not directly generate many of these signals. Instead, the 8085A has the signals A8 through A15, AD0 through AD7, ALE, IO/$\overline{\text{M}}$, $\overline{\text{RD}}$, and $\overline{\text{WR}}$. By using some *very simple* external logic (two commonly available integrated circuits), we can derive the complete 16-bit address bus (A0–A15), the 8-bit data bus (D0–D7), and the four control signals: $\overline{\text{MEMR}}$, $\overline{\text{MEMW}}$, $\overline{\text{I/O R}}$ ($\overline{\text{IN}}$), and $\overline{\text{I/O W}}$ ($\overline{\text{OUT}}$).

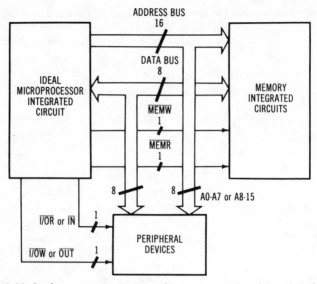

Fig. 1-11. A microcomputer system with memory and peripheral devices.

The High Address Bus (Output)

As you would expect, address lines A8 through A15 contain the *high-order byte of a 16-bit address,* or *the high address,* when the 8085A is addressing memory. During the execution of an IN (input) or OUT (output) instruction, the 8-bit device address will be present on address lines A8 through A15.

The Multiplexed Address/Data Bus (Input/Output)

To save a number of pins on the 8085A 40-pin integrated circuit package, the engineers who designed the 8085A decided to combine the 8 low-order bits (the low address) of the 16-bit address with 8-bit bi-directional data bus (Fig. 1-12). Of course, the 8085A has to generate some type of signal for memory and peripheral devices, so that they know what type of information is on the address/data bus. The signal used for this purpose is *Address Latch Enable,* or *ALE.* When the ALE signal is a logic one, the low address is on the address/data bus. When ALE is a logic zero, the address/data bus is being used as a bidirectional data bus. The least significant bit of the address/data bus is called AD0 and the most significant bit is called AD7.

In many systems the address/data bus is demultiplexed, so that the microcomputer has a 16-bit address bus and an 8-bit bidirectional data bus. However, there are also some very sophisticated integrated circuits that actually demultiplex the address/data bus *internally!* This means that the address/data bus (AD0 through AD7) and ALE are wired

Courtesy Intel Corp.

Fig. 1-12. Multiplexed address/data bus timing.

directly to these integrated circuits. The internal logic then "grabs" the low address from the bus when ALE is a logic one. At all other times these lines are used as the bidirectional data bus. In fact, by using these sophisticated integrated circuits. you can construct a fully operational, powerful microcomputer with only three integrated circuits. Intel has designed five integrated circuits that operate in this manner including two combination R/W memory, I/O, and timer chips, two read-only-memory and I/O chips and an R/W memory chip. In Chapter 2 we will actually discuss the circuitry that can be used to demultiplex the address/data bus, splitting apart the address and data bus functions.

Read and Write Control Signals (Output)

The 8085A also does not have $\overline{\text{MEMR}}$, $\overline{\text{MEMW}}$, $\overline{\text{I/O R}}$, and $\overline{\text{I/O W}}$ signals. It does, however, generate the signals IO/$\overline{\text{M}}$, $\overline{\text{RD}}$, and $\overline{\text{WR}}$, which can be gated together to generate the four memory and I/O read and write signals.

IO/$\overline{\text{M}}$ (Output)

The IO/$\overline{\text{M}}$ signal (pronounced eye-oh memory bar) is used by both I/O and memory devices. If the 8085A is addressing an I/O device, by executing either an IN or OUT instruction, the IO/$\overline{\text{M}}$ signal will be a logic one. If the 8085A is addressing memory during either a memory read or memory write operation, the IO/$\overline{\text{M}}$ signal will be a logic zero.

$\overline{\text{RD}}$ (Output)

The $\overline{\text{RD}}$ signal (pronounced read bar) is a logic zero whenever the 8085A is reading information from an input device (during the execution of an IN instruction) or when it is reading information from a memory device. This signal can be gated with IO/$\overline{\text{M}}$ to generate the $\overline{\text{I/O R}}$ ($\overline{\text{IN}}$) and $\overline{\text{MEMR}}$ signals.

$\overline{\text{WR}}$ (Output)

The $\overline{\text{WR}}$ signal (pronounced write bar) is a logic zero whenever the 8085A is writing information to an output device (during the execution of an OUT instruction) or when it is writing information to a memory device. This signal can be gated with IO/$\overline{\text{M}}$ to generate the $\overline{\text{I/O W}}$ ($\overline{\text{OUT}}$) and $\overline{\text{MEMW}}$ signals.

29

In the next chapter we will discuss how the signals IO/$\overline{\text{M}}$, $\overline{\text{RD}}$, and $\overline{\text{WR}}$ are gated together to generate the memory and I/O control signals that we have already discussed. It should be noted that some of the 8085A-family integrated circuits (those chips that are designed to work specifically with the 8085A) can be wired directly to the IO/$\overline{\text{M}}$, $\overline{\text{WR}}$, and $\overline{\text{RD}}$ signals generated by the 8085A integrated circuit. These special integrated circuits generate the appropriate control signals from these signals internally and are discussed in Chapter 7.

Miscellaneous Signals

There are a number of output signals and one input signal of the 8085A that we have not discussed in detail. These signals are S_1, S_0, SOD, and SID. The S_0 and S_1 signals generated by the 8085A are used to generate *advance* information about what the 8085A will be doing in the next machine cycle. These signals are rarely used. One nice feature of these two signals is that when they are combined with ALE, the result will tell us whether the 8085A has halted (executed a halt or HLT instruction).

The SOD output pin and the SID input pin of the 8085A microprocessor integrated circuit can be used to (1) control simple external or peripheral devices or (2) communicate with an asynchronous serial teletypewriter or crt. These two signals and their application will be discussed in Chapter 6.

MICROPROCESSOR/MICROCOMPUTER TIMING

Just as the microprocessor is the "heart" of the microcomputer system, the clock applied to the clock inputs of the microprocessor is the "heart" of the microprocessor. The frequency of the clock that is used to drive the microprocessor will determine how fast the microprocessor can operate (within certain specified limits established by the manufacturer). *All other signals that are generated by the 8085A are derived from this clock.*

As an example, consider Fig. 1-13. Even though the 8085A is executing only one instruction (the STA instruction), it reads three 8-bit bytes from memory and then writes an 8-bit byte into memory. Regardless of what instruction the 8085A will execute next, the 8085A first has to read the STA instruction from memory into the instruction register IR (M_1). As expected, the 16-bit address in the program counter (PC) is used to address the memory location that contains the instruction. As a result of reading the instruction into the IR, the IR determines what other operations have to be performed to "execute" the instruction. In Fig. 1-13 two additional memory reads (M_2 and M_3) and one memory write (M_4) have to be performed. Once these operations are performed,

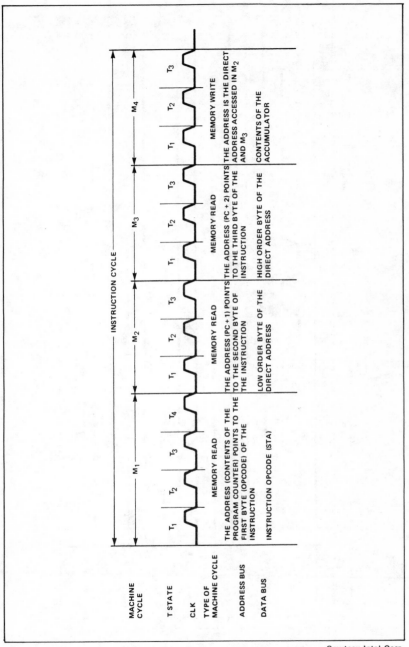

The figure shows timing waveforms with the following row labels and content:

MACHINE CYCLE: M₁ — M₂ — M₃ — M₄, all spanning the INSTRUCTION CYCLE.

T STATE:
- M₁: T₁, T₂, T₃, T₄
- M₂: T₁, T₂, T₃
- M₃: T₁, T₂, T₃
- M₄: T₁, T₂, T₃

CLK

TYPE OF MACHINE CYCLE:
- M₁: MEMORY READ
- M₂: MEMORY READ
- M₃: MEMORY READ
- M₄: MEMORY WRITE

ADDRESS BUS:
- M₁: THE ADDRESS (CONTENTS OF THE PROGRAM COUNTER) POINTS TO THE FIRST BYTE (OPCODE) OF THE INSTRUCTION
- M₂: THE ADDRESS (PC + 1) POINTS TO THE SECOND BYTE OF THE INSTRUCTION
- M₃: THE ADDRESS (PC + 2) POINTS TO THE THIRD BYTE OF THE INSTRUCTION
- M₄: THE ADDRESS IS THE DIRECT ADDRESS ACCESSED IN M₂ AND M₃

DATA BUS:
- M₁: INSTRUCTION OPCODE (STA)
- M₂: LOW ORDER BYTE OF THE DIRECT ADDRESS
- M₃: HIGH ORDER BYTE OF THE DIRECT ADDRESS
- M₄: CONTENTS OF THE ACCUMULATOR

Courtesy Intel Corp.

Fig. 1-13. Typical instruction timing and operations.

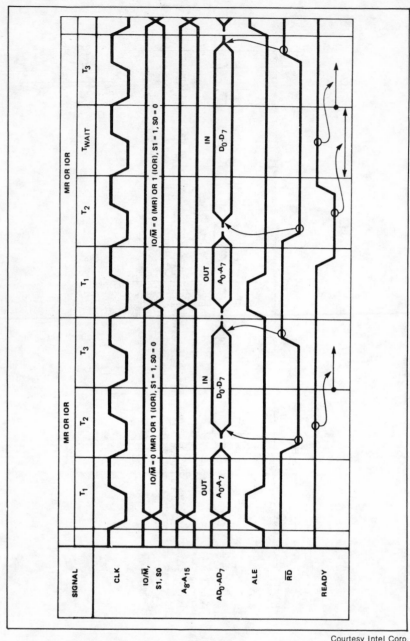

Courtesy Intel Corp.

Fig. 1-14. The machine cycles for reading from memory or an I/O (peripheral) devive.

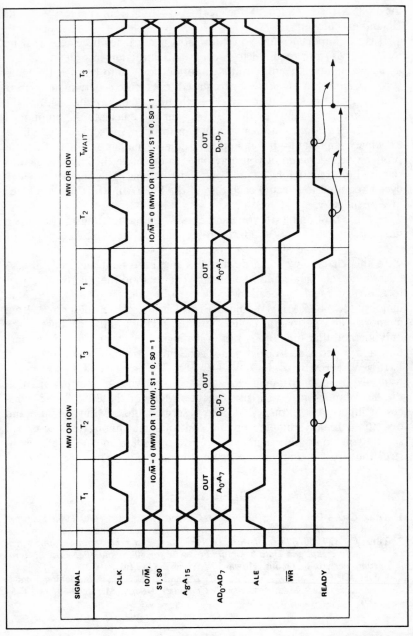

Courtesy Intel Corp.

Fig. 1-15. The machine cycles for writing to memory or an I/O (peripheral) device.

33

the 8085A reads (fetches) the next instruction from memory into the IR and executes it.

It is not important that you know how many machine cycles (M_1 up to M_4 or M_5) are required to execute an instruction in order to *design* a microcomputer system. What is important for you to know is the number of *T states,* or *clock cycles,* required to execute a particular instruction. Knowing this number and the cycle time (clock frequency, *not* the clock input frequency) or the 8085A, you can calculate the amount of time required to execute a particular instruction. In some cases this is extremely important—for example, in time-dependent tasks. In fact, for proper *system operation* you may have to calculate the amount of time required to execute long sequences of instructions. The number of clock cycles required to execute each one of the 8085A instructions are listed in Appendix A.

In Figs. 1-14 and 1-15 you can actually see the relationships between most of the commonly used control signals of the 8085A. Do not be concerned with the S0 and S1 notation.

In this chapter we have discussed a number of the different 8085A buses, control signals and operations. The method that the 8085A uses to address a memory location (with a 16-bit address) and *control* that memory location ($\overline{\text{MEMW}}$ and $\overline{\text{MEMR}}$) has also been described. Both memories and peripheral devices use the address and data buses. The only method that the 8085A has to distinguish between a memory location and a peripheral device is by generating a different control signal ($\overline{\text{MEMW}}$, $\overline{\text{MEMR}}$, or $\overline{\text{I/O W}}$, $\overline{\text{I/O R}}$). The internal 8085A registers were also mentioned along with the different types of instructions that the 8085A microprocessor can execute. Many of the 8085A microprocessor inputs and outputs were also described, along with their use and operation. Finally, simple bus and control signal timing was described so that you would have some idea of how the 8085A actually fetches instructions from memory and executes them.

REFERENCES

1. Titus, C. A., Rony, P. R., Larsen, D. G., and J. A. Titus *8080/8085 Software Design, Book 1,* Indianapolis: Howard W. Sams & Co., Inc., 1978.
2. Titus, C. A. *8080/8085 Software Design, Book 2: Asynchronous Communications, Interrupt and Data Structure Software for 8080- and 8085-Based Microcomputers,* Indianapolis: Howard W. Sams & Co., Inc., 1979.
3. Larsen, D. G., Rony, P. R., Titus, C. A., and J. A. Titus "Interfacing Fundamentals: Direct Memory Access," *Computer Design,* March 1979, pp. 176–180.

BIBLIOGRAPHY

1. *MCS-85 User's Manual, September 1978,* Intel Corp., Santa Clara, CA 95051.

PROBLEMS

1-1. List the various buses that the 8085A microprocessor has and state whether information flows in one direction and, if so, give the direction of data flow (into the processor or out of the processor), or whether data flows in both directions.

1-2. Is a logic one considered to be +5 V or ground? What voltage level is required for a logic zero?

1-3. List the various registers contained within the 8085A and state whether they are 8-bit or 16-bit registers.

1-4. What are the five basic types of instructions that the 8085A can execute?

1-5. What are the 8085A input/output (I/O) instructions? What I/O control signals are generated when these instructions are executed?

1-6. What are the voltage and current (power) requirements of the 8085A?

1-7. What is the maximum clock frequency (minimum cycle time) for the 8085A and the 8085A-2?

1-8. List the different types of external clock sources that can be used with the 8085A.

1-9. List any 30 pin numbers between 1 and 40. Determine the name of each of these 30 pins, determine if the pin is used to output information, input information, or both, and describe the function of the pin in five or ten words.

1-10. How is the time required to execute an assembly language instruction calculated?

CHAPTER 2

Basic System Control

In this chapter we will discuss a number of topics, including (1) the design of a clock generator, (2) the demultiplexing of the address/data bus, (3) the generation of the control signals $\overline{\text{MEMR}}$, $\overline{\text{MEMW}}$, $\overline{\text{I/O R}}$ ($\overline{\text{IN}}$), and $\overline{\text{I/O W}}$ ($\overline{\text{OUT}}$) from the signals $\overline{\text{RD}}$, $\overline{\text{WR}}$, and IO/$\overline{\text{M}}$, and (4) the circuitry required to reset the 8085A microprocessor. At the end of the chapter you will have the opportunity to apply your knowledge of the 8085A and its control signals to three microcomputer designs.

CLOCK SOURCE FOR THE 8085A

There are four different methods that can be used to clock the 8085A microprocessor, including (1) an external TTL-compatible clock, (2) a resistor-capacitor (*RC*) network and (3) a quartz crystal. All of these methods will work, but there are advantages and disadvantages to each method.

Clock Frequency Limits

Regardless of the clocking method used you cannot simply clock the 8085A at any frequency that you desire. *Intel has specified that the 8085A must have a minimum clock period of 320 ns and a maximum clock period of 2000 ns.* Any clock frequency applied to the X1 and X2 inputs of the 8085A microprocessor is *divided by two* by the 8085A. Therefore the external clock must have a minimum clock period of 160 ns and a maximum clock period of 1000 ns. In terms of frequency the 8085A requires a clock frequency of between 1 MHz (minimum) and 6.25 MHz (maximum). If you use a clock whose frequency is within these two limits, and apply this clock to the 8085A correctly, the 8085A will operate correctly.

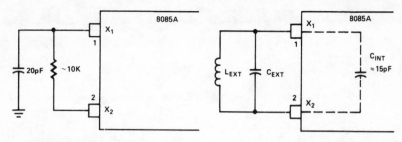

(A) *RC* circuit clock driver.   (B) *LC* tuned circuit clock driver.

Courtesy Intel Corp.

Fig. 2-1. Using an *RC* or *LC* network for the 8085A clock source.

Using a Resistor-Capacitor (*RC*) Network

Perhaps the easiest and least expensive method that you can use to generate a clock input for the 8085A is with an RC network. These two components are wired to the 8085A clock inputs (X1 and X2) as shown in Fig. 2-1A.

As you might expect, this method has a number of characteristics that make it a poor choice among the three possibilities. Any changes in the resistance or capacitance of these two components will cause the clock frequency of the network, and thus of the 8085A, to change. This means that if you have to produce a number of 8085A-based microcomputers, all with the same *cycle time,* carefully matched (and expensive) resistors and capacitors will have to be used. If you only need one microcomputer system and the clock frequency and stability are not that important, an *RC* network can be used.

In many instances the microcomputer is programmed to generate time delays. Time delays of from 5 μs to seconds, minutes, or hours can be generated by having the 8085A execute a *sequence* of instructions that requires a known number of clock cycles to be executed. Depending upon the application, these instructions may be executed once or 100,000 times. However, if a time delay program is written for a microcomputer system that uses an *RC* network for a clock source, the time delay generated on another microcomputer system that uses a similar *RC* network will probably be somewhat different.

Intel Corporation states, "Variations in the on-chip timing generation can cause a wide variation in frequency when using the *RC* mode."[1] Because we have no control over how the 8085A operates internally, the use of an *RC* network is not recommended. However, a resistance of 10 kilohms and a capacitance of 22 pF will generate a clock frequency of about 3 MHz.

It is also possible to use a parallel-resonant inductor-capacitor (*LC*) network as the clock source for the 8085A. This circuit should not be used for frequencies above 5 MHz (Fig. 2-1B), however.

Using an External TTL Oscillator

In some situations an 8085A-based microcomputer may be added to equipment to upgrade the equipment. The equipment may already contain a "master clock" that is used to synchronize all internal and external operations. In this case you may want to synchronize the 8085A operation to that of the rest of the system.

Simply using the same clock does not ensure that the systems are synchronized, however. The 8085A must still execute a program to be useful, and the time required to execute the program may vary, depending on the data being processed. Therefore it may be particularly difficult to get the equipment to operate effectively with the microcomputer. Since most users will not use an external TTL-compatible clock (see Fig. 2-2), we will not discuss this topic further.

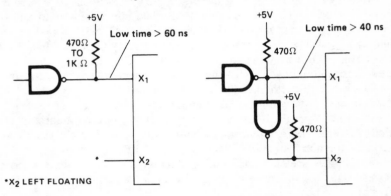

(A) 1- to 6-MHz input frequency external clock driver circuit.

(B) 1- to 10-MHz input frequency external clock driver circuit.

Courtesy Intel Corp.

Fig. 2-2. Using an external TTL-compatible oscillator to clock the 8085A.

Using a Quartz Crystal

The most frequently used method of generating a clock signal for the microprocessor is a quartz crystal. Quartz crystals have very good temperature stability and can be purchased accurate to one part in 100,000 or one part in 1,000,000. This means that a 4-MHz crystal might actually have a frequency between 3.9996 and 4.0004 MHz or between 3.99996 and 4.00004 MHz.

The circuit in Fig. 2-3 illustrates how a parallel-resonant crystal and two low-value capacitors are wired to the X1 and X2 inputs of the 8085A chip. Of course, the crystal must be within the frequency range of 1 and 6.25 MHz (1 and 10 MHz for the 8085A-2). NOTE: For NEC 8085As the 20-pF capacitors are required for crystal frequencies less than 6 MHz only.

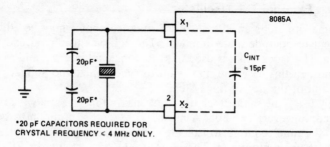

Courtesy Intel Corp.

Fig. 2-3. Wiring a quartz crystal to the 8085A microprocessor.

Circuitry within the 8085A divides this clock frequency by two, before it is used to generate control signals, gate information onto and off of the data bus, and so on. The "divided-by-two" clock signal is also output by the 8085A on the CLK (OUT) pin (pin 37, see Fig. 1-3). Most 8085A-based microcomputer systems do not use this signal. However, it is required by some of the "family" integrated circuits that Intel designed for use with the 8085A microprocessor (see Chapter 7 for descriptions of these integrated circuits).

As a final note, the authors recommend that you use a quartz crystal clock in your 8085A-based microcomputer designs. These crystals have good temperature stability (they do not "drift"), they cost about $5 each, and there are only small timing differences between microcomputer systems that use the same clock frequency, that is, the same frequency crystal.

DEMULTIPLEXING THE ADDRESS/DATA BUS

As mentioned in Chapter 1 the 8085A multiplexes the low-order 8 bits of an address with 8-bit data on the address/data bus. When the address latch enable (ALE) signal is a logic one, this bus contains address information, and when it is a logic zero, the bus contains data. Unfortunately, most peripheral devices and memory integrated circuits expect *separate* address and data information, that is, they have separate address and data pins. This means that the address/data bus has to be demultiplexed before these devices can be used with the microprocessor. By demultiplexing the bus the 8085A can send a 16-bit address and 8 bits of data to a device simultaneously. To demultiplex the bus we must use one or more integrated circuits that can *latch* or remember, the address (A0 through A7) bits present on this bus when the ALE signal is a logic one. These latch devices must remember *and* output the low-order address until a new low-order address is placed on the multiplexed address/data bus, and the ALE signal is a logic one, indicating its presence.

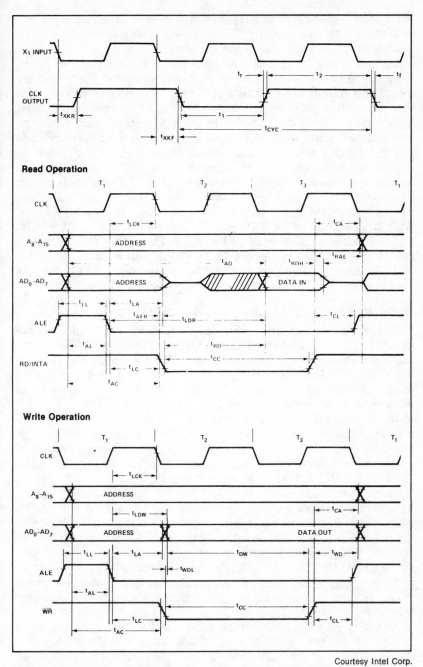

Courtesy Intel Corp.

Fig. 2-4. The timing relationships of many of the 8085A signals (see Table 2-1).

41

Regardless of the type of integrated circuits used to latch the address from the address/data bus, the ICs must meet certain requirements. The address/data bus and ALE signal can only sink and source a certain amount of current to drive external integrated circuits. Also, Intel states, "The falling edge of ALE is set to guarantee setup and hold times for the address information."[2] This means that the logic one to logic zero transition (the *negative* or *trailing edge*) of the ALE signal must be used to activate the latch circuitry. There are a number of latch-type integrated circuits that can be used. We will discuss three of them and then you will design a number of microcomputers using them.

Some important facts about the timing of the 8085A ALE signal can be obtained by examining Fig. 2-4 and Table 2-1. The address on the multiplexed address/data bus is valid at least 90 ns (t_{AL}) before the trailing edge of ALE. The address hold time after the trailing edge of ALE (t_{LA}) is a minimum of 100 ns. We can also see that the ALE pulse is generated for a minimum of 140 ns (t_{LL}). These times assume that an 8085A with a 320-ns cycle time (6.25 MHz) is being used. For a 10-MHz 8085A-2 the address is valid for 50 ns before, and 50 ns after, the trailing edge of ALE. The ALE pulse width is a minimum of 80 ns.

Using an 8-Bit Octal Latch—The SN74LS373

One of the simplest latch integrated circuits that can be used to demultiplex the address/data bus is the SN74LS373 octal (8-bit) D-type transparent latch. The function table and pin configuration for this integrated circuit are shown in Fig. 2-5. This integrated circuit contains the required electronics so that an 8-bit value at the inputs to the latch can be latched, or stored in the chip, by controlling the enable (G) input of the chip. If this device is used to demultiplex the address/data bus, it must (1) be fast enough to latch the address when the trailing edge of ALE occurs and (2) have input power (voltage and current) requirements that are within the limits established for the 8085A. The data sheet for the SN74LS373 is shown in Appendix B.

From the function table in Fig. 2-5A, you can see that the SN74LS373 has an output control input and an enable (G) input. In our design we will assume that the output control input (signal) is wired directly to ground. If the enable (G) input is a logic one, the data present at any D input will be output to the appropriate Q output. Note that as long as the enable (G) input is held at a logic one, the D inputs can change, and the Q outputs will change accordingly. *However, when the enable (G) input goes from a logic one to a logic zero, the data present at the inputs will be latched.*

As you might guess from this last statement, the ALE signal generated by the 8085A can be used to enable the latch and the latch inputs would be wired to the multiplexed address/data bus. The eight outputs of the latch would represent the low-order, or the 8 least significant, bits

Table 2-1. The Timing Requirements and Characteristics of the 8085A and 8085A-2 (See Fig. 2-4)

$T_A = 0°C$ to $70°C$; $V_{CC} = 5V \pm 5\%$; $V_{SS} = 0V$

Symbol	Parameter	8085A [2]		8085A-2 [2] (Preliminary)		Units
		Min.	Max.	Min.	Max.	
t_{CYC}	CLK Cycle Period	320	2000	200	2000	ns
t_1	CLK Low Time	80		40		ns
t_2	CLK High Time	120		70		ns
t_r, t_f	CLK Rise and Fall Time		30		30	ns
t_{XKR}	X_1 Rising to CLK Rising	30	120	30	100	ns
t_{XKF}	X_1 Rising to CLK Falling	30	150	30	110	ns
t_{AC}	A_{8-15} Valid to Leading Edge of Control [1]	270		115		ns
t_{ACL}	A_{0-7} Valid to Leading Edge of Control	240		115		ns
t_{AD}	A_{0-15} Valid to Valid Data In		575		350	ns
t_{AFR}	Address Float After Leading Edge of READ (INTA)		0		0	ns
t_{AL}	A_{8-15} Valid Before Trailing Edge of ALE [1]	115		50		ns
t_{ALL}	A_{0-7} Valid Before Trailing Edge of ALE	90		50		ns
t_{ARY}	READY Valid from Address Valid		220		100	ns
t_{CA}	Address (A_8-A_{15}) Valid After Control	120		60		ns
t_{CC}	Width of Control Low (RD, WR, INTA) Edge of ALE	400		230		ns
t_{CL}	Trailing Edge of Control to Leading Edge of ALE	50		25		ns
t_{DW}	Data Valid to Trailing Edge of WRITE	420		230		ns
t_{HABE}	HLDA to Bus Enable		210		150	ns
t_{HABF}	Bus Float After HLDA		210		150	ns
t_{HACK}	HLDA Valid to TRailing Edge of CLK	110		40		ns
t_{HDH}	HOLD Hold Time	0		0		ns
t_{HDS}	HOLD Setup Time to Trailing Edge of CLK	170		120		ns
t_{INH}	INTR Hold Time	0		0		ns
t_{INS}	INTR, RST, and TRAP Setup Time to Falling Edge of CLK	160		150		ns
t_{LA}	Address Hold Time After ALE	100		50		ns
t_{LC}	Trailing Edge of ALE to Leading Edge of Control	130		60		ns
t_{LCK}	ALE Low During CLK High	100		50		ns
t_{LDR}	ALE to Valid Data During Read		460		270	ns
t_{LDW}	ALE to Valid Data During Write		200		120	ns
t_{LL}	ALE Width	140		80		ns
t_{LRY}	ALE to READY Stable		110		30	ns
t_{RAE}	Trailing Edge of READ to Re-Enabling of Address	150		90		ns
t_{RD}	READ (or INTA) to Valid Data		300		150	ns
t_{RV}	Control Trailing Edge to Leading Edge of Next Control	400		220		ns
t_{RDH}	Data Hold Time After READ INTA [3]	0		0		ns
t_{RYH}	READY Hold Time	0		0		ns
t_{RYS}	READY Setup Time to Leading Edge of CLK	110		100		ns
t_{WD}	Data Valid After Trailing Edge of WRITE	100		60		ns
t_{WDL}	LEADING Edge of WRITE to Data Valid		40		20	ns

Notes:
1. A_8-A_{15} address Specs apply to IO/$\overline{M}$, S_0, and S_1 except A_8-A_{15} are undefined during T_4-T_6 of OF cycle whereas IO/$\overline{M}$, S_0, and S_1 are stable.
2. Test conditions: t_{CYC} = 320ns (8085A)/200ns (8085A-2); C_L = 150pF.
3. Data hold time is guaranteed under all loading conditions.

Courtesy Intel Corp.

of an address (A0 through A7). However, is the SN74LS373 electrically compatible with the 8085A?

Before we can answer this question we must determine the amount of current that the 8085A can sink at the logic zero voltage level and source at the logic one voltage level. These voltages and currents are summarized in Table 2-2. From this table you can see that a logic zero generated by the 8085A is represented by a voltage less than 0.45 V (V_{OL}). At this voltage the 8085A can sink 2 mA of current (I_{OL}). For a logic one of the 8085A generates voltages greater than 2.4 V (V_{OH}) and can source or supply -400 μA of current (I_{OH}). *All currents that are sourced by an integrated circuit are negative.* From Table 2-2 we can also see that the 8085A will assume that any voltage less than 0.8 V is a logic zero (V_{IL}) and any voltage greater than 2.0 V on one of its inputs is a logic one (V_{IH}). The input leakage currents represent the current required to drive one of the 8085A inputs to a logic one or a logic zero. For a logic one the input pin must be driven by more than 10 μA of current, and for a logic zero the integrated circuit must sink the -10 μA that the 8085A sources on its input pin.

OUTPUT CONTROL	ENABLE G	D	OUTPUT
L	H	H	H
L	H	L	L
L	L	X	Q_0
H	X	X	Z

(A) Function table.

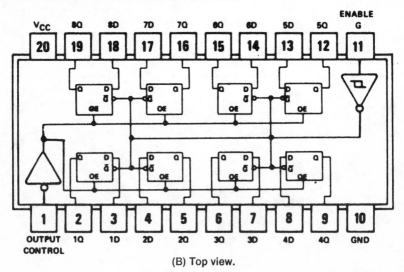

(B) Top view.

Fig. 2-5. The function table, pin configuration, and

44

Can the 8085A drive the SN74LS373? Yes, it can. The logic zero voltage output by the 8085A is a maximum of 0.45 V with a sink current of 2 mA. The SN74LS373 will accept any voltage less than 0.8 V as a logic zero and will source −0.4 mA of current to the 8085A. Therefore the logic zero voltage and current requirements are compatible. When the 8085A generates a logic one a voltage equal to or greater than 2.4 V will be produced, with a source current capability of −400 μA. The

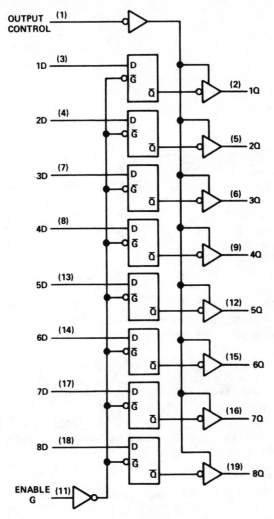

(C) Transparent latches.

block diagram for the SN74LS373 octal D-type transparent latch.

Table 2-2. The DC Characteristics of the 8085A and 8085A-2

(T_A = 0°C to 70°C; V_{CC} = 5V ±5%; V_{SS} = 0V; unless otherwise specified)

Symbol	Parameter	Min.	Max.	Units	Test Conditions
V_{IL}	Input Low Voltage	-0.5	+0.8	V	
V_{IH}	Input High Voltage	2.0	V_{CC} +0.5	V	
V_{OL}	Output Low Voltage		0.45	V	I_{OL} = 2mA
V_{OH}	Output High Voltage	2.4		V	I_{OH} = -400μA
I_{CC}	Power Supply Current		170	mA	
I_{IL}	Input Leakage		±10	μA	V_{in} = V_{CC}
I_{LO}	Output Leakage		±10	μA	0.45V $\leqslant$ V_{out} $\leqslant$ V_{CC}
V_{ILR}	Input Low Level, RESET	-0.5	+0.8	V	
V_{IHR}	Input High Level, RESET	2.4	V_{CC} +0.5	V	
V_{HY}	Hysteresis, RESET	0.25		V	

SN74LS373 assumes that any voltage greater than 2 V is a logic one, and the SN74LS373 will sink 20 μA of current at this logic (voltage) level. As you have seen, the voltage and current requirements and capabilities of the 8085A and the SN74LS373 are compatible, but is the SN74LS373 *fast enough* to be used with the 8085A?

The SN74LS373 requires a minimum (positive) pulse width of 15 ns on the enable (G) input to latch the data on its inputs. As you know, the minimum pulse width of the ALE signal generated by the 8085A (8085A-2) is 140 ns (80 ns). Therefore the octal latch is certainly fast enough to use the ALE signal to demultiplex the address/data bus. One important point to remember about the ALE signal is that the address will be on the address/data bus for a minimum of 90 ns (8085A) before the trailing edge of ALE (50 ns for the 8085A-2). The address will remain on the address/data bus a minimum of 100 ns (8085A) after the trailing edge of the ALE signal (50 ns for the 8085A-2). This means that the latch used to demultiplex the address/data bus must latch the address information from the bus on the *trailing edge* of the ALE signal. The SN74LS373 does exactly this. Keep in mind, however, that not all circuits latch on the trailing edge of a signal. Fig. 2-6 contains the schematic for wiring the SN74LS373 to the 8085A. The electrical specifications for the SN74LS373 that were used in this discussion were obtained from Appendix B.

The 8212 Latch

The 8212 is an 8-bit latch that is housed in a 24-pin integrated circuit. The 8212 can be used as an 8-bit latch, an input port, an output port, or as an interrupt instruction port. Because the 8212 can be used in so many different roles, the integrated circuit not only contains an 8-bit latch, but also some additional circuitry. Intel, along with most of the

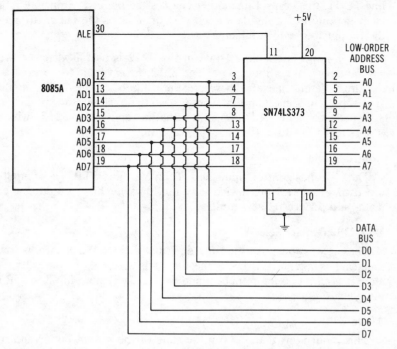

Fig. 2-6. Wiring the SN74LS373 to the 8085A multiplexed address/data bus.

8080A second sources [National Semiconductor, Texas Instruments, Advanced Micro Devices, and Nippon Electric Company (NEC)], manufactures the 8212 or its equivalent (SN74S412).

The pin configuration and block diagram for the 8212 are shown in Fig. 2-7. Unfortunately, because the 8212 can be used to solve so many problems, it is not "straightforward" to design an address demultiplexer using it. The functional description of the 8212 that follows was obtained from Intel Corporation's *MCS-85 User's Manual.*[1]

Data Latch

The eight flip-flops that make up the data latch are of the "D" type design. The output (Q) of the flip-flop will follow the data input (D) while the clock (C) is high. Latching will occur when the clock (C) returns low.

The data latch is cleared by an asynchronous reset input ($\overline{\text{CLR}}$). NOTE: Clock (C) overrides reset $\overline{\text{CLR}}$.

Output Buffer

The outputs of the data latch (Q) are connected to three-state, noninverting output buffers. These buffers have a common control line (EN); this control line either enables the buffer to transmit data from the outputs of the data latch (Q) or disables the buffer, forcing the output into a high-impedance state (three-state).

The high-impedance output state of the 8212 is useful when we are using the device as an input port. The 8212, however, is to be used as the address demultiplexer. Therefore the outputs of the 8212 should always represent some address. The 8212 outputs should not be in the high-impedance state. Additional information about the 8212, which was obtained from Intel Corporation, follows.

Control Logic

The 8212 has control inputs $\overline{DS1}$, DS2, MD, and STB. These inputs are used to control the device selection, data latching, output buffer state, and service request flip-flop.

$\overline{DS1}$, DS2 (Device Select)

These two inputs are used for device selection. When $\overline{DS1}$ is low and DS2 is high ($\overline{DS1} \cdot DS2$) the device is selected. In the selected state the output buffer is enabled and the service request flip-flop (SR) is asynchronously set.

Mode

This input is used to control the state of the output buffer and to determine the source of the clock input (C) to the data latch. When MD is high (output mode) the output buffers are enabled and the

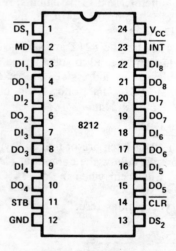

(A) Pin configuration.

$DI_1 \cdot DI_8$	DATA IN
$DO_1 \cdot DO_8$	DATA OUT
$\overline{DS_1} \cdot DS_2$	DEVICE SELECT
MD	MODE
STB	STROBE
$\overline{INT}$	INTERRUPT (ACTIVE LOW)
$\overline{CLR}$	CLEAR (ACTIVE LOW)

(B) Logic diagram.

Fig. 2-7. The pin configuration and logic

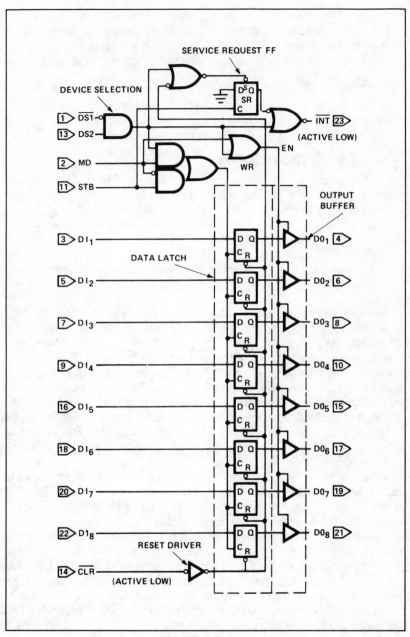

(C) Pin names.

Courtesy Intel Corp.

diagram for the 8212 8-bit latch.

source of the clock (C) to the data latch is from the device selection logic ($\overline{\text{DS1}} \cdot \text{DS2}$). When MD is low (input mode) the output buffer state is determined by the device selection logic ($\overline{\text{DS1}} \cdot \text{DS2}$) and the source of the clock (C) to the data latch is the STB (strobe) input.

Strobe

This input is used as the clock (C) to the data latch for the input mode (MD=0) and synchronously to reset the service request flip-flop (SR). Note that the SR flip-flop is negative-edge triggered.

Service Request (SR) Flip-Flop

The SR flip-flop is used to generate and control interrupts in microcomputer systems. It is asynchronously set by the $\overline{\text{CLR}}$ input (active low). When the SR flip-flop is set it is in the noninterrupting state.

The output of the SR flip-flop (Q) is connected to an inverting input of a NOR gate. The other input of the NOR gate is noninverting and is connected to the device selection logic ($\overline{\text{DS1}} \cdot \text{DS2}$). The output of the NOR gate ($\overline{\text{INT}}$) is active low (interrupting state) for connection to active low-priority generating circuits.

Since we are not using the 8212 with any interrupts, we have no need to use the service request flip-flop. Based on this description of the 8212, could you design a system that uses it to demultiplex the address/data bus? One way of using it would be to wire the $\overline{\text{CLR}}$ input to +5 V. This means that the flip-flops in the 8212 are no longer cleared to zero, so they can have information clocked into them. The MD input would also be wired to +5 V, so that the output (three-state) buffers of the 8212 are always enabled. The source of the clock for the D flip-flops will be $\overline{\text{DS1}}$ and DS2. Since the ALE signal is a logic one pulse, $\overline{\text{DS1}}$ would be wired to ground and DS2 would be wired to the ALE pin of the 8085A microprocessor integrated circuit.

What do we do with the STB input and $\overline{\text{INT}}$ output? The STB input can be wired to either ground or +5 V, while the $\overline{\text{INT}}$ output of the 8212 is not wired to *anything*, since the service request (SR) flip-flop output is not used for anything in this configuration.

Can the 8212 be wired to the 8085A in a different manner, and still operate correctly? Yes, it can. Again, the $\overline{\text{CLR}}$ input would be wired to +5 V. The MD input would be wired to ground, so that the $\overline{\text{DS1}}$ and DS2 inputs are used to enable the output buffers and so that the STB input is used to clock the data into the flip flops. This means that the $\overline{\text{DS1}}$ input is wired to ground and that the DS2 input is wired to +5 V. This will cause the latched address to always be output by the 8212. The ALE signal would then be wired to the STB input.

Can the 8212 actually be used as the address latch in an 8085A-based microcomputer system? Let us examine the electrical characteristics of

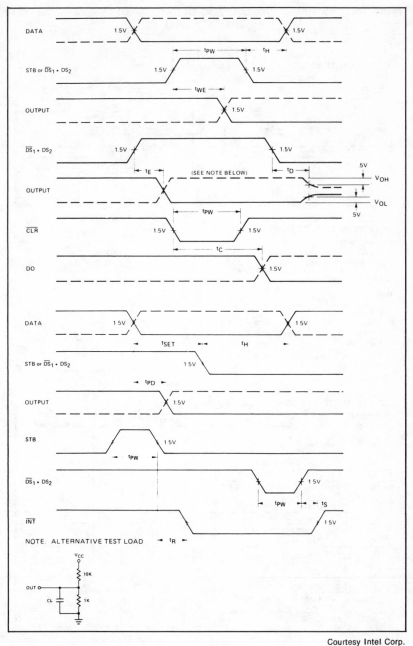

Courtesy Intel Corp.

Fig. 2-8. The timing relationships of the input and output signals of the 8212 (see Table 2-3).

Table 2-3. The Timing, Voltage, and Current Requirements of the 8212 (See Fig. 2-8)

AC CHARACTERISTICS $T_A = 0°C$ to $+70°C$, $V_{CC} = +5V \pm 5\%$

Symbol	Parameter	Limits			Unit	Test Conditions
		Min.	Typ.	Max.		
t_{PW}	Pulse Width	30			ns	
t_{PD}	Data to Output Delay			30	ns	Note 1
t_{WE}	Write Enable to Output Delay			40	ns	Note 1
t_{SET}	Data Set Up Time	15			ns	
t_H	Data Hold Time	20			ns	
t_R	Reset to Output Delay			40	ns	Note 1
t_S	Set to Output Delay			30	ns	Note 1
t_E	Output Enable/Disable Time			45	ns	Note 1
t_C	Clear to Output Delay			55	ns	Note 1

SWITCHING CHARACTERISTICS

Conditions of Test

Input Pulse Amplitude = 2.5V
Input Rise and Fall Times 5ns
Between 1V and 2V Measurements made at 1.5V
with 15mA and 30pF Test Load

Note 1:

Test	C_L^*	R_1	R_2
t_{PD}, t_{WE}, t_R, t_S, t_C	30pF	300Ω	600Ω
t_E, ENABLE↑	30pF	10KΩ	1KΩ
t_E, ENABLE↓	30pF	300Ω	600Ω
t_E, DISABLE↑	5pF	300Ω	600Ω
t_E, DISABLE↓	5pF	10KΩ	1KΩ

*Includes probe and jig capacitance.

Test Load
15mA & 30pF

*INCLUDING JIG & PROBE CAPACITANCE

DC CHARACTERISTICS $T_A = 0°C$ to $+75°C$, $V_{CC} = +5V \pm 5\%$

Symbol	Parameter	Limits			Unit	Test Conditions
		Min.	Typ.	Max.		
I_F	Input Load Current, ACK, DS_2, CR, DI_1-DI_8 Inputs			-.25	mA	$V_F = .45V$
I_F	Input Load Current MD Input			-.75	mA	$V_F = .45V$
I_F	Input Load Current DS_1 Input			-1.0	mA	$V_F = .45V$
I_R	Input Leakage Current, ACK, DS, CR, DI_1-DI_8 Inputs			10	μA	$V_R \leq V_{CC}$
I_R	Input Leakage Current MO Input			30	μA	$V_R \leq V_{CC}$
I_R	Input Leakage Current DS_1 Input			40	μA	$V_R \leq V_{CC}$
V_C	Input Forward Voltage Clamp			-1	V	$I_C = -5mA$
V_{IL}	Input "Low" Voltage			.85	V	
V_{IH}	Input "High" Voltage	2.0			V	
V_{OL}	Output "Low" Voltage			.45	V	$I_{OL} = 15mA$
V_{OH}	Output "High" Voltage	3.65	4.0		V	$I_{OH} = -1mA$
I_{SC}	Short Circuit Output Current	-15		-75	mA	$V_O = 0V$, $V_{CC} = 5V$
$|I_O|$	Output Leakage Current High Impedance State			20	μA	$V_O = .45V/5.25V$
I_{CC}	Power Supply Current		90	130	mA	

Courtesy Intel Corp.

this integrated circuit. The timing requirements and electrical characteristics of the 8212 are shown in Fig. 2-8 and are listed in Table 2-3.

As expected, the electrical requirements of the 8212 are within the drive capabilities of the 8085A. Each of the 8085A outputs can sink 2 mA at 0.45 V (maximum) for a logic zero and can source −400 μA at 2.4 V (minimum) for a logic one. The data inputs of the 8212 each source −0.25 mA at 0.45 V and sink 10 μA at 5.25 V. The maximum logic zero voltage level is 0.85 V and a minimum of 2.0 V for a logic one. If the ALE signal is wired to the DS2 input, it must be capable of sinking −0.25 mA at 0.45 V and sourcing 10 μA at a maximum of 5.25 V. The input requirements of the STB signal have not been listed in Table 2-3 by Intel, but are probably similar to the input requirements of the MD input. An address demultiplexing circuit that uses the 8212, and which was designed by Intel, is shown in Fig. 2-9. In this circuit ALE is wired to the DS2 input.

The SN74LS374

The descriptions of both the SN74LS373 and SN74LS374 are listed at the beginning of Appendix B. We already know that the SN74LS373 can be used to demultiplex the address/data bus, but can the SN74LS374 also be used? In particular, examine the function table and description of the SN74LS374 *very carefully,* in order to answer this question.

The SN74LS374 is electrically compatible with the 8085A with respect to its input voltage and current requirements. However, the information present at its 8 data inputs is clocked into the integrated circuit on the *positive edge (the logic zero to logic one transition)* of the clock signal. As we already know, the address is on the address/data bus just before (90 ns, 8085A; 50 ns, 8085A-2) and just after (100 ns, 8085A; 50 ns, 8085A-2) *the trailing or negative edge (the logic one to logic zero transition)* of the ALE signal. This means that the SN74LS374 would be clocked on the leading or positive edge of the ALE signal, and this would cause unknown information to be latched into the device.

Of course, by using additional integrated circuits we could make the SN74LS374 "work with" the address/data bus and the ALE signal. However, one of our design goals is to keep the microcomputer circuitry to a minimum and thereby reduce the cost of the integrated circuits, the cost of the printed-circuit board, integrated-circuit sockets, etc. Therefore, unless you have many thousand of the SN74LS374 in stock, and you need to "use them up," there is no reason why they should be used. It is better to use the SN74LS373 or 8212, since they can be wired directly to the 8085A microprocessor.

The SN7475

One of the most popular and least expensive latches is the SN7475 4-bit bistable latch. It is possible that we may be able to save some

8085A Low-Order Address Latch

The 8085A microprocessor uses a multiplexed address/data bus that contains the low order 8-bits of address information during the first part of a machine cycle. The same bus contains data at a later time in the cycle. An address latch enable (ALE) signal is provided by the 8085A to be used by the 8212 to latch the address so that it may be available through the whole machine cycle. Note: In this configuration, the MODE input is tied high, keeping the 8212's output buffers turned on at all times.

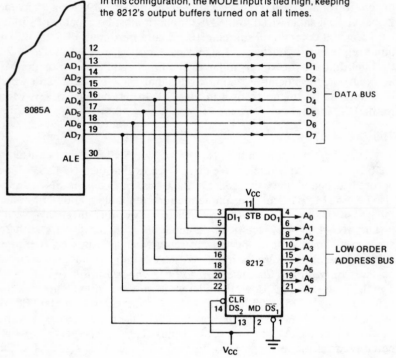

Courtesy Intel Corp.

Fig. 2-9. Using an 8212 8-bit latch to demultiplex the 8085A address/data bus.

money by using two of these devices to demultiplex the address/data bus. The specification sheets for the SN7475, along with the SN74L75 and SN74LS75, are included in Appendix B. The SN7475 is very similar to the SN74LS373, because if the enable (G) inputs are at a logic one, the data outputs will change to reflect any changes on the data inputs. Once the enable (G) inputs go from a logic one to a logic zero, the data present at the inputs will be latched and will be output constantly. Only when the enable (G) inputs go back to a logic one, can the outputs change, and only if the inputs change.

Note that the SN7475 has two enable (G) inputs. Each input controls two of the four flip-flops contained in the chip. As you can see from the data sheet, the device is extremely fast, so it will have no trouble latching the address from the address/data bus when the ALE signal is a logic one. However, what are the input voltage and current requirements of this device?

A number of different types of SN7475-type latches (SN7475, SN74-L75, and SN74LS75) are shown in Appendix B. The voltage and current requirements of these devices are summarized in Table 2-4.

From Table 2-4 you should be able to conclude that none of these devices can be wired directly to the 8085A integrated circuit, in order to demultiplex the address/data bus. For example, the data (D) input requirements of the SN7475 are 80 μA at 2.4 V and −3.2 mA at 0.4 V. The 8085A can only source −400 μA (2.4 V) and sink 2 mA (0.45 V). Therefore the 8085A sinks less current than is required by the SN7475 for a logic zero, so they cannot be used together.

It might appear that the SN74L75 would work, because the data (D) input currents are less. But the enable (G) inputs will source −3.2 mA at 0.4 V that the 8085A must sink. Again, this is too much current.

By far the best device of the three is the SN74LS75. The data inputs of the SN74LS75 sink 20 μA (2.7 V) and source −0.4 mA (0.4 V), which is within the current capabilities of the 8080A address/data pins. It also appears that the enable inputs are also compatible with the 8085A (80 μA *vs.* 400 μA; −1.6 mA *vs.* 2 mA). *However, the ALE signal must drive four enable inputs, two in each latch integrated circuit.* Therefore the current and voltage requirements of all four enable inputs are 320 μA at 2.7 V minimum and −6.4 mA at 0.4 V maximum. As you can see, the ALE signal cannot directly drive all four of the enable inputs. If you re-examine Table 2-4, you will see that the ALE signal does not have enough "power" to drive four of the enable inputs of any of these latches (SN7475, SN74L75, or SN74LS75). In conclusion, additional circuitry would be required if SN7475-type latches are used to demultiplex the address/data bus.

At this point we should note that the ALE signal is used to latch both memory addresses (during a memory read and memory write) and I/O device addresses (during an I/O read or I/O write). You can verify this by re-examining Figs. 1-14 and 1-15 in Chapter 1.

Data Bus Drive Capability

As soon as an address demultiplexer is added to the 8085A microcomputer system, the drive capabilities of the address/data bus are decreased. This is what you would expect, because the address/data bus pins in the 8085A integrated circuit have to source current to the address demultiplexer and sink current from the address demultiplexer. The sink and source currents for the two integrated circuits that we have used to demultiplex the address/data bus, the SN74LS373 and the 8212, are summarized in Table 2-5.

Table 2-4. The Voltage and Current Requirements of the SN7475, SN74L75, and SN74LS75

SN7475

PARAMETER		TEST CONDITIONS†		MIN	TYP‡	MAX	UNIT
V_{IH}	High-level input voltage			2			V
V_{IL}	Low-level input voltage					0.8	V
V_{IK}	Input clamp voltage	V_{CC} = MIN,	I_I = −12 mA			−1.5	V
V_{OH}	High-level output voltage	V_{CC} = MIN, V_{IH} = 2 V, V_{IL} = 0.8 V,	I_{OH} = −400 µA	2.4	3.4		V
V_{OL}	Low-level output voltage	V_{CC} = MIN, V_{IH} = 2 V, V_{IL} = 0.8 V,	I_{OL} = 16 mA		0.2	0.4	V
I_I	Input current at maximum input voltage	V_{CC} = MAX,	V_I = 5.5 V			1	mA
I_{IH}	High-level input current	D input	V_{CC} = MAX, V_I = 2.4 V			80	µA
		G input				160	
I_{IL}	Low-level input current	D input	V_{CC} = MAX, V_I = 0.4 V			−3.2	mA
		G input				−6.4	
I_{OS}	Short-circuit output current §	V_{CC} = MAX	SN54'	−20		−57	mA
			SN74'	−18		−57	
I_{CC}	Supply current	V_{CC} = MAX, See Note 3	SN54'		32	46	mA
			SN74'		32	53	

SN74L75

PARAMETER		TEST CONDITIONS†		MIN	TYP‡	MAX	UNIT
V_{IH}	High-level input voltage			2			V
V_{IL}	Low-level input voltage					0.8	V
V_{IK}	Input clamp voltage	V_{CC} = MIN,	I_I = −12 mA			−1.5	V
V_{OH}	High-level output voltage	V_{CC} = MIN, V_{IH} = 2 V, V_{IL} = 0.8 V,	I_{OH} = −200 µA	2.4	3.4		V
V_{OL}	Low-level output voltage	V_{CC} = MIN, V_{IH} = 2 V, V_{IL} = 0.8 V,	I_{OL} = 8 mA		0.2	0.4	V
I_I	Input current at maximum input voltage	V_{CC} = MAX,	V_I = 5.5 V			1	mA
I_{IH}	High-level input current	D input	V_{CC} = MAX, V_I = 2.4 V			40	µA
		G input				80	
I_{IL}	Low-level input current	D input	V_{CC} = MAX, V_I = 0.4 V			−1.6	mA
		G input				−3.2	
I_{OS}	Short-circuit output current §	V_{CC} = MAX	SN54L'	−10		−29	mA
			SN74L'	−9		−29	
I_{CC}	Supply current	V_{CC} = MAX, See Note 3	SN54L'		16	23	mA
			SN74L'		16	27	

SN74LS75

PARAMETER		TEST CONDITIONS†		SN54LS75 SN54LS77			SN74LS75			UNIT
				MIN	TYP‡	MAX	MIN	TYP‡	MAX	
V_{IH}	High-level input voltage			2			2			V
V_{IL}	Low-level input voltage					0.7			0.8	V
V_{IK}	Input clamp voltage	V_{CC} = MIN,	I_I = −18 mA			−1.5			−1.5	V
V_{OH}	High-level output voltage	V_{CC} = MIN, V_{IH} = 2 V, V_{IL} = V_{IL} max,	I_{OH} = −400 µA	2.5	3.5		2.7	3.5		V
V_{OL}	Low-level output voltage	V_{CC} = MIN, V_{IH} = 2 V, V_{IL} = V_{IL} max	I_{OL} = 4 mA		0.25	0.4		0.25	0.4	V
			I_{OL} = 8 mA					0.35	0.5	
I_I	Input current at maximum input voltage	V_{CC} = MAX, V_I = 7 V	D input			0.1			0.1	mA
			G input			0.4			0.4	
I_{IH}	High-level input current	V_{CC} = MAX, V_I = 2.7 V	D input			20			20	µA
			G input			80			80	
I_{IL}	Low-level input current	V_{CC} = MAX, V_I = 0.4 V	D input			−0.4			−0.4	mA
			G input			−1.6			−1.6	
I_{OS}	Short-circuit output current §	V_{CC} = MAX		−20		−100	−20		−100	mA
I_{CC}	Supply current	V_{CC} = MAX, See Note 2	'LS75		6.3	12		6.3	12	mA
			'LS77		6.9	13				

† For conditions shown as MIN or MAX, use the appropriate value specified under recommended operating conditions.
‡ All typical values are at V_{CC} = 5 V, T_A = 25°C.
§ Not more than one output should be shorted at a time, and duration of the short-circuit should not exceed one second
NOTE 2, 3: I_{CC} is tested with all inputs grounded and all outputs open.

Courtesy Texas Instruments, Inc.

	SN74LS373	8212
Logic Zero Input Logic One Input	− 0.4 mA/0.8 V max 20 μA/2.0 V min	− 0.25 mA/0.45 V max 10 μA/2.0 V min
Logic Zero Output Logic One Output	12 mA/0.4 V max − 2.6 mA/2.4 V min	15 mA/0.45 V max − 16 mA/2.4 V min

From this table you can see that the SN74LS373 requires the 8085A to source more current to it, and requires the 8085A to sink more current from it, than the 8212 does. If the SN74LS373 is used, this means that the data bus will have −380 μA of source current and 1.60 mA of sink current "left over" to drive other integrated circuits (memories or interface chips). Since the 8212 requires less current, more current will be left for use by other chips. If the 8212 is used, the data bus will have −390 μA of source current and 1.75 mA of sink current left over. The 8212 is a smaller load to the data bus.

When considering address/data bus demultiplexers, we should also consider the output current capabilities of the chips used. Typically, the SN74LS373 can sink 12 mA at 0.4 V maximum and source −2.6 mA at 2.4 V minimum. Again, the 8212 is better, because it can sink 15 mA at 0.45 V maximum and source −16 mA at 2.4 V minimum. Based on these electrical characteristics, the 8212 would be the better of the two to be used as the address/data bus demultiplexer.

GENERATING THE $\overline{\text{MEMR}}$, $\overline{\text{MEMW}}$, $\overline{\text{I/O R}}$, AND $\overline{\text{I/O W}}$ CONTROL SIGNALS

When the 8085A is reading information from memory or a peripheral device, the $\overline{\text{RD}}$ signal (a logic zero pulse) is generated. Likewise, when the 8085A is writing information to memory or a peripheral device, the $\overline{\text{WR}}$ signal (a logic zero pulse) is generated. The only signal that the 8085A generates to distinguish between a memory location and a peripheral device is the IO/$\overline{\text{M}}$ signal. This signal is a logic one when the 8085A is communicating with a peripheral device, and it is a logic zero when the 8085A is communicating with a memory location. Table 2-6 contains a summary of the different combinations of these three signals. The four combinations of these signals that we are interested in are summarized in Table 2-7.

Generating $\overline{\text{MEMR}}$

To generate the $\overline{\text{MEMR}}$ signal (pronounced memory read bar), the logic zero state of IO/$\overline{\text{M}}$ must be *gated* with $\overline{\text{RD}}$. The output of the gate must only be a logic zero when both inputs are a logic zero. The pin

Table 2-6. The Truth Table for All of the Combinations of RD, WR, and IO/M

RD	WR	IO/M	Condition
0	0	0	Not Allowed
0	0	1	Not Allowed
0	1	0	Memory Read
0	1	1	I/O Read
1	0	0	Memory Write
1	0	1	I/O Write
1	1	0	No External Access
1	1	1	No External Access

Table 2-7. The Combinations of RD, WR, and IO/M for Memory and Peripheral Operations

RD	WR	IO/M	Condition
0	1	0	Memory Read
0	1	1	I/O Read
1	0	0	Memory Write
1	0	1	I/O Write

configurations and truth tables for six common integrated circuits that contain gates, are shown in Fig. 2-10. Although there are many combinations of gates that will do the job, only a single SN7432-type OR gate is required. The truth table for an OR gate in this application is shown in Table 2-8, and the OR gate is wired as shown in Fig. 2-11. The 8085A

Table 2-8. The Truth Table for RD and IO/M so that the MEMR Signal Is Generated

RD	IO/M	MEMR
0	0	0
0	1	1
1	0	1
1	1	1

might generate the sequence of signals shown in Fig. 2-12, but only when *both* RD and IO/M are logic zeroes at the same time, will the output of the OR gate (MEMR) be a logic zero.

In Fig. 2-11 you can see that the RD signal generated by the 8085A is pulled up to +5 V by a 10,000-ohm (10-kilohm) resistor. This is done to prevent spurious RD signals from being generated when the microprocessor is in the hold state or when internal operations are being performed that do not require memory or peripheral devices to be accessed. The hold state was mentioned briefly in Chapter 1, when the function of the HOLD and HLDA pins were discussed. These pins are used by direct memory access (dma) devices so that they can access the microcomputer memory *without* using the microprocessor.

Will the $\overline{\text{RD}}$ and IO/$\overline{\text{M}}$ outputs of the 8085A be able to "drive" the inputs of this OR gate? Yes, these two signals have enough drive capability for some type of OR gate. Even though we want to use an OR gate in this circuit, there are a number of different OR gates to choose from. For example, an SN7432, SN74L32, SN74S32, or SN74LS32 might be used. What are the differences between these four OR gates?

The differences are tabulated in Tables 2-9 and 2-10. As you can see, the SN74LS32 is a reasonably "fast" gate with a propagation delay (the time it takes for a change on an input to be reflected in a change on an

Table 2-9. Typical Input Current Requirements (One Load) of SN54/SN74 Series Logic

SERIES	NOMINAL VALUE OF INPUT PULL-UP RESISTOR	MAXIMUM HIGH-LEVEL INPUT CURRENT	MAXIMUM LOW-LEVEL INPUT CURRENT
54/74	4 kΩ	40 μA	−1.6 mA
54H/74H	2.8 kΩ	50 μA	−2 mA
54L/74L †	40 kΩ	10 μA	−0.18 mA
	8 kΩ	20 μA	−0.8 mA
54LS/74LS	18 kΩ	20 μA	−0.4 mA
54S/74S	2.8 kΩ	50 μA	−2 mA

†Series 54L/74L has two different types of standard inputs as shown.

output) of only 9.5 ns. The SN74LS32 also has relatively low logic zero and logic one input current requirements. Although the SN74L32 has lower input current requirements, the propagation delay of this type of gate may be too long for use with microprocessors. Therefore, for almost all microcomputer applications the SN74LS-type of gates and functions

Table 2-10. Typical SN54/SN74 "Family" Performance Characteristics

SERIES	GATES			FLIP-FLOPS
	Speed-Power Product	Propagation Delay Time	Power Dissipation	Clock Input Frequency Range
54LS/74LS	19 pJ	9.5 ns	2 mW	dc to 45 MHz
54L/74L	33 pJ	33 ns	1 mW	dc to 3 MHz
54S/74S	57 pJ	3 ns	19 mW	dc to 125 MHz
54/74	100 pJ	10 ns	10 mW	dc to 35 MHz
54H/74H	132 pJ	6 ns	22 mW	dc to 50 MHz

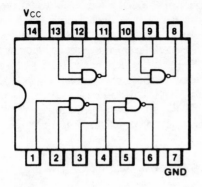

INPUTS		OUTPUT
A	B	Q
0	0	1
0	1	1
1	0	1
1	1	0

(A) NAND gate, SN7400 type.

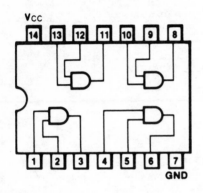

INPUTS		OUTPUT
A	B	Q
0	0	0
0	1	0
1	0	0
1	1	1

(B) AND gate, SN7408 type.

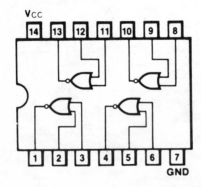

INPUTS		OUTPUT
A	B	Q
0	0	1
0	1	0
1	0	0
1	0	0

(C) NOR gate, SN7402 type.

Fig. 2-10. The pin configuration and

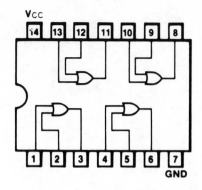

INPUTS		OUTPUT
A	B	Q
0	0	0
0	1	1
1	0	1
1	1	1

(D) OR gate, SN7432 type.

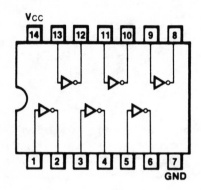

INPUT A	OUTPUT Q
0	1
1	0

(E) Inverter, SN7404 type.

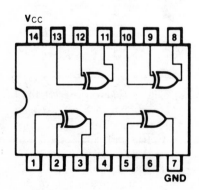

INPUTS		OUTPUT
A	B	Q
0	0	0
0	1	1
1	0	1
1	1	0

(F) Exclusive-OR gate, SN7486 type.

Courtesy Fairchild Camera and Instrument Corp.

truth tables for some of the common gates.

61

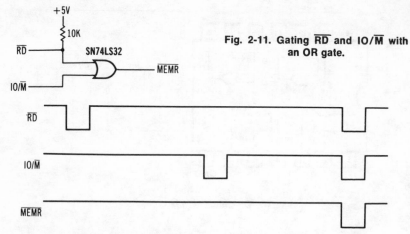

Fig. 2-11. Gating $\overline{\text{RD}}$ and IO/$\overline{\text{M}}$ with an OR gate.

Fig. 2-12. Possible combination of the $\overline{\text{RD}}$ and IO/$\overline{\text{M}}$ control signals.

will do very well. Based on this we would use an SN74LS32 OR gate to gate $\overline{\text{RD}}$ and IO/$\overline{\text{M}}$ together to generate the $\overline{\text{MEMR}}$ signal.

Generating $\overline{\text{MEMW}}$

It should be very easy for you to determine how to generate the $\overline{\text{MEMW}}$ signal (pronounced memory write bar). As expected, IO/$\overline{\text{M}}$ has to be gated with $\overline{\text{WR}}$. The output of the gate that is used in this design must only be a logic zero when both inputs (IO/$\overline{\text{M}}$ and $\overline{\text{WR}}$) are logic zeroes (Table 2-11). The writers hope that you have come to the con-

Table 2-11. The Truth Table for $\overline{\text{WR}}$ and IO/$\overline{\text{M}}$ so that the $\overline{\text{MEMW}}$ Signal Is Generated

$\overline{\text{WR}}$	IO/$\overline{\text{M}}$	$\overline{\text{MEMW}}$
0	0	0
0	1	1
1	0	1
1	1	1

clusion that an OR gate (SN74LS32) can be used to generate the $\overline{\text{MEMW}}$ signal. The gating of $\overline{\text{WR}}$ and IO/$\overline{\text{M}}$ is shown in Figs. 2-13 and 2-14.

If both OR gates (Figs. 2-11 and 2-13) are wired to the microprocessor chip, one OR gate input will be wired to $\overline{\text{RD}}$ and one of the inputs of the other OR gate will be wired to $\overline{\text{WR}}$. The remaining two inputs (one from each gate) will be wired to the same 8085A output, IO/$\overline{\text{M}}$. Based on Table 2-9 the logic one input source current requirements of the two OR gates (SN74LS32) is only 40 μA. The logic zero input sink current that is generated by the OR gates is -0.8 mA. This means that the 8085A must source -40 μA and sink 1.3 mA (0.5 mA due to the resistor, 0.8

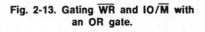
Fig. 2-13. Gating $\overline{WR}$ and IO/$\overline{M}$ with
an OR gate.

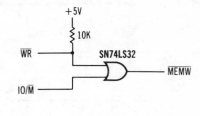

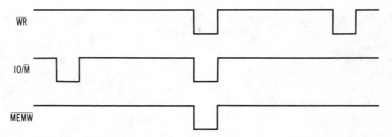

Fig. 2-14. Possible combinations of the $\overline{WR}$ and IO/$\overline{M}$ control signals.

mA due to the OR gates). This is well within the limits specified for the 8085A.

In Fig. 2-13 you can see that $\overline{WR}$ signal generated by the 8085A is also pulled up to +5 V with a pullup resistor. Again, this is to prevent spurious pulses from being placed on the $\overline{WR}$ line when the microprocessor is either in the hold state or when the 8085A is performing some internal operation. In all future diagrams where $\overline{RD}$ and $\overline{WR}$ are used you will see these same pullup resistors.

Generating $\overline{I/O\ R}$ ($\overline{IN}$)

To generate the $\overline{I/O\ R}$ signal (pronounced eye-oh read bar), the IO/$\overline{M}$ signal must be a logic one while the $\overline{RD}$ signal is a logic zero. This signal is also often called $\overline{IN}$ (pronounced in bar). Only when these two signals are in these states should the output of a gate ($\overline{I/O\ R}$) be a logic zero. This is shown in Fig. 2-15. A truth table for the combination of these two signals appears in Table 2-12.

Unfortunately, we can not use a single gate, such as a NAND, AND, OR, or exclusive-OR gate, to generate this signal. There are, however, a num-

Table 2-12. The Truth Table for $\overline{RD}$ and IO/$\overline{M}$ so that the
$\overline{I/O\ R}$ or $\overline{IN}$ Signal Is Generated

$\overline{RD}$	IO/$\overline{M}$	$\overline{I/O\ R}$ ($\overline{IN}$)
0	0	1
0	1	0
1	0	1
1	1	1

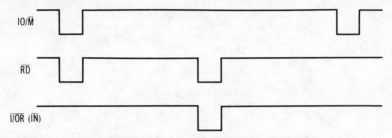

Fig. 2-15. Possible combinations of the $\overline{\text{RD}}$ and IO/$\overline{\text{M}}$ control signals to generate the $\overline{\text{I/O R}}$ ($\overline{\text{IN}}$) signal.

ber of different gating solutions to this problem, including the one shown in Fig. 2-16. Another possible solution is shown in Fig. 2-17.

So far, by generating $\overline{\text{MEMR}}$, $\overline{\text{MEMW}}$, and $\overline{\text{I/O R}}$ ($\overline{\text{IN}}$), the inputs to three gates are wired to the IO/$\overline{\text{M}}$ output signal of the 8085A integrated circuit. Even so, the 8085A will operate properly.

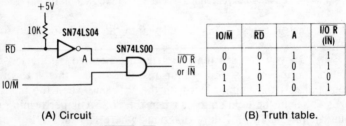

IO/$\overline{\text{M}}$	$\overline{\text{RD}}$	A	$\overline{\text{I/O R}}$ ($\overline{\text{IN}}$)
0	0	1	1
0	1	0	1
1	0	1	0
1	1	0	1

(A) Circuit   (B) Truth table.

Fig. 2-16. Generating the $\overline{\text{I/O R}}$ ($\overline{\text{IN}}$) signal with an inverter and a NAND gate.

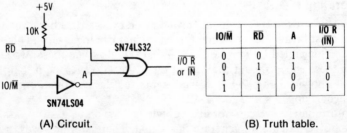

IO/$\overline{\text{M}}$	$\overline{\text{RD}}$	A	$\overline{\text{I/O R}}$ ($\overline{\text{IN}}$)
0	0	1	1
0	1	1	1
1	0	0	0
1	1	0	1

(A) Circuit.   (B) Truth table.

Fig. 2-17. Generating the $\overline{\text{I/O R}}$ ($\overline{\text{IN}}$) signal wih an inverter and an OR gate.

Generating $\overline{\text{I/O W}}$ ($\overline{\text{OUT}}$)

The $\overline{\text{I/O W}}$ signal (pronounced eye-oh write bar) is also often called $\overline{\text{OUT}}$ (pronounced out bar), and is generated when the IO/$\overline{\text{M}}$ signal is a logic one and the $\overline{\text{WR}}$ signal is a logic zero (see Fig. 2-18). A truth table for the four combinations of IO/$\overline{\text{M}}$ and $\overline{\text{WR}}$ is shown in Table

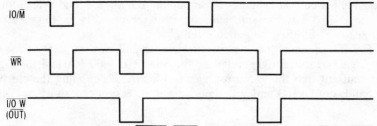

Fig. 2-18. Generating the I/O W (OUT) control signal from IO/M̄ and W̄R̄.

Table 2-13. The Truth Table for W̄R̄ and IO/M̄ so that the I/O W or OUT Signal Is Generated

W̄R̄	IO/M̄	I/O W (OUT)
0	0	1
0	1	0
1	0	1
1	1	1

2-13. As you would expect we can use an inverter and a NAND gate or an inverter and an OR gate to generate this signal. Since we have used OR gates in a number of previous examples, we will use one in combination with an inverter, to generate the I/O W (OUT) control signal. The resulting circuitry is shown in Fig. 2-19.

Generating MEMR̄, MEMW̄, I/O R̄ (IN), and I/O W̄ (OUT) Together

Now that we have discussed how all of these signals are generated with some simple, external circuitry, you should be able to design the required circuitry that will generate all four of these control signals. Therefore, design and draw the schematic diagram for a circuit that can be used to generate all four of the memory and I/O control signals. You may use any gates that appear in Fig. 2-10 in your design.

One solution to this problem is shown in Fig. 2-20. This particular solution requires one SN74LS04 inverter and one SN74LS32 OR gate

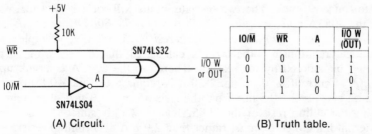

(A) Circuit.   (B) Truth table.

Fig. 2-19. Generating the I/O W̄ signal with an inverter and an OR gate.

integrated circuit. How much current do the IO/$\overline{M}$, RD, and WR outputs of the 8085A have to sink and source if the circuitry in Fig. 2-20 is wired to the 8085A integrated circuit?

The IO/$\overline{M}$ signal has to drive an inverter and two OR gate inputs, so the logic one current generated by the 8085A is −60 μA and the logic zero current that this pin must sink is 1.2 mA. Calculating the current demands on the $\overline{RD}$ and $\overline{WR}$ signals is not as easy, because we not only

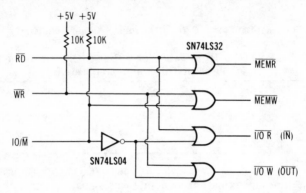

Fig. 2-20. Using OR gates and inverters to generate the $\overline{MEMR}$, $\overline{MEMW}$, $\overline{I/O\ R}$ ($\overline{IN}$), and $\overline{I/O\ W}$ ($\overline{OUT}$) control signals.

have the $\overline{RD}$ and $\overline{WR}$ signals wired to two OR gates, but also to +5 V through a 10-kilohm resistor. In the logic one state the $\overline{RD}$ and $\overline{WR}$ pins will have to source −40 μA for the inputs of the OR gates. If we assume that the logic one is represented by +5 V, then most of this source current will be generated by the 8085A and some will come from the +5 V through the pullup resistor. The amount of current from the 8085A will be determined by the internal resistance of the circuitry that drives these two pins. In general, we can assume that all of the source current comes from the 8085A. Therefore the 8085A can still generate up to −400 μA of source current.

When the 8085A places a logic zero on the $\overline{RD}$ or $\overline{WR}$ pins, current from both the inputs of the OR gates *and* from the 10-kilohm pullup resistor must be sunk. The two OR gate inputs will source −0.4 mA each, so the 8085A must sink this, *but in addition the 8085A must sink −0.5 mA of source current from the pullup resistor.* Using a very simple mathematical relationship, the writers calculated that 0.5 mA of current would be sourced by the resistor. Therefore the 8085A can sink up to 2 mA of current, and in Fig. 2-20 it is required to sink −0.8 mA from the OR gates and −0.5 mA from the resistor, or −1.3 mA of current. By using the pullup resistor the 8085A can now only sink −1.5 mA from external integrated circuits, rather than 2.0 mA. The pullup resistors on $\overline{RD}$ and $\overline{WR}$ must be used, however.

Are there any other designs that can be used to generate these same signals? Yes, one of them is shown in Fig. 2-21. Although this new design requires the same number of integrated circuits, three inverters and four NAND gates (SN74LS00) are used. This is two more gates that our previous design in Fig. 2-20. However, this new design does have one advantage over our previous design. Do you know what this particular advantage is?

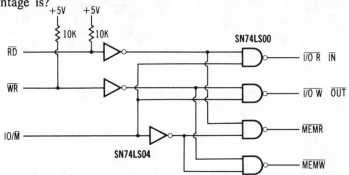

Fig. 2-21. Using inverters and NAND gates to generate the $\overline{\text{MEMR}}$, $\overline{\text{MEMW}}$, $\overline{\text{I/O R}}$ ($\overline{\text{IN}}$), and $\overline{\text{I/O W}}$ ($\overline{\text{OUT}}$) control signals.

The IO/$\overline{\text{M}}$ signal still has to drive three inputs, but the $\overline{\text{RD}}$ and $\overline{\text{WR}}$ outputs only have to drive one inverter input each. This means that the $\overline{\text{RD}}$ and $\overline{\text{WR}}$ signals can be used to drive more gates than the $\overline{\text{RD}}$ and $\overline{\text{WR}}$ signals shown in Fig. 2-20. Surprisingly enough, we can use a single integrated circuit, rather than the two integrated circuits shown in Fig. 2-20 and 2-21, to generate all four of these control signals.

The Single Chip Solution—The SN74LS42

The pin configuration, logic diagram, and truth table for the SN74-LS42 4-line-to-10-line decoder are shown in Fig. 2-22. Even though the internal organization of this integrated circuit is complex, you can still see the use of inverters and four-input NAND gates to construct a *decoder*. Although we did not use this term to describe the circuitry in the previous section, that is what we designed. The decoder for the control signals decodes the different states of the IO/$\overline{\text{M}}$, $\overline{\text{RD}}$, and $\overline{\text{WR}}$ signals, and generates logic zeroes on its appropriate outputs.

Even though the SN74LS42 decoder has four inputs, it cannot decode all 2^4 or 16 possible input states (0000, 0001, . . . , 1110, 1111). Instead, the SN74LS42 can decode the logic states between 0000 and 1001. The A input is assigned the decimal value one, the B input is assigned the decimal value two, C is assigned four, and D is assigned eight. Therefore the decoder decodes the states between 0_{10} (0000) and 9_{10} (1001), or ten possible states—thus the name *4-line-to-10-line decoder* for the chip.

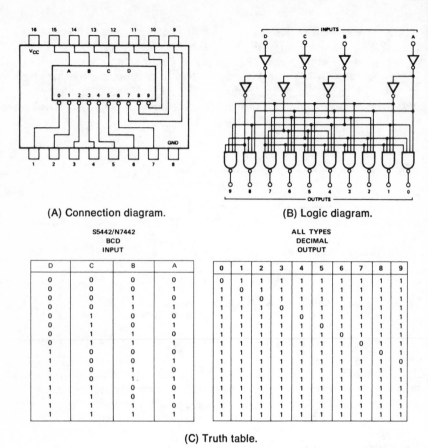

(A) Connection diagram.

(B) Logic diagram.

S5442/N7442
BCD
INPUT

ALL TYPES
DECIMAL
OUTPUT

D	C	B	A		0	1	2	3	4	5	6	7	8	9
0	0	0	0		0	1	1	1	1	1	1	1	1	1
0	0	0	1		1	0	1	1	1	1	1	1	1	1
0	0	1	0		1	1	0	1	1	1	1	1	1	1
0	0	1	1		1	1	1	0	1	1	1	1	1	1
0	1	0	0		1	1	1	1	0	1	1	1	1	1
0	1	0	1		1	1	1	1	1	0	1	1	1	1
0	1	1	0		1	1	1	1	1	1	0	1	1	1
0	1	1	1		1	1	1	1	1	1	1	0	1	1
1	0	0	0		1	1	1	1	1	1	1	1	0	1
1	0	0	1		1	1	1	1	1	1	1	1	1	0
1	0	1	0		1	1	1	1	1	1	1	1	1	1
1	0	1	1		1	1	1	1	1	1	1	1	1	1
1	1	0	0		1	1	1	1	1	1	1	1	1	1
1	1	0	1		1	1	1	1	1	1	1	1	1	1
1	1	1	0		1	1	1	1	1	1	1	1	1	1
1	1	1	1		1	1	1	1	1	1	1	1	1	1

(C) Truth table.

Courtesy Signetics Corp.

Fig. 2-22. The truth table, logic diagram, and pin configuration for the SN74LS42 4-line-to-10-line decoder.

How is this integrated circuit used to generate the required control signals? We have three signals generated by the 8085A and four inputs to the SN74LS42. Which inputs are used? The combinations of IO/$\overline{M}$, $\overline{RD}$, and $\overline{WR}$ that we are interested in are shown in Table 2-7. Based on the information in this table you would not wire any of the three signals generated by the 8085A to the D input of the SN74LS42. Instead, the D input would be wired directly to ground. The $\overline{RD}$, $\overline{WR}$, and IO/$\overline{M}$ signals would then be wired in *any combination* to the A, B, and C inputs of the decoder.

Assume that the 8085A signals are wired to the SN74LS42 decoder as shown in Fig. 2-23. At which outputs will the logic zero pulses for the control signals be present? To determine which outputs will represent which control signals a truth table must be generated (Table 2-14). As

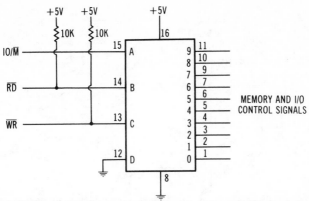

Fig. 2-23. Using an SN74LS42 to generate memory and I/O control signals.

Table 2-14. The Pin Assignments for the Control Signals Generated by
the SN74LS42 4-Line-to-10-Line Decoder

GND (D)	$\overline{\text{WR}}$ (C)	$\overline{\text{RD}}$ (B)	IO/$\overline{\text{M}}$ (A)	Control Signal	Output	Pin
0	0	1	1	$\overline{\text{I/O W (OUT)}}$	3	4
0	1	0	1	$\overline{\text{I/O R (IN)}}$	5	6
0	0	1	0	$\overline{\text{MEMW}}$	2	3
0	1	0	0	$\overline{\text{MEMR}}$	4	5

you can see from Table 2-14 the control signals will be output on outputs
2 through 5 (pins 3 through 6). Note that because of the inverters built
into the inputs of the SN74LS42, the IO/$\overline{\text{M}}$, $\overline{\text{RD}}$, and $\overline{\text{WR}}$ signals only
have to drive a single gate. However, the pullup resistors on the $\overline{\text{RD}}$ and
$\overline{\text{WR}}$ lines increase the amount of current that the 8085A must sink.

Using the SN74LS155

Using the SN74LS155 decoder (Fig. 2-24), design the circuitry nec-
essary to generate the four control signals $\overline{\text{MEMR}}$, $\overline{\text{MEMW}}$, $\overline{\text{I/O R}}$, and
$\overline{\text{I/O W}}$. You may use any of the integrated circuits that we discussed
previously (Fig. 2-10).

Unfortunately, we cannot generate all of the control signals using just
one of the 2-line-to-4-line decoders contained in the SN74LS155; both
must be used. As you can see from the truth table in Fig. 2-24, the two
strobe inputs (1G and 2G) should not be wired to either $\overline{\text{RD}}$, $\overline{\text{WR}}$, or
IO/$\overline{\text{M}}$. Instead, both of these inputs would be wired to ground. Although
we could wire $\overline{\text{RD}}$, $\overline{\text{WR}}$, and IO/$\overline{\text{M}}$ in any combination to the A, B, and
data inputs (both 1C and 2C), it will be easiest to determine the "active
outputs" of both decoders by wiring IO/$\overline{\text{M}}$ to both data (1C and 2C)
inputs. If we assume that $\overline{\text{RD}}$ is wired to the A input, and that $\overline{\text{WR}}$ is
wired to the B input, which outputs can be used for the $\overline{\text{MEMR}}$,
$\overline{\text{MEMW}}$, $\overline{\text{I/O R}}$ (IN), and $\overline{\text{I/O W}}$ (OUT) signals?

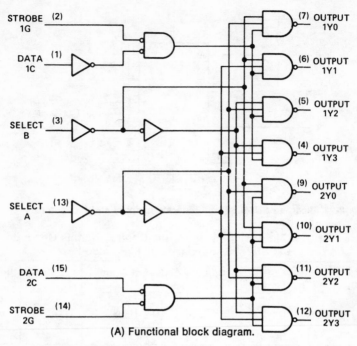

(A) Functional block diagram.

INPUTS				OUTPUTS			
SELECT		STROBE	DATA	1Y0	1Y1	1Y2	1Y3
B	A	1G	1C				
X	X	H	X	H	H	H	H
L	L	L	H	L	H	H	H
L	H	L	H	H	L	H	H
H	L	L	H	H	H	L	H
H	H	L	H	H	H	H	L
X	X	X	L	H	H	H	H

INPUTS				OUTPUTS			
SELECT		STROBE	DATA	2Y0	2Y1	2Y2	2Y3
B	A	2G	2C				
X	X	H	X	H	H	H	H
L	L	L	L	L	H	H	H
L	H	L	L	H	L	H	H
H	L	L	L	H	H	L	H
H	H	L	L	H	H	H	L
X	X	X	H	H	H	H	H

(B) Function tables: 2-line-to-4-line decoder or 1-line-to-4-line multiplexer.

Courtesy Texas Instruments, Inc.

Fig. 2-24. The truth table, pin configuration, and logic diagram for the SN74LS155 dual 2-line-to-4-line decoder.

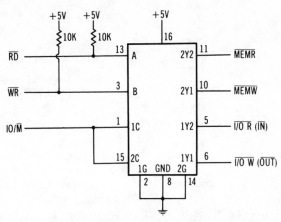

Fig. 2-25. Using the SN74LS155 to generate memory and I/O control signals.

The IO/$\overline{\text{M}}$ signal is wired to both decoders, so the memory control signals ($\overline{\text{MEMR}}$ and $\overline{\text{MEMW}}$) will be generated by the "2" decoder. When IO/$\overline{\text{M}}$ is a logic one, the I/O control signals [$\overline{\text{I/O R}}$ ($\overline{\text{IN}}$) and $\overline{\text{I/O W}}$ ($\overline{\text{OUT}}$)] will be generated by the "1" decoder. If the $\overline{\text{RD}}$ signal is wired to the A input and $\overline{\text{WR}}$ is wired to the B input, the control signals will be generated as shown in Table 2-15. The SN74LS155 in Fig. 2-25

Table 2-15. The Pin Assignments for the Control Signals Generated by the SN74LS155 Dual 2-Line-to-4-Line Decoder

Control Signal	Output	Pin
$\overline{\text{MEMR}}$	2Y2	11
$\overline{\text{MEMW}}$	2Y1	10
$\overline{\text{I/O R}}$ ($\overline{\text{IN}}$)	1Y2	5
$\overline{\text{I/O W}}$ ($\overline{\text{OUT}}$)	1Y1	6

is wired so that these four control signals will be present on the 2Y2, 2Y1, 1Y2, and 1Y1 outputs.

RESETTING THE 8085A MICROPROCESSOR

As was mentioned in Chapter 1 a resistor, capacitor, and push button are often used to reset the 8085A. A typical reset circuit is shown in Fig. 2-26. The diode in series with the 50-kilohm resistor prevents voltages greater than 5.6 V from being applied to the $\overline{\text{RESET IN}}$ input.

PRELIMINARY 8085A MICROCOMPUTER DESIGN

In this chapter and all of the remaining chapters you will have the opportunity to design parts of an 8085A-based microcomputer. In gen-

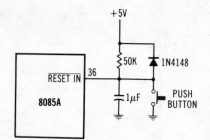

Fig. 2-26. A typical reset circuit for the 8085A.

eral, you will just be asked to apply the signals and techniques that were discussed in this chapter to the design of the microcomputer. This means that in the following preliminary designs you will have the opportunity to apply your knowledge of the address/data bus, control signals, microprocessor reset circuitry, and TTL integrated circuits to the design of an 8085A-based microcomputer.

In this and the previous chapter we discussed the use of many of the signals of the 8085A. In this section you will have your first opportunity to design part of an 8085-based microcomputer system. We have not discussed how memory integrated circuits are used or how I/O devices are wired to the microcomputer buses. Therefore your designs at this point will not be for a completely operational microcomputer. Good luck.

Preliminary Address Demultiplexer, Control-Signal Design Number 1

Using an 8085A, an SN74LS373, and an SN74LS42, design a microcomputer system that has a cycle time of 400 ns. You may use any additional components, such as resistors, capacitors, crystals, etc., that you require, but you may not use any additional integrated circuits.

The microcomputer design that you should have created should be very similar to the design shown in Fig. 2-27. Some specific design points that you should look for in your design include:

1. Is power applied to all of the integrated circuits? For the 8085A, +5 V to pin 40, ground to pin 20. For the SN74LS42, +5 V to pin 16, ground to pin 8. For the SN74LS373, +5 V to pin 20, ground to pin 10.
2. Is the output control pin of the SN74LS373 wired to ground? This means that the low address is always output by the SN74-LS373.
3. Is the D input of the SN74LS42 wired to ground?
4. Is the ALE signal wired to the enable (G) input of the SN74-LS373?

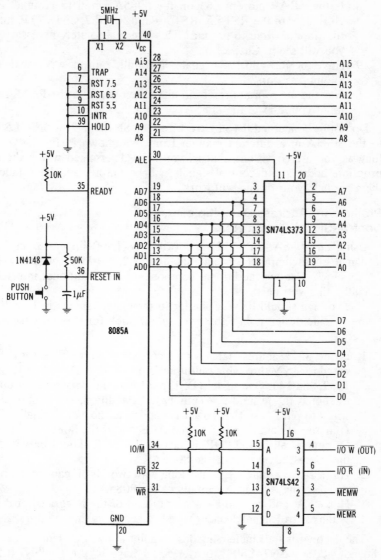

Fig. 2-27. A 400-ns 8085A-based microcomputer with an address latch and control signal decoder.

5. Is a 5-MHz crystal used? It would be difficult to get an accurate *RC* network for the clock generation circuitry.
6. Is the READY pin (pin 35) on the 8085A wired to +5 V?
7. Is the HOLD pin (pin 39) on the 8085A wired to ground?

8. Is the TRAP pin (pin 6) on the 8085A wired to ground? Op-
   TIONAL: Are the RST5.5, RST5.6 and RST7.7, and INTR interrupt inputs wired to ground? This is not absolutely necessary, as
   you will see in Chapter 6.
9. Have the RD and WR signals been pulled up to +5 V with 10-
   kilohm resistors?
10. Has the appropriate reset circuitry been wired to the RESET IN
    input (pin 36) of the 8085A?

Do not be concerned if you have wired the SN74LS42 or SN74LS373
to the 8085A in a different manner from that shown in Fig. 2-27. As
long as you are consistent, that is, you have determined where the appropriate address and control signals will be output, and have labeled
them as such, your design will work.

Preliminary Address-Demultiplexer, Control-Signal Design No. 2

Using an 8085A, an 8212, and two SN74LS00 integrated circuits,
design a microcomputer system that uses a 2.000-MHz quartz crystal
for its clock. Use any additional components (no additional integrated
circuits) that you need.

Your design should be very similar to the system shown in Fig. 2-28.
Some specific design points that you should look for in your design include:

1. Is the 8212 address latch wired correctly? Three pins should be
   wired to +5 V through a pullup resistor (STB, MD, and $\overline{CLR}$; pins
   11, 2, and 14). One signal ($\overline{DS1}$, pin 1) should be wired to ground,
   as should the ground pin (pin 12). In addition, +5 V should be
   wired to pin 24, so that power is applied to the 8212. Finally, DS2
   (pin 13) should be wired to the ALE pin of the 8085A (pin 30).
   Of course, all of the "DI" inputs of the 8212 should be wired to
   the address/data pins of the 8085A.
2. Has a 2-MHz quartz crystal, along with two 20-pF capacitors, been
   wired to the X1 and X2 inputs of the 8085A?
3. Has +5 V and ground been wired to all of the integrated circuits?
4. Is the control signal decoder wired correctly, as shown in Fig. 2-21?

The decoder is the challenging design point in this problem. Since you
did not get any SN74LS04 inverters, you have to use the SN74LS00
NAND gates as inverters where required. This is done by wiring one of
the NAND gate inputs to +5 V through a 1-kilohm pullup resistor and the
remaining input is the input of the "inverter." This means that there are
only two possible logic states—when one input is at a logic zero and the
other input is at a logic one, or when both inputs are at logic one. The
"inversion function" can be proved by examining the truth table for the
NAND gate in Fig. 2-10 for these two cases.

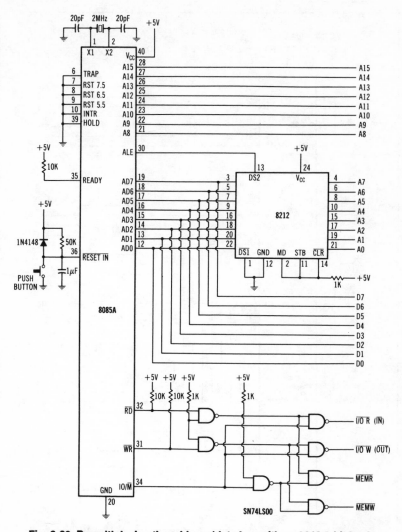

Fig. 2-28. Demultiplexing the address/data bus with an 8212 8-bit latch.

Preliminary Address-Demultiplexer,
Control-Signal Design No. 3

Using an 8085A-2, two SN74LS75 latches, and an SN74LS155, design a microcomputer that has a 500-ns cycle time. You may use any additional *integrated circuits* or components (resistors, capacitors, crystals, etc.) that you require.

Your design should be very similar to that shown in Fig. 2-29. Some specific design points that you should look for in your design include:

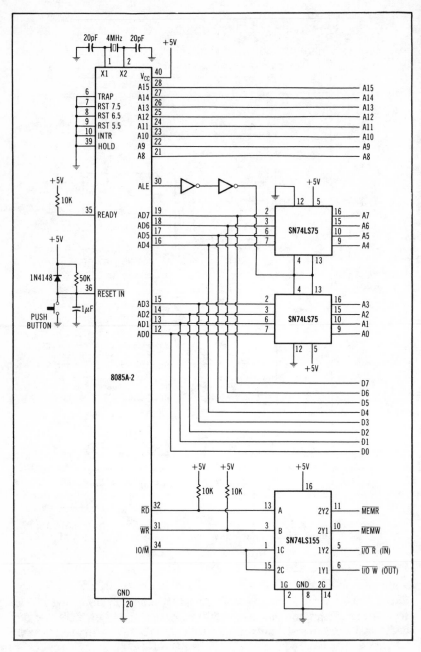

Fig. 2-29. Using an SN74LS155 decoder and two SN74LS75 latches in an 8085A-based microcomputer design.

1. Has a 4-MHz crystal along with two 20-pF capacitors been wired to the X1 and X2 inputs of the 8085A-2?
2. Have both decoders in the SN74LS155 been used to generate the required memory and peripheral (I/O) control signals?
3. Have both strobe inputs (1G and 2G) been wired to ground?
4. Have the two SN74LS75 latches been wired to the microprocessor address/data pins correctly?
5. Has ALE been buffered with two SN74LS04 inverters (or equivalent)?
6. Have all four latch enable inputs been wired together to the output of the second inverter?
7. Have the $\overline{RD}$ and $\overline{WR}$ outputs of the 8085A-2 been pulled up to +5 V with 10-kilohm resistors?

Wiring the latches to the microprocessor is the challenge in this design. At the beginning of this chapter we noted that SN74LS75 latches would require additional circuitry if they are used to demultiplex the address/data bus. The data inputs of the SN74LS75s would be wired directly to the address/data bus. However, the four enable inputs to the latches source more current (−6.4 mA) than the ALE output can sink (2 mA). Therefore two SN74LS04 inverters are used to buffer the ALE signal. The ALE signal drives one input rather than four. The output of the second inverter is the *same positive pulse* as the ALE signal, only it is slightly delayed (19 ns; Table 2-10). The output of an SN74LS04 can sink 8 mA at 0.4 V maximum and can source −400 μA at 3.4 V minimum.

CONCLUSION

In this chapter we have discussed a number of different clock designs, address/data bus demultiplexer designs, and control signal decoder designs. Based on these a number of preliminary microcomputer systems were designed. Some of the important points to remember in designing an 8085A-based microcomputer system include: (1) the drive capabilities of the 8085A outputs, (2) the drive requirements of external circuitry, (3) the timing requirements of the 8085A, and (4) the timing requirements of external circuitry.

By demultiplexing the address/data bus we now have a 16-bit address bus and an 8-bit bidirectional data bus. As we will see in the following chapters, the address bus will be used by both memory and peripheral devices. When the 8085A accesses memory it generates a 16-bit address and places it on the address bus, and when the 8085A accesses peripheral (I/O) devices it generates an 8-bit device address, which it places on A0 through A7 and also on A8 through A15. Although the "data bus" still has an address on it when the ALE signal is a logic one, only data are present on the data bus when one of the four control signals ($\overline{\text{MEMR}}$, $\overline{\text{MEMW}}$, $\overline{\text{I/O R}}$ ($\overline{\text{IN}}$), and $\overline{\text{I/O W}}$ ($\overline{\text{OUT}}$)) is active.

REFERENCES

1. *MCS-85 User's Manual, September 1978,* Intel Corp., Santa Clara, CA 95051, 1978, page 5–5.
2. *ibid.,* page 5–2.

PROBLEMS

2-1. Design the clock circuitry required for use with a 3.567-MHz quartz crystal.

2-2. Design the clock circuitry for an 8085A-2 so that it can be clocked by an 8-MHz TTL-compatible clock.

2-3. Some latches latch information present on their inputs on the positive edge (logic zero to logic one transition) of the clock signal. Is it possible to use this type of latch to demultiplex the address/data bus? If it is possible, design the required circuitry to perform this task.

2-4. The input current requirements of the data inputs of the SN7475 4-bit bistable latch are 80 μA at 2.4 V minimum and -3.2 mA at 0.4 V maximum. Design the required circuitry so that two of these latches can be used to demultiplex the address/data bus.

2-5. When the ALE signal is a logic one, the S1 and S0 outputs of the microprocessor contain *status information.* In particular, if the 8085A executes a halt (HLT) instruction, S1 and S0 will be logic zeroes when ALE is a logic one. Design the circuitry for a *halt indicator*. This circuitry should generate a logic zero when the microprocessor halts, and a logic one at all other times.

2-6. What are the advantages and disadvantages of using a resistor-capacitor network versus a quartz crystal to clock the 8085A?

2-7. Design a control signal decoder, using only NOR gates, so that the signals $\overline{MEMR}$, $\overline{MEMW}$, $\overline{IN}$, and $\overline{OUT}$ are generated.

2-8. If the 8085A is wired to a 6.144-MHz quartz crystal, what is the cycle time of the microprocessor?

2-9. What are the voltage and current levels generated (output) by the 8085A for a logic zero and a logic one?

2-10. What is the minimum duration of the $\overline{WR}$ pulse generated by an 8085A with a 320-ns cycle time?

CHAPTER 3

Memory Systems—
Memory Decoding

In this chapter we will discuss the electronics required to select one memory location out of a possible 65,536. Of course, to do this a memory address must be on the address bus. The external electronics must *decode* this address and then select the memory integrated circuit that contains the appropriate memory location. This circuitry can be designed and constructed using a number of different methods and integrated circuits. We will discuss the most popular methods, and then you will have an opportunity to design your own memory decoders.

MEMORY SYSTEMS

As you have seen in the two previous chapters, the microprocessor generates a 16-bit memory address so that a specific memory location can be addressed. The microprocessor also uses the 8-bit data bus and the memory control signals $\overline{\text{MEMR}}$ and $\overline{\text{MEMW}}$ to control the flow of data on the data bus. Of course, when the 8085A generates an address, only one out of many memory locations should "recognize" the address and therefore respond to the memory control signals. The addressed memory location would then gate information from the data bus to the memory location (memory write) or gate information onto the data bus from the memory location (memory read).

As an example, suppose that there are six people in a classroom. One person is the teacher and the remaining people are the students. The teacher might say, "I have information for the person who lives at 1208 Elm Street, and the information is: bring your lunch tomorrow." As the teacher is saying this, all of the students ask themselves if they live at 1208 Elm Street. If one student lives at this address, he or she listens to the rest of the message. The students who do not live at 1208 Elm Street, realize that this is not their address, so they do not listen to the rest of the message. What if no one lives at 1208 Elm Street? The teacher will still "output" or generate the address and information, but, since no one recognizes the address, no one receives the information.

The microcomputer memory operates in a very similar manner. When an address is placed on the address bus by the microprocessor, external logic determines which one of many memory locations is being addressed. The memory location will then be accessed by the microprocessor during either a read or write operation. In our teacher/student example, information was "written" to the students.

Fortunately, there is more than one memory location in a memory integrated circuit. If there were only one 8-bit memory location in an integrated circuit, you would need 65,536 integrated circuits to use all of the microprocessor "address space." Instead, because there are so many memory locations in a single integrated circuit, you can actually have all 65,536 8-bit memory locations in eight integrated circuits! Typically, memory integrated circuits have between 1024 (1K) and 4096 (4K) words or memory locations, with either 1, 4, or 8 bits of information per address.

Let us assume that we have an "ideal" read-only memory (ROM) integrated circuit that contains 1024 8-bit memory locations. This ROM was programmed by someone else and it contains a sequence of instructions that we would like to execute on our 8085A-based microcomputer. A block diagram for this "ideal" ROM is shown in Fig. 3-1. How would this integrated circuit be wired to the microcomputer address and data buses?

One of the first questions that we must answer is: where will the 8085A read its first instruction from? We know that when the 8085A is reset it fetches the first instruction from memory location zero. Therefore our ROM must be wired to the microprocessor so that when the 8085A puts a memory address of zero on the address bus there is a memory location within the ROM that "recognizes" this address and places its contents on the data bus, which the 8085A assumes to be an instruction. This means that the ROM would have to be wired to the microprocessor buses as shown in Fig. 3-2. As you can see, since there are only 1024 (1K) 8-bit words in the ROM, address lines A10 through A15 are not used; they are not wired to the ROM, since the ROM has no provision for recognizing these particular address signals. It contains only the circuitry necessary to recognize an address on address lines A0 through A9. Where did the address signals A0–A7 come from? These signals are generated by the address/data bus demultiplexer that was discussed in the last chapter.

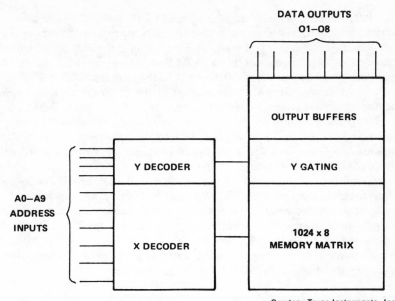

Courtesy Texas Instruments, Inc.

Fig. 3-1. An "ideal" 1024 8-bit word read-only memory (ROM).

When the 8085A outputs a memory address of zero, how is one memory location out of a possible 1024 memory locations selected? In Fig. 3-1 you can see that decoders contained *within* the integrated circuit decode the 10-bit ($2^{10} = 1024$) address and select one 8-bit memory location. The instruction in this memory location is then output on the

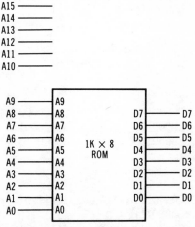

Fig. 3-2. Wiring an ideal read-only memory to the microcomputer address and data buses.

data bus. Suppose we need to add a second 1K×8 ROM to the microcomputer system, because our program has grown from 882 memory
locations to 1956 memory locations. Even though we only needed 882
locations initially, we cannot buy a ROM that contains only 882 memory
locations. We have to use a 1024-word ROM and ignore the last 142
memory locations. Since the new version of the program requires 1956
memory locations, we will have to use two 1K-(1024-) word ROMs, or
a total of 2048 memory locations. As you will see in the next chapter
we could use a single 2048-word ROM to do the job. Regardless of the
number of ROMs used, for a 1956-step program 92 memory locations
out of 2048 memory locations will not be used.

Assuming that 1K ROMs are used, how will the second ROM be
wired to the address and data buses? Before we can answer this question,
we must determine what addresses the ROMs should respond to. Even
though the microprocessor generates a 16-bit address the first ROM was
only wired to 10 of the 16 possible address lines. We know, however,
that when the 8085A is reset, it outputs an address of zero. Therefore the
addresses that the first 1K ROM will respond to are:

High Address	Low Address
00000000	00000000
00000000	00000001
00000000	00000010
•	•
•	•
•	•
00000011	11111101
00000011	11111110
00000011	11111111

When the second 1K ROM is added to the system, it should respond to
the next 1024 sequential addresses from:

High Address	Low Address
00000100	00000000
00000100	00000001
00000100	00000010
•	•
•	•
•	•
00000111	11111101
00000111	11111110
00000111	11111111

As you can see, the first memory location in the first 1K ROM has an address of 00000000 00000000 and the first address in the second 1K ROM has an address of 00000100 00000000. The only difference between these two addresses is that bit A10 in the address is a logic zero when the first ROM is addressed, and it is a logic one when the second ROM is addressed. In fact, this is also true when the memory addresses for the first ROM are compared with the memory addresses for the second ROM.

Based on this the inputs A0 through A9 of the second ROM would also be wired to the ten least significant address lines in the address bus. External circuitry that uses A10 would also have to be added to distinguish or *select* one ROM or the other. However, once these "chip select" signals are generated, how can they be wired to the ROMs? In Fig. 3-1 there are no additional inputs shown. Fig. 3-3 contains the block diagram for a more "realistic" ROM, and, even though they are not shown in the diagram, there are at least two pins that are used to supply power to the ROM.

As you can see in Fig. 3-3 the ROM manufacturer *provides a chip select* or $\overline{CS}$ input on the ROM. For most ROMs this signal must be a logic zero to *enable* or *select* the ROM. By enabling the ROM the content of the addressed memory location is output by the output buffers onto the data bus. If the chip is not selected ($\overline{CS} = 1$), the address on

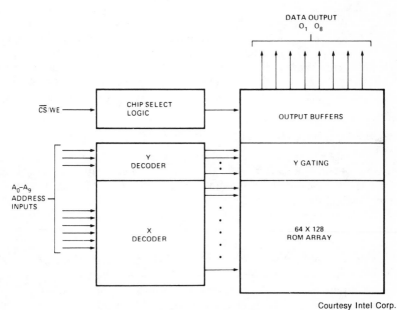

Courtesy Intel Corp.

Fig. 3-3. A "real" ROM block diagram.

lines A0 through A9 will still be decoded and a memory location will be selected internally. However, the content of the memory location will *not* be placed on the data bus, because the logic one on the CS input prevents the information from being transferred onto the data bus by the three-state output buffers. We will discuss ROMs and how they are used in microcomputer systems in great detail in the next chapter. At this point we simply want to use them to illustrate the concepts of addressing memory and chip select signals.

We now know, in general, how ROMs are wired to the microcomputer buses. All of the data lines of the ROMs are wired to the appropriately labeled signals in the data bus, and all of the address lines are wired to the appropriately labeled lines in the address bus. The only way that the microcomputer can distinguish one ROM from the other is through the use of the CS inputs of the ROMs. In the next section we will discuss circuitry that can be used to select one ROM or the other, *but never both at the same time.*

ADDRESS DECODING

In the previous section of this chapter we observed that the address lines of both 1K×8 ROMs are wired to address lines A0 through A9. This means that address lines A10 through A15 (six lines) may be used in various combinations, to select one or the other 1K ROM in our two-ROM system. In fact, if we use all six of the lines, there are 2^6 or 64 possible combinations of ones and zeros that we can use to select the 1K ROMs. This means that we can have up to 64 of these ROMs wired to the microcomputer, and that we can uniquely address or select each one of them. There are a number of different integrated circuits that we can wire to lines A10 through A15, so that one or the other 1K ROM is selected. In fact, we can use *decoders* or *comparators,* and use them to *absolutely* or *nonabsolutely* address memory.

Using Decoders—the SN74LS42

In Chapter 2 we used two different decoders to decode (the different states of) the signals $\overline{RD}$, $\overline{WR}$, and $IO/\overline{M}$, and generate the control signals $\overline{MEMR}$, $\overline{MEMW}$, $\overline{I/O\ R}$ (IN), and $\overline{I/O\ W}$ (OUT). For review, the pin configuration, block diagram, and truth table for the SN74LS42 4-line-to-10-line decoder are shown in Fig. 3-4. How would this integrated circuit be wired to the microcomputer buses, so that one of the two 1K×8 ROMs is selected?

As you would expect, the A, B, C, and D inputs would be wired to the address bus, and the outputs, 0 through 9, would be wired to the chip select inputs of the ROMs. However, since the decoder does not "fully decode" the D input, that is, there are not eight decoded outputs on the SN74LS42 that go to a logic zero when the D input is a logic one, the

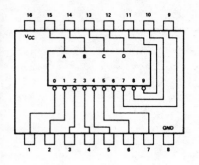

(A) Connection diagram.

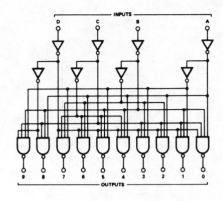

(B) Logic diagram.

S5442/N7442 BCD INPUT				ALL TYPES DECIMAL OUTPUT										
D	C	B	A	0	1	2	3	4	5	6	7	8	9
0	0	0	0	0	1	1	1	1	1	1	1	1	1
0	0	0	1	1	0	1	1	1	1	1	1	1	1
0	0	1	0	1	1	0	1	1	1	1	1	1	1
0	0	1	1	1	1	1	0	1	1	1	1	1	1
0	1	0	0	1	1	1	1	0	1	1	1	1	1
0	1	0	1	1	1	1	1	1	0	1	1	1	1
0	1	1	0	1	1	1	1	1	1	0	1	1	1
0	1	1	1	1	1	1	1	1	1	1	0	1	1
1	0	0	0	1	1	1	1	1	1	1	1	0	1
1	0	0	1	1	1	1	1	1	1	1	1	1	0
1	0	1	0	1	1	1	1	1	1	1	1	1	1
1	0	1	1	1	1	1	1	1	1	1	1	1	1
1	1	0	0	1	1	1	1	1	1	1	1	1	1
1	1	0	1	1	1	1	1	1	1	1	1	1	1
1	1	1	0	1	1	1	1	1	1	1	1	1	1
1	1	1	1	1	1	1	1	1	1	1	1	1	1

(C) Truth table.

Courtesy Signetics Corp.

Fig. 3-4. The pin configuration, logic diagram, and truth table for the SN74LS42 4-line-to-10-line decoder.

D input would normally be grounded. Address line A10 would be wired to the A input, A11 to the B input, and A12 to the C input. Which output of the decoder would be wired to the $\overline{CS}$ input of the ROM that is to contain memory location zero? The zero output (pin 1), which is a logic zero only when the A, B, C, and D inputs are a logic zero, would be wired to the $\overline{CS}$ input of the ROM. Which output would be wired to the $\overline{CS}$ input of the ROM with addresses 00000100 00000000 through 00000111 11111111? The $\overline{CS}$ input of the second ROM would be wired to the one output (pin 2) of the SN74LS42. These interconnections are shown in Fig. 3-5.

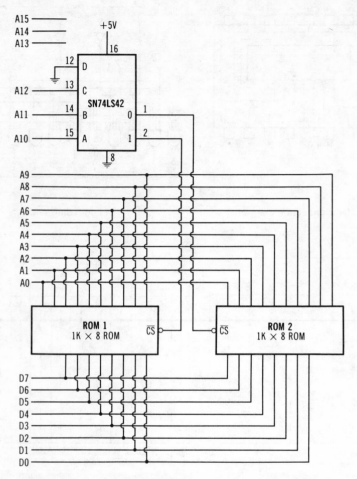

Fig. 3-5. Using an SN74LS42 decoder to select one of two ROMs.

Based on Fig. 3-5, which ROM, ROM 1 or ROM 2, contains memory location zero? ROM 2 contains this memory location, because the zero output of the decoder is wired to the $\overline{CS}$ input of ROM 2. This output of the decoder will only go to a logic zero when the A, B, C, and D inputs (A10, A11, and A12) are logic zeros. Which addresses will the microprocessor be able to generate, and still address ROM 2? We know that the address lines A10, A11, and A12 must be logic zeros for this ROM to be selected. Therefore A0 through A9 can assume any one of 2^{10} or 1024 possible combinations of ones and zeros, where each combination represents a different memory address. Therefore ROM 2 will be addressed when the addresses:

High Address	Low Address
00000000	00000000
00000000	00000001
00000000	00000010
•	•
•	•
•	•
00000011	11111101
00000011	11111110
00000011	11111111

are present on the address bus. If the microprocessor generates the next consecutive address, 00000100 00000000, it will actually be addressing the first memory location in the next ROM, or ROM 1. This will cause the $\overline{CS}$ input of ROM 2 to go to a logic one, and the $\overline{CS}$ input of ROM 1 will go to a logic zero. In fact, the addresses:

High Address	Low Address
00000100	00000000
00000100	00000001
00000100	00000010
•	•
•	•
•	•
00000111	11111101
00000111	11111110
00000111	11111111

will all cause ROM 1 to be accessed by the microprocessor. If the microprocessor generates any of the 1024 possible addresses between 00000100 00000000 and 00000111 11111111, it will be reading instructions or data from ROM 1. Of course, we cannot write data into either of these two ROMs by executing an instruction that causes a memory-write operation to occur. In fact, if you look at the block diagram of the ROM in Fig. 3-3, you will see that there is no signal such as $\overline{MEMW}$ or $\overline{WR}$ connected to the ROM.

Nonabsolute vs. Absolute Decoding

Suppose that the 8085A microprocessor fetches an instruction from memory location 11100000 00000. Does this memory location "exist," based on Fig. 3-5, and, if it does, "where" is it? To answer these questions, you have to examine Fig. 3-5 very carefully. When the microprocessor places address 11100000 00000000 on the address bus, bits A15, A14, and A13 will not be used by the decoder shown in Fig. 3-5, so they will have *no* effect on determining which ROM is selected, if one is.

Address bits A12, A11, and A10 are wired to the SN74LS42 decoder, and since they are logic zeros, the zero output of the decoder will be a logic zero, so ROM 2 is selected. Address bits A0 through A9 are also logic zeros, so they will be decoded internally by the ROM so that memory location zero is selected and the content of this memory location will be output on the data bus. *In fact, the microprocessor can generate eight different addresses that will cause the content of the first memory location in ROM 2 to be output on the data bus.* These addresses are summarized in Chart 3-1.

Chart 3-1. Addressing Memory Location 0 With Eight Different Memory Addresses

High Address	Low Address
00000000	00000000
00100000	00000000
01000000	00000000
01100000	00000000
10000000	00000000
10100000	00000000
11000000	00000000
11100000	00000000

The fact that we do not have a *single, absolute memory address* that represents each memory location means that *nonabsolute addressing* has been used. If any address lines (signals) have not been used in the decoder section of the memory chip select circuitry, then nonabsolute addressing has been used in the microcomputer system. Can you think of a single integrated circuit that we could add to the circuitry in Fig. 3-5 so that each memory location in the two ROMs is absolutely addressed? Another SN74LS42 could be used. The whole circuit is shown in Fig. 3-6.

In Fig. 3-6 address lines A15, A14, and A13 have been wired to the C, B, and A inputs of the SN74LS42 decoder (the A decoder), rather than allowing them to remain unconnected. The zero output of this decoder, which will only be a logic zero when address lines A15, A14, and A13 are logic zeroes, is wired to the D input of the second SN74LS42 decoder, the B decoder. This logic zero "enables" the B decoder, which is wired to address lines A12, A11, and A10. If this SN74LS42 is enabled, the zero output will be a logic zero if the address 000 is present on address lines A12, A11, and A10. This logic zero output by the B decoder will cause ROM 2 to be enabled. If address 001 is present on A12, A11, and A10, ROM 1 will be selected.

By wiring the zero output of the A decoder to the D input of the B decoder, the B decoder is only enabled when the address 000 is present on the A15, A14, and A13 address lines. From Fig. 3-4 we know that if the D input of the decoder is a logic one, only two outputs (8 and 9) can go to a logic zero. Therefore, if the D input of the B decoder is a logic one, it will be impossible to select either of the two ROMs, regardless of the address on A12, A11, and A10. *This is absolute addressing,* that is, an entire 16-bit address is used to select a memory location. The six most significant bits are decoded by the SN74LS42 decoders and the ten least significant bits are decoded within the ROMs.

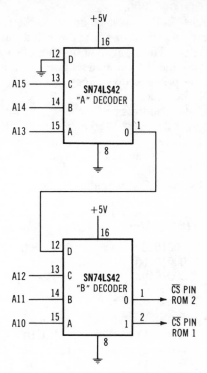

Fig. 3-6. Using two SN74LS42 decoders to absolutely decode a memory address.

In this configuration the D input of the B decoder is used to enable the decoder. When enabled, the output that is in the logic zero state will be determined by the states of the A, B, and C inputs. Therefore the SN74LS42 is being used as a *3-line-to-8-line decoder,* rather than a 4-line-to-10-line decoder.

Which ROM will be selected now if the decoder in Fig. 3-6 is used and if the addresses in Chart 3-1 are placed on the address bus by the microprocessor? For example, suppose that the address 10100000 00000000 is on the address bus. Will ROM 2 or will ROM 1 be selected (enabled)? Neither ROM will be selected. This is what you would expect with absolute addressing. The 101 on address lines A15, A14, and A13 will cause output 5 of the A decoder to go to a logic zero, and output 0, which is wired to the B decoder, will go to a logic one. This means that the B decoder will decode the number 1000, so output 8 of the B decoder will go to a logic zero. All the other outputs of the decoder will be at a logic one. Because of this, neither ROM will be selected. In fact, there is only one 16-bit address in Chart 3-1 that will cause ROM 2 to be selected. What is this address? The address that will cause ROM 2 to be selected is 00000000 00000000.

If additional 1K×8 ROMs must be added to the microcomputer system, how would they be wired to the address and data buses, and how would they be selected? The eight data outputs of the ROMs would be wired to the data bus, and the ten address lines (A0 through A9) would be wired to the appropriate address lines in the address bus. The chip select signals would be generated by the B decoder shown in Fig. 3-6. What would the memory address be for the ROM that is selected by output 5 (pin 6) of the B decoder? We know that for this output to go to a logic zero, (1) the three most significant address lines, A15, A14, and A13, must be zero and (2) the address on address lines A12, A11, and A10 must be 101. Therefore the 1K of "address space" that would be allocated or used by this ROM would be:

High Address	Low Address
00010100	00000000
00010100	00000001
00010100	00000010
•	•
•	•
•	•
00010111	11111101
00010111	11111110
00010111	11111111

What is the maximum amount of memory that can be absolutely selected or decoded using the decoder in Fig. 3-6? Outputs 0 through 7 of the decoder could be used to select 1K ROMs, so a maximum of eight 1K×8 ROMs, or 8192 words of memory or memory locations could be selected. How many SN74LS42 decoders would be required to absolutely decode all 64K of the microprocessor address space into 1K blocks? Nine decoders would be required: one A-type decoder and eight B-type decoders. Each output between zero and seven of the A-type decoder would be used to enable one B-type decoder. Each of the B-type decoders can select up to 8K of memory, so with eight B-type decoders all 64K of the microprocessor address space is decoded into 1K blocks. There are 64 "1K" chip selects.

The SN74LS154 Decoder

The pin configuration, logic diagram, and truth table for the *SN74LS-154 4-line-to-16-line decoder* are shown in Fig. 3-7. As you can see, this integrated circuit decodes all possible input states ($2^4 = 16$). The outputs of this device are active in the logic zero state and, like the SN74LS 42 decoder, only one output can be in the logic zero state at any one time. Of course, by decoding all possible input states this integrated circuit is larger than the SN74LS42 (24 pins *vs.* 16 pins), but this also means that fewer integrated circuits are required to decode the entire 64K of address space of the microprocessor. One nice feature of the SN74LS154 is that it not only has four fully decoded inputs, *but it also has two enable inputs (G1 and G2) that must both be in the logic zero state for the decoder to decode the four inputs (A, B, C, and D)*.

Since these two enable inputs must be a logic zero for the decoder to "decode," this single integrated circuit can be used to absolutely decode the first 16K of the microprocessor address space into 1K blocks. The schematic for the circuit is shown in Fig. 3-8. One requirement of this design is that it has to be used to select a ROM that contains memory location zero (00000000 00000000). By wiring address lines A15 and A14 directly to the two enable inputs (G1 and G2), we ensure that the SN74LS154 will decode the lowest 16K in the microprocessor address space. The address lines A13, A12, A11, and A10 are wired to the D, C, B, and A inputs of the decoder. Although A10 does not have to be connected to the A input, nor A11 to the B input, nor A12 to C, nor A13 to D, doing all this makes it very easy to determine which output represents which 1K block. Which outputs of the SN74LS154 decoder in Fig. 3-8 will be a logic zero when the addresses in Chart 3-2 are placed on the address bus?

Chart 3-2. Test Addresses for Use With an Absolute Memory Address Decoder (Fig. 3-8)

High Address	Low Address
10010101	11111010
01001110	11011011
00110010	10000001
00101000	00111000
00001000	10111011
00111111	11100000

Based on the schematic shown in Fig. 3-8, the first two addresses will not cause any of the decoder outputs to go to a logic zero. If either A15 or A14 or both is a logic one, the decoder will not be enabled, since these addresses are wired directly to the enable inputs of the decoder. The remaining four addresses will cause one of the 16 outputs to go to a logic zero, because the two most significant address bits are logic zeros.

Only address bits A13, A12, A11, and A10 will determine which output will go to a logic zero, so the remaining ten bits in the address can be ignored. This means that the third address will cause the 12 output (1100) to go to a logic zero. The remaining three addresses will cause the 10 (1010), 2 (0010), and 15 (1111) outputs to go to a logic zero.

If more than 16K of memory is to be used with the microcomputer that uses the decoder shown in Fig. 3-8, how would all of this memory be decoded? Since the SN74LS154 already decodes the first 16K of the microprocessor address space, any additional memory would have to be selected with another decoder. There are many different ways that this decoder can be added, including the methods which are shown in Figs. 3-9 and 3-10.

In Fig. 3-9 we have used an inverter (SN74LS04) so that the SN74-LS154 decoder is only enabled when A15 is a logic zero and A14 is a

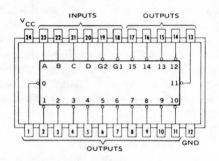

(A) Connection diagram

INPUTS						OUTPUTS															
G1	G2	D	C	B	A	0	1	2	3	4	5	6	7	8	9	10	11	12	13	14	15
L	L	L	L	L	L	L	H	H	H	H	H	H	H	H	H	H	H	H	H	H	H
L	L	L	L	L	H	H	L	H	H	H	H	H	H	H	H	H	H	H	H	H	H
L	L	L	L	H	L	H	H	L	H	H	H	H	H	H	H	H	H	H	H	H	H
L	L	L	L	H	H	H	H	H	L	H	H	H	H	H	H	H	H	H	H	H	H
L	L	L	H	L	L	H	H	H	H	L	H	H	H	H	H	H	H	H	H	H	H
L	L	L	H	L	H	H	H	H	H	H	L	H	H	H	H	H	H	H	H	H	H
L	L	L	H	H	L	H	H	H	H	H	H	L	H	H	H	H	H	H	H	H	H
L	L	L	H	H	H	H	H	H	H	H	H	H	L	H	H	H	H	H	H	H	H
L	L	H	L	L	L	H	H	H	H	H	H	H	H	L	H	H	H	H	H	H	H
L	L	H	L	L	H	H	H	H	H	H	H	H	H	H	L	H	H	H	H	H	H
L	L	H	L	H	L	H	H	H	H	H	H	H	H	H	H	L	H	H	H	H	H
L	L	H	L	H	H	H	H	H	H	H	H	H	H	H	H	H	L	H	H	H	H
L	L	H	H	L	L	H	H	H	H	H	H	H	H	H	H	H	H	L	H	H	H
L	L	H	H	L	H	H	H	H	H	H	H	H	H	H	H	H	H	H	L	H	H
L	L	H	H	H	L	H	H	H	H	H	H	H	H	H	H	H	H	H	H	L	H
L	L	H	H	H	H	H	H	H	H	H	H	H	H	H	H	H	H	H	H	H	L
L	H	X	X	X	X	H	H	H	H	H	H	H	H	H	H	H	H	H	H	H	H
H	L	X	X	X	X	H	H	H	H	H	H	H	H	H	H	H	H	H	H	H	H
H	H	X	X	X	X	H	H	H	H	H	H	H	H	H	H	H	H	H	H	H	H

H = high level, L = low level, X = irrelevant

(B) Logic diagram.

Fig. 3-7. The pin configuration, logic diagram, and truth

logic one (01). This means that this decoder generates the next 16 consecutive 1K chip selects, starting where the decoder in Fig. 3-8 "left off." In Fig. 3-10 a second decoder (SN74LS42) has been used to enable the 4-line-to-16-line decoder. Which output of the SN74LS42 will be used to enable the SN74LS154? There are only four reasonable choices, since the SN74LS42 only decodes two address bits, A15 and A14. The one output (pin 2) would be used to enable the SN74LS154. The zero output would not be used, because A15 and A14 would have to be a logic zero (00) to enable the decoder, and this combination is already used by the first 16K decoder in Fig. 3-8.

If we need to decode all 64K of the microprocessor address space into 1K blocks, how many decoders will be required if we use the method shown in Fig. 3-9? We will only need four decoders (SN74LS154) and

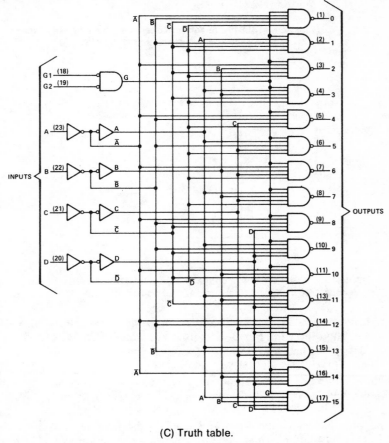

(C) Truth table.

Courtesy Texas Instruments, Inc.

table for the SN74LS154 4-line-to-16-line decoder.

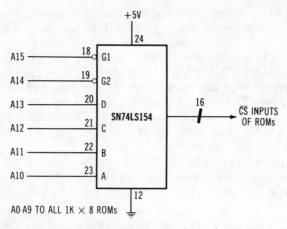

Fig. 3-8. Using an SN74LS154 decoder to absolutely decode 16K of the microprocessor address space into 1K blocks.

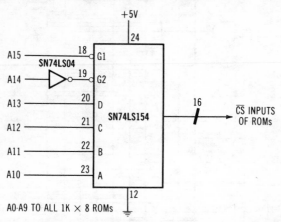

Fig. 3-9. Using an SN74LS154 decoder and an SN74LS04 inverter to absolutely decode 16K of the microprocessor address space into 1K blocks.

one inverter integrated circuit (containing six inverters—an SN74LS04). If the method shown in Fig. 3-10 is used, we would need five decoders— one SN74LS42 and four SN75LS154s. The "inverter method" is shown in Fig. 3-11 and the SN74LS42 method is shown in Fig. 3-12. Which method is better? Both methods require the same number of integrated circuits, but the SN74LS04 inverter is less expensive than the SN74LS42 decoder. If the SN74LS42 is used, however, the A15 and A14 address lines only have to drive one 74LS load. If the inverters are used, the A15 and A14 address lines have to drive two enable inputs and one inverter input. The microprocessor has enough drive capability for either

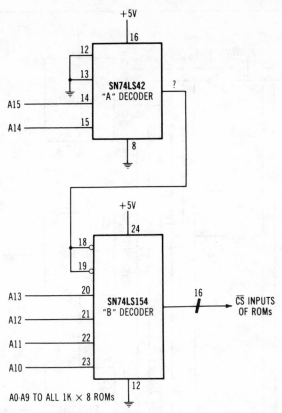

Fig. 3-10. Using an SN74LS42 to enable an SN74LS154 decoder so that 16K of the microprocessor address space is absolutely decoded.

method, but we would be inclined to use the SN74LS42 method, simply because of its lower drive requirements. Also, the SN74LS42 method (Fig. 3-12) may be easier to troubleshoot if something goes wrong.

You have now seen a number of different decoding methods that can be used to select one of many memory integrated circuits. Unfortunately the decoding schemes that are *really required to select ROMs are not as simple as they seem.* We have not discussed one flaw in these ROM decoding methods; this will be discussed in detail in the next chapter. In the next section you will be shown another way to decode memory addresses, using *digital comparators.*

Using Comparators—The SN74LS85

The SN74LS85 4-bit comparator can compare two 4-bit numbers, and if the numbers are equal an output of the integrated circuit will go to a logic one. The pin configuration, logic diagram, and truth table for this

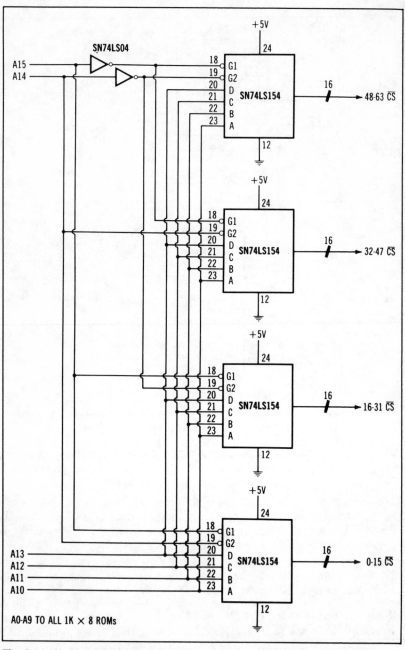

Fig. 3-11. Absolutely decoding all 64K of the microprocessor address space into 1K blocks using inverters and SN74LS154 decoders.

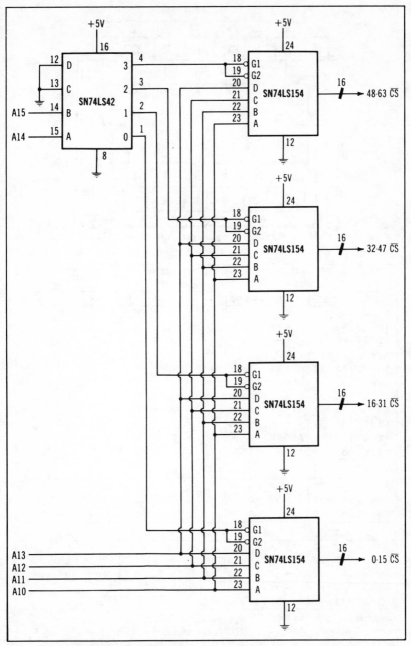

Fig. 3-12. Absolutely decoding all 64K of the microprocessor address space into 1K blocks using SN74LS42 and SN74LS154 decoders.

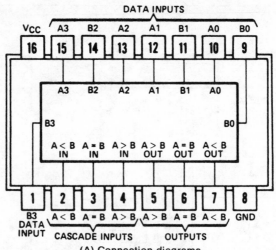

DATA INPUTS

(A) Connection diagrams.

COMPARING INPUTS				CASCADING INPUTS			OUTPUTS		
A3, B3	A2, B2	A1, B1	A0, B0	A > B	A < B	A = B	A > B	A < B	A = B
A3 > B3	X	X	X	X	X	X	H	L	L
A3 < B3	X	X	X	X	X	X	L	H	L
A3 = B3	A2 > B2	X	X	X	X	X	H	L	L
A3 = B3	A2 < B2	X	X	X	X	X	L	H	L
A3 = B2	A2 = B2	A1 > B1	X	X	X	X	H	L	L
A3 = B3	A2 = B2	A1 < B1	X	X	X	X	L	H	L
A3 = B3	A2 = B2	A1 = B1	A0 > B0	X	X	X	H	L	L
A3 = B3	A2 = B2	A1 = B1	A0 < B0	X	X	X	L	H	L
A3 = B3	A2 = B2	A1 = B1	A0 = B0	H	L	L	H	L	L
A3 = B3	A2 = B2	A1 = B1	A0 = B0	L	H	L	L	H	L
A3 = B3	A2 = B2	A1 = B1	A0 = B0	L	L	H	L	L	H

'85, 'LS85, 'S85

A3 = B3	A2 = B2	A1 = B1	A0 = B0	X	X	H	L	L	H
A3 = B3	A2 = B2	A1 = B1	A0 = B0	H	H	L	L	L	L
A3 = B3	A2 = B2	A1 = B1	A0 = B0	L	L	L	H	H	L

'L85

A3 = B3	A2 = B2	A1 = B1	A0 = B0	L	H	H	L	H	H
A3 = B3	A2 = B2	A1 = B1	A0 = B0	H	L	H	H	L	H
A3 = B3	A2 = B2	A1 = B1	A0 = B0	H	H	H	H	H	H
A3 = B3	A2 = B2	A1 = B1	A0 = B0	H	H	L	H	H	L
A3 = B3	A2 = B2	A1 = B1	A0 = B0	L	L	L	L	L	L

H = high level, L = low level, X = irrelevant

(B) Truth tables.

Courtesy Texas Instruments, Inc.

**Fig. 3-13. The pin configurations and truth table for the SN74LS85
4-bit comparator.**

device are shown in Fig. 3-13. This devices can be used to enable decoders, such as the SN74LS42 or SN74LS154, as shown in Fig. 3-14.

To add some variety to our discussion the decoder shown in Fig. 3-14 decodes a portion of the microprocessor address space into 256 word blocks. As you can see, the comparator compares the 4-bit values on address lines A15, A14, A13, and A12 (the A inputs) to the B inputs of the comparator. All of the B inputs are grounded, or logic zeroes, so the A=B output (pin 6) will only go to a logic one if address lines A15

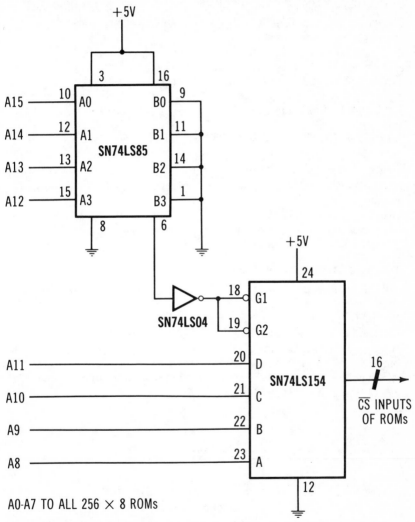

Fig. 3-14. Using a comparator to enable a decoder so that the first 4K of the microprocessor address space is decoded into 256-word blocks.

through A12 are logic zeros. When the A=B output does go to a logic one the inverter inverts it to a logic zero, so the SN74LS154 decoder is enabled. This decoder decodes the address on address lines A11, A10, A9, and A8 and generates a logic zero on one of its outputs to enable one of the 256×8 ROMs.

How much of the microprocessor address space is decoded by this circuitry? Address lines A0 through A7 go to the memory integrated circuits, which means that they must each contain 256 words. The SN74LS-154 decoder can generate 16 chip selects, so this decoding method decodes 16 × 256 or 4096 (4K) words (memory locations) of the microprocessor address space.

What addresses will be decoded if inputs B0, B2, and B3 of the comparator are wired to +5 V and the B1 input is wired to ground? This means that A15, A14, A13, and A12 will have to be in the 1, 0, 1, and 1 states, respectively, in order to enable the decoder. The addresses 10110000 00000000 through 10111111 11111111 will be decoded.

Additional Nonabsolute Decoder Designs

Quite often the cost of a single decoder integrated circuit cannot be tolerated. This is particularly true in small, well-defined microcomputer systems. If this is the case, nonabsolute decoding can be used. In Figs. 3-2 and 3-5 nonabsolute decoding was used, but in Fig. 3-5 a decoder was used. The question is: how are a number of memory integrated circuits used in a microcomputer system when nonabsolute decoding must be used and the system must be low-cost?

A Simple Two-Memory System

We have already seen (Fig. 3-2) a microprocessor that is wired to a single memory integrated circuit, even though the $\overline{\text{CS}}$ input was not shown. In this figure the $\overline{\text{CS}}$ input could simply be wired to ground. (Remember, in the next chapter we will see how ROMs are *really* selected.) This means that the memory would always be enabled or selected. Of course, with two ROMs, such as 1K×8 ROMs, we have to have a simple, inexpensive way of selecting one ROM or the other. One way of doing this is shown in Fig. 3-15.

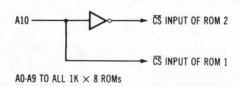

Fig. 3-15. A nonabsolute decoding method for two 1K × 8 ROMs.

In Fig. 3-15 a single inverter is used so that the logic level of A10 is used to determine which of the two ROMs is selected. If A10 is a logic zero, ROM 1 is selected, and if A10 is a logic one, ROM 2 is selected. Of course, since the 16-bit address that the microprocessor generates is not absolutely decoded, there are a number of different addresses that will cause one of the ROMs to be selected. The important point is that both ROMs cannot be selected at the same time. Some of these addresses are tabulated in Chart 3-3. In fact, A15 through A11 can assume any one of 32 possible values, so there are $2^5 \times 1024$, or 32×1024, or 32,768 different addresses that will cause one or the other ROM to be selected.

Chart 3-3. Nonabsolute Decoding Two 1K × 8 ROMs

ROM 1 Addresses		ROM 2 Addresses	
01101011	10111111	00110100	11000000
11111011	00011001	00111111	00000000
00000001	11111111	11000100	11111111
11000000	11110000	10101100	11000101

Even so, one ROM (ROM 1) occupies the first 1K of the microprocessor address space (along with a number of other 1K blocks) and the second ROM (ROM 2) occupies the second 1K of the microprocessor address space (and many other 1K blocks too).

A large number of additional ROMs can be added to the microcomputer system, even though they are not absolutely decoded. *However, no two memories may occupy the same address space and put data onto the data bus at the same time.* In Fig. 3-16 four 1K×8 ROMs have been added to the microcomputer. Since the ROMs in Fig. 3-16 have not been absolutely decoded, extreme care must be exercised when the software is written, since it is possible to select two or more ROMs at once!

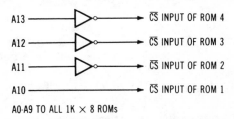

Fig. 3-16. A nonabsolute decoding method for four 1K × 8 ROMs.

What are the address boundaries of the four ROMs? ROM 1 occupies the microprocessor address space from zero to 00000011 11111111. Since address bits A13, A12, and A11 are logic zeroes for any of these 1024 addresses, the inverters cause logic ones to be present at the $\overline{CS}$ inputs of ROM 2, ROM 3, and ROM 4, so they are not selected by any of these addresses. To select ROM 2, A10 must be a logic one so that ROM 1 is not selected, and A12 and A13 must be logic zeroes so that ROM 3 and ROM 4 are not selected. To select ROM 3, A10 would have to be a logic one, A11 and A13 would have to be zero, and A12 would have to be a logic one. To select ROM 4, A10 would be a logic one, A11 and A12 would be logic zeroes, and A13 a logic one. All of these states, along with the ROM selected, are listed in Chart 3-4. The

Chart 3-4. The States of A13, A12, A11, and A10 so That One of Four ROMs in a Nonabsolutely Decoded Microcomputer System Is Selected

A13	A12	A11	A10	ROM Selected
0	0	0	0	ROM 1
0	0	1	1	ROM 2
0	1	0	1	ROM 3
1	0	0	1	ROM 4

address space for each ROM is listed in Chart 3-5. As you can see from Chart 3-5 there are gaps in the address space of the microprocessor where there is no memory. Of course, this design must use an inverter (SN74LS04), but they are less expensive than decoders. Another solution to this problem that the semiconductor manufacturers found was to give some ROMs three or even four chip select inputs. When the ROM

Chart 3-5. The Address Space for Four Nonabsolutely Decoded 1K × 8 ROMs

ROM 1	00000000	00000000 to 00000011	11111111
ROM 2	00001100	00000000 to 00001111	11111111
ROM 3	00010100	00000000 to 00010111	11111111
ROM 4	00100100	00000000 to 00100111	11111111

is programmed at the factory the chip select inputs are also "programmed." This means that you could purchase a ROM where two of the chip selects would have to be logic ones and two would have to be logic zeros, in order to select the ROM. With four chip select inputs, there are 16 different ways that the chip selects can be programmed.

ELECTRICAL CHARACTERISTICS OF MEMORY ADDRESS DECODERS

In all of our memory address decoder designs we have used SN74LS TTL integrated circuits. These types of chips have input requirements of 20 μA sink at 2.7 V (minimum) for a logic one and -0.4 mA source at 0.8 V (maximum) for a logic zero. In general, the outputs of these devices can source -400 μA at 2.0 V minimum for a logic one and can sink 8 mA at 0.4 V maximum for a logic zero. In many of the decoder designs in this chapter an address pin output of the 8085A has only been required to drive a single input pin of a decoder. In Fig. 3-5 A10, A11, and A12 drive the A, B, and C inputs of an SN74LS42. The output pins of the 8085A can source -400 μA at 2.4 V minumum for a logic one and can sink 2 mA at 0.45 V maximum for a logic zero. As you can see, the 8085A can source -400 μA, but the decoder only needs 20 μA and the 8085A can sink 2 mA while the decoder will only source -0.4 mA. Therefore the address outputs of the 8085A can easily drive the decoder inputs shown in Fig. 3-5.

In Fig. 3-6, 3-8, 3-9, and 3-10 the address outputs of the 8085A drive only a single 74LS TTL input. As you know from the preceding discussion the 8085A has more than enough sink and source current capabilities to drive these devices. In Figs. 3-11, the A10, A11, A12, and A13 address outputs of the 8085A have to drive four inputs, one in each SN74LS154 decoder used. Also, the A14 and A15 address signals have to drive an inverter input and two decoder inputs. To drive four 74LS TTL inputs at least 80 μA of source current will be required and -1.6 mA of current will have to be sunk. This is within the capability of the 8085A. As you might guess, if the address outputs can drive four 74LS TTL loads, other address outputs (A14 and A15) can drive three 74LS TTL loads.

The 8085A has enough drive capability so that a number of 74LS TTL loads can be wired to an individual output pin. However, how much drive capability do the outputs of the decoders have? In general, the output of a 74LS TTL chip can drive the inputs of at least 10 or 15 other 74LS TTL chips. For example, this means that a single output of a decoder or the output of a gate could drive a single enable input in ten other decoders at the same time. The signal would not have to be buffered to increase its current capabilities. At times, signals do not have enough current capabilities, so they must be buffered. This topic will be discussed in detail in another chapter.

PRELIMINARY DECODER DESIGN

In this section you will have the opportunity to test your knowledge of memory addressing and address decoders. We know that the microprocessor always generates a 16-bit address, and as a result of this memory address a data value can be read from or written into memory. As we saw in Chapter 2, however, the memories also have to be controlled by one of the memory control signals: $\overline{\text{MEMR}}$ or $\overline{\text{MEMW}}$. The state or logic level of each of these two signals determines whether the memories place information on the data bus or gate information off of the data bus. In this chapter we did not discuss how these memory control signals are used. They will be discussed in the next two chapters. All of the memories used in the examples in this chapter were read-only memories (ROMs), and we will continue to use ROMs in our preliminary designs.

Preliminary Memory Address Decoder Design No. 1

Using two SN74LS42 4-line-to-10-line decoders, absolutely decode 5K of the microprocessor address space, starting at memory location zero, into 1K blocks. No additional integrated circuits may be used.

A design that meets these requirements is shown in Fig. 3-17. Some design points that you should check for in your design include:

1. Has the D input of the A decoder been wired to ground?
2. Have the A, B, and C inputs of the A decoder been wired to A13, A14, and A15? Although these connections do not have to be made in any specific order, the decoder is "easier to work with" if the least significant address bit (A13) is wired to the least significant decoder input (A).
3. Has the appropriate output (output 0 in Fig. 3-17) been used to enable the B decoder, by being wired to the D input?
4. Have the A, B, and C inputs of the B decoder been wired to address bits A10, A11, and A12? Again, they do not have to be wired

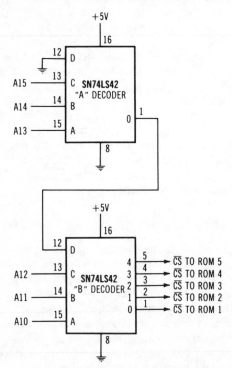

Fig. 3-17. Generating five 1K chip selects with absolute decoding.

in this order, but the authors recommend that A be wired to A10, B to A11, and C to A12. If this is done, outputs 0 through 4 (five outputs) can be used to select the 1K×8 ROMs.

5. Has power been applied correctly to both decoder integrated circuits (+5 V to pin 16, ground to pin 8)?

If 1K blocks are to be decoded, we know that address lines A0 through A9 (2^{10} or 1024) will be wired directly to the ROMs. This means that address lines A10 through A15 must be wired to the decoders. All six of these signals must be used, because one of the design requirements was that absolute decoding be used.

Preliminary Memory Address Decoder Design No. 2

Using an SN74LS42 and an SN74LS154, absolutely decode 6K of the address space of the microprocessor, starting at 00010100 00000000, into 1K blocks. Further decode the 1K blocks starting at 00100000 00000000 into four 256-word blocks. This is done so that we can use five 1K×8 and four 256-word ROMs in the microcomputer system. No additional integrated circuits may be used in this design. We have assumed that we have other memories wired to the microprocessor so that when it is reset it can fetch an instruction from one of these other memories and execute it.

Your decoder design should be very similar to the design shown in Fig. 3-18. Some specific design points that you should look for in your design include:

1. Is the A decoder the SN74LS154 and the B decoder the SN74-LS42?
2. Has the SN74LS154 been enabled (G1 and G2) by address bits A15 and A14?
3. Have outputs 5, 6, 7, 9, and 10 of the SN74LS154 decoder been used to select one of the five 1K×8 ROMs?
4. Has output 8 of the SN74LS154 been used to enable the SN74LS42 so that address bits A8 and A9 are decoded?
5. Have address lines A0 through A9 been wired to the five 1K×8 ROMs and A0 through A7 to all four 256×8 ROMs?

Preliminary Memory Address Decoder Design No. 3

Using any commonly available gates (NAND, AND, NOR, OR, exclusive OR, or inverters; Fig. 2-10), nonabsolutely decode 2K of the microprocessor address space, starting at memory location zero, into 512-word blocks. No decoders, such as the SN74LS42, SN74LS154, or SN74LS-155, may be used in this design.

Your design should be similar to the one shown in Fig. 3-19. Some design points that you should look for in your design include:

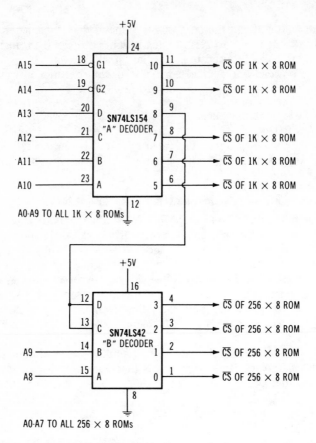

Fig. 3-18. An absolute decoder that can be used with 1K × 8 and 256 × 8 ROMs.

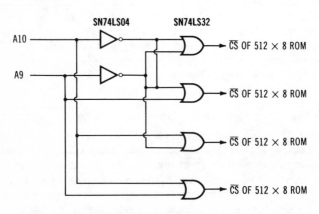

Fig. 3-19. A nonabsolute decoder for four 512 × 8 ROMs.

1. Are only address lines A9 and A10 used in the decoder design?
2. Have inverters or "invert functions" been implemented in the design?
3. Have A0 through A8 been wired to all four 512×8 ROMs?

From the design in Fig. 3-19, which addresses will cause the four different chip selects to be generated? When address zero is on the address bus, the OR gate at the bottom of the figure will generate a logic zero chip select signal. In fact, all of the addresses between zero and 00000001 11111111 will cause this chip select signal to be generated. The address boundaries for the other three chip select signals are shown in Chart 3-6.

Chart 3-6. The Address Space for Four Nonabsolutely Decoded 512 × 8 ROMs

ROM 1	00000000	00000000 to	00000001	11111111
ROM 2	00000010	00000000 to	00000011	11111111
ROM 3	00000100	00000000 to	00000101	11111111
ROM 4	00000110	00000000 to	00000111	11111111

CONCLUSION

In this chapter we have discussed a number of different methods that we can use to select one memory location (integrated circuit) among many. Decoders, comparators, or gates can be used. Depending on the application, these integrated circuits can be used to absolutely decode or nonabsolutely decode blocks of memory. As we have seen, these two methods have their advantages and disadvantages. Generally, unless one is in a situation in which cost, size, or power consumption is particularly important, absolute memory address decoding should be used. If the latter has been used in the microcomputer system, additional memory can be added easily. If nonabsolute decoding has been used, considerable effort may be required; the decoding logic may have to be modified to accommodate additional memory.

Although we have limited our examples to 256-, 512-, and 1024-word × 8-bit ROMs, there are many memory integrated circuits that contain only 1 or 4 bits of information in each word. This means that eight 1-bit or two 4-bit memory integrated circuits would have to be connected to the *same chip select signal*. In general, this does not present any problems, since the $\overline{CS}$ signal generated by the decoder or gate has sufficient drive capability. This will be discussed further in Chapter 5, when we discuss read/write (R/W) memories. We will see in Chapter 4 that most ROMs are 8 bits wide, so a particular $\overline{CS}$ signal is usually only wired to one ROM.

As we will learn in the next chapter we cannot simply wire a decoder to the address bus of the microprocessor, to generate chip select signals for ROMs. To keep our discussion simple, without introducing a number of new topics, we have not been concerned about this. *Therefore do not use any of the decoder designs that we have discussed in this chapter, to select read-only memories.* They have been provided as examples of how the address bus may be decoded and of how several different decoding schemes may be configured. As such, these designs have served their instructional purpose, which is quite important for an understanding of information in the following chapters, even though these particular circuits should not be used.

PROBLEMS

3-1. Which control signals that are used to control memory are generated by the microprocessor or the external decoder logic?

3-2. *Exactly* how many words of memory are contained in a 1K×8 read-only memory (ROM)?

3-3. What is the difference between absolute and nonabsolute address decoding?

3-4. A 4K (4096-word) ROM is selected when the microprocessor is reset. What are the first and last memory addresses that will cause this ROM to be selected? Assume that absolute address decoding has been used. What is the next consecutive address that will cause a different memory integrated circuit in the microcomputer system to be selected?

3-5. If ROM 1 in Fig. 3-5 is wired to output 6 (pin 7) and ROM 2 is wired to output 9 (pin 11), what will the addresses for the 1K×8 ROMs be?

3-6. In Fig. 3-5 what would the addresses for ROM 1 and ROM 2 be if A13 is wired to the D input, rather than the D input being wired to ground?

3-7. Design an absolute address decoder that decodes addresses 11000000 00000000 through 11111111 11111111 into sixteen 1K blocks. Only two integrated circuits may be used in this design, and only one of them may be a decoder integrated circuit.

3-8. Assume that the decoder design shown in Fig. 3-11 has been used in a microcomputer system. However, no SN74LS04 inverters are available for use in the decoding logic. Can an SN74L04 or an SN7404 be used in this design? If so, state which can and cannot be used. If either of these two chips can be used, determine how much of the current capabilities of the address bus are used up and how much is left over for use by other devices wired to the address signals A14 and A15.

3-9. Nonabsolute address decoding has been used in Fig. 3-16. State which ROM or ROMs will be selected when the addresses listed below are placed on the address bus by the microprocessor.

Address		ROM 1	ROM 2	ROM 3	ROM 4
00010101	01110101	___	___	___	___
00101000	11010010	___	___	___	___
01111010	10000000	___	___	___	___
00110100	00111101	___	___	___	___
00100011	11000000	___	___	___	___
00011100	00101101	___	___	___	___
00010100	11111111	___	___	___	___
11010101	00010110	___	___	___	___
00000100	00000111	___	___	___	___

3-10. How many additional ROMs can be selected by the "B" decoder shown in Fig. 3-17? Has absolute or nonabsolute address decoding been used?

3-11. How much current is required to drive the A9 and A10 inputs of the decoder shown in Fig. 3-19?

3-12. List some of the decoder examples shown in this chapter that can actually be used in a microcomputer system to select ROMs.

CHAPTER 4

Read-Only Memories

Read-only memories are an integral part of most microcomputer systems. When power is first applied to an Apple, PET 2001, or TRS-80 microcomputer, the BASIC interpreter contained in read-only memory (ROM) is executed. If we had to load the BASIC interpreter into the microcomputer from audio cassette each time power is applied, it would take from 30 seconds to 5 minutes. Therefore it is very important that we have the ability to store programs and/or data *permanently* in memory, regardless of whether or not power is applied to the microcomputer system. In fact, the popularity of microcomputers is due in large part to the availability of different types of ROMs.

TYPICAL ROM CHARACTERISTICS

As we saw in the last chapter, read-only memories have address and chip select inputs and data outputs. Read-only memories also have to be powered, and this may be done by one, two, or three different power supply voltages. Typical power supply voltages are +5 V, +12 V, and −5 V. Another characteristic of ROMs (and other memories in general) is their *access time*. When the microprocessor generates a memory address, it takes the selected ROM a certain amount of time to recognize the address and output the content of the specified memory location. This can be seen in Fig. 4-1. The times t_A, t_{CO}, and t_{DF} for this particular 2K × 8 ROM (the Intel 2316E) are listed in Table 4-1.

In Fig. 4-1 it is easy to see that the ROM requires a specific amount of time (t_A) to output the content of the addressed memory location. In general, if the ROM has an access time of 575 ns or less, it can be used with very little effort in an 8085A-based microcomputer system. Since the 8085A-2 can be used at 10 MHz, memories that have access

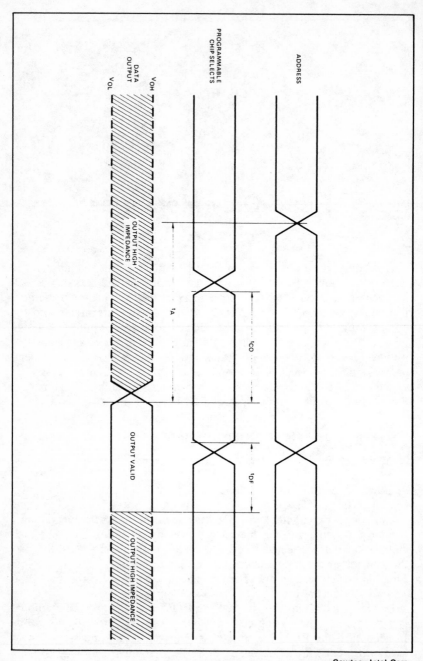

Courtesy Intel Corp.

Fig. 4-1. The ac waveforms for the Intel 2316E mask ROM.

Table 4-1. AC Characteristics of the Intel 2316A 2K × 8 Mask ROM

$T_A = 0°C$ to $+70°C$, $V_{CC} = +5V \pm 10\%$, unless otherwise specified.

SYMBOL	PARAMETER	LIMITS		UNIT
		MIN.	MAX.	
t_A	Address to Output Delay Time		450	ns
t_{CO}	Chip Select to Output Enable Delay Time		120	ns
t_{DF}	Chip Deselect to Output Data Float Delay Time	10	100	ns

Courtesy Intel Corp.

times of 350 ns can be easily used. At the end of this chapter and the end of the next chapter, you will see how memories that have longer access times than this are used with the 8085A and 8085A-2.

There are basically three different types of read-only memories that are ordinarily used in microcomputer systems: (1) mask-programmed read-only memories (mask ROM), (2) programmable read-only memories (PROM), and (3) erasable, programmable read-only memories (EPROM). Another type of read-only memory that is not very popular at this time is the electrically alterable read-only memory (EAROM). In our discussions, if the term ROM is used, the authors mean any type of ROM (mask ROM, PROM, or EPROM). If the authors mean only mask ROM, they will use the term "mask ROM."

Mask ROM

The mask ROM can only be programmed by the semiconductor manufacturers while the integrated circuit is being made. This involves a considerable amount of effort, so the manufacturers usually charge the purchaser a $1000 or $2000 mask charge, and, in addition, an order for at least 250 of the mask ROMs must be placed. The most popular types of mask ROMs have configurations of 1024 words, 8 bits wide (1K × 8); 2048 words, 8 bits wide (2K × 8); and 4096 words, 8 bits wide (4K × 8). These devices may cost between $5 and $25, depending on the quantity and configuration of the memory. Some typical mask ROMs are listed in Table 4-2.

Programmable ROM

The programmable read-only memory (PROM) is a semiconductor device that contains a number of very small electrical fuses. To program the device *the user selectively blows out the fuses*. The schematic diagram for a PROM is shown in Fig. 4-2. A picture of a blown fuse and a fuse that is intact can be seen in Fig. 4-3. In general, if a fuse is present, it represents a logic one, and if it has been "blown," it represents a logic zero. To blow out the fuse the user has to apply a high-voltage, high-current (20–30 V at 20–50 mA) pulse to one of the PROM out-

Table 4-2. Some Typical Mask ROMs and Their Specifications

Manufacturer	Name	Configuration	Power Supplies	Access Time
Texas Instruments	TMS 4732	4K × 8	+ 5	450 ns
Texas Instruments	TMS 4700	1K × 8	+ 5, + 12, − 5	450 ns
Texas Instruments	TMS 4800	2K × 8	+ 5, − 12	700 ns
Fairchild	F68316	2K × 8	+ 5	500 ns
National	MM5242	1K × 8	+ 5	450 ns
National	MM5246	2K × 8	+ 5	450 ns
Intel	2308	1K × 8	+ 5, + 12, − 5	450 ns
Intel	2316E	2K × 8	+ 5	450 ns
Intel	2332	4K × 8	+ 5	N/A*
Intel	2364	8K × 8	+ 5	N/A*

*N/A = not available.

puts. Unfortunately, a bit within the PROM can only be programmed (blown) once, so they are not as popular as many manufacturers had hoped. For instance, to program 10011101 into one of a PROM's memory locations, you would apply a programming pulse to the D1, D5, and

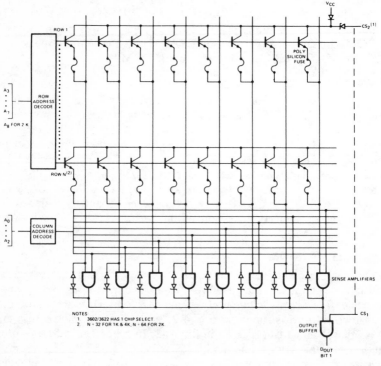

Courtesy Intel Corp.

Fig. 4-2. The schematic diagram for a programmable ROM (PROM).

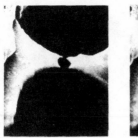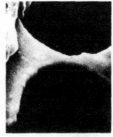

Fig. 4-3. A fuse that has been blown and a fuse that is intact in a PROM.

D6 outputs of the PROM. After doing this, however, suppose you realize that a 10111101 should have been programmed into the PROM. This means that D5 should be a logic one, rather than a logic zero. Since there is no way to replace a blown fuse in the integrated circuit, it would be thrown away, and a new PROM would have to be programmed. Since, in the initial phases of developing a program, both program instructions and data values change *often,* PROMs should not be used. These devices are only used when a program has been developed (and operates properly), and 50 or 100 copies of the program are required. This quantity is not enough to make the mask ROM an economical alternative. PROMs are available in a number of word lengths and word sizes. Typically, they contain 32 to 1024 four- or eight-bit words.

Erasable, Programmable ROM

The most popular ROM is the erasable, programmable read-only memory (EPROM). The Intel Corporation pioneered the design and use of this device. This type of ROM can be programmed by the user, and if the content (data, program, etc.) of the EPROM is incorrect, *the content of the EPROM can be erased by exposing it to ultraviolet (uv) light.* To have this "erase" feature EPROMs have transparent quartz windows so that the ultraviolet light can actually illuminate the silicon integrated circuit chip (Fig. 4-4). Different EPROMS require different uv light intensities and exposure times to be erased. You should refer to the manufacturer's literature for programming, erasure, and electrical characteristics. It is recommended that small, opaque labels be placed on the quartz windows of all EPROMs to prevent accidental exposure due to sunlight or fluorescent light. The labels also give you the capability of labeling the EPROMs so that you know what program or version of a program is contained in the EPROM.

Surprisingly enough, there are only four or five different EPROMs that are popular, so this makes the designer's choice that much easier.

Fig. 4-4. Typical erasable, programmable ROMs with their quartz lids.

These different EPROMs and some of their features are summarized in Table 4-3. A summary of EPROM manufacturers and their products is shown in Table 4-4. The 2708 1K × 8 EPROM is the most popular EPROM today, because it costs less than $10. It is also manufactured by the largest number of semiconductor firms. In fact, the ROM block

Table 4-3. Commonly Available EPROMs and Their Specifications

Name	Configuration	Power Supplies	Access Time
1702A	256 × 8	+5, −9	650–1700 ns
2708	1K × 8	+5, +12, −5	450 ns
2516/2716*	2K × 8	+5	450 ns
2532/2732*	4K × 8	+5	450 ns

*Access times based on the 2516 and 2532.

Table 4-4. EPROM Manufacturers

Device Name	Configuration	Manufacturers
1702A	256 × 8	Intel, AMD, Mostek, National
2708	1K × 8	Intel, Mostek, National, Signetics, Motorola, Fairchild, Texas Instruments, Electronic Arrays
TMS 2716*	2K × 8	Texas Instruments, Motorola
2716*	2K × 8	Texas Instruments, Motorola, Intel, Mostek, NEC, Electronic Arrays
2532/2732†	4K × 8	Texas Instruments, Intel

*The TMS 2716 and 2716 differ in pinouts and power supplies.
†The 2532 and 2732 differ in pinouts.

APPLICATIONS INFORMATION

Ease of Conversion From TMS 2708 To TMS 2716

A. The TMS 2716 and TMS 2708 have compatible timing, voltage and current parameters in both modes.

B. The TMS 2716 requires less power than the TMS 2708.

C. The pinouts are compatible. (See below.)

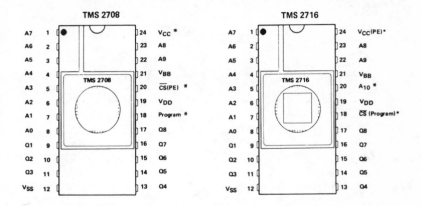

As can be seen from the above diagrams, only three pins* are modified in going from TMS 2708 to TMS 2716:

1. The additional address pin required for the 16K EPROM is located on pin 20 which displaces the $\overline{CS}$/PE functions on the TMS 2708.

2. Since the V_{CC} is not required during programming, the PE function shares pin 24 with V_{CC} on the TMS 2716.

3. The $\overline{CS}$ function and program function are mutually exclusive during normal read mode (and are self-actuated complementary during the program/verify mode) and share pin 18 on the TMS 2716.

The diagrams below show how these three pins are actually utilized in the read mode and in the program mode. Only pins 18, 20, and 24 need to be shown, as all other pin connections are identical.

If the TMS 2708 is used. (1)pin 18 is wired to ground and (2)pin 20 is used as the CS input. If the TMS 2716 is used. (1)pin 18 is used as the CS input and (2)pin 20 is used for the additional address input (A10).

Courtesy Texas Instruments, Inc.

Fig. 4-5. Comparing the TMS 2708 (1K × 8) and the TMS 2716 (2K × 8) EPROMs.

diagram that we used in the last chapter (Fig. 3-3) is that of the 2708. As you can see from Table 4-4, there are a number of 2K × 8 EPROMs that are available. Two are manufactured by Texas Instruments and one is manufactured by Intel Corporation. The TMS 2716 (Texas Instruments) has a pinout that is very similar to the 2708. This can be seen in Fig. 4-5. In fact, to upgrade, or increase, the amount of memory using EPROMs in a microcomputer system by a factor of two, TMS

2716 EPROMs (2K × 8) can be used in a microcomputer designed for 2708s (1K × 8) by changing the functions of only two pins.

Both Intel and Texas Instruments make 2K × 8 and 4K × 8 EPROMs, but, in general, these devices are not pin-for-pin compatible. The pin configurations for these EPROMs are shown in Figs. 4-6 and 4-7. As you can see from Figs. 4-5, 4-6, and 4-7, the functions of pins 18, 19, 20, and 21 are the only features that change between the 1K × 8 (2708), 2K × 8 (TMS 2516, TMS 2716, and Intel 2716), and the

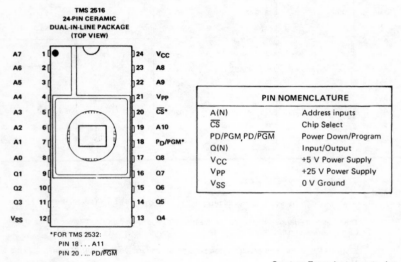

Courtesy Texas Instruments, Inc.

Fig. 4-6 .The pin configurations for the Texas Instruments TMS 2516 and TMS 2532 EPROMs.

4K × 8 (TMS 2535 and Intel 2732) EPROMs. This is a good feature in one respect, because it means that we can use a 4K × 8 EPROM in a socket designed for a 1K × 8 EPROM, with only four changes. It also means, however, that a Texas Instruments 4K × 8 EPROM cannot be used in a socket designed for an Intel 4K × 8 EPROM, without some changes (or *vice versa*).

Another nice feature of the 2K × 8 and 4K × 8 EPROMs (except the TMS 2716) is the fact that they only require +5 V for operation. This, combined with the single-voltage power requirements of the microprocessor integrated circuit and any external TTL logic, means that a microcomputer system can easily be designed that can derive its power from an automobile battery (with appropriate 5-V regulators) or from solar cells!

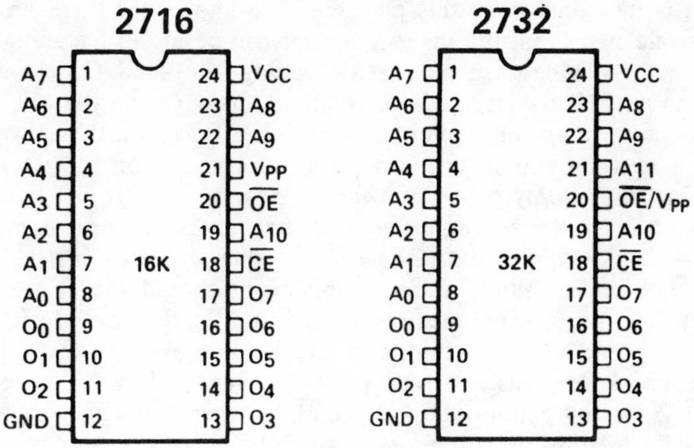

2716	2732
A7 □ 1 24 □ VCC	A7 □ 1 24 □ VCC
A6 □ 2 23 □ A8	A6 □ 2 23 □ A8
A5 □ 3 22 □ A9	A5 □ 3 22 □ A9
A4 □ 4 21 □ VPP	A4 □ 4 21 □ A11
A3 □ 5 20 □ $\overline{OE}$	A3 □ 5 20 □ $\overline{OE}$/VPP
A2 □ 6 19 □ A10	A2 □ 6 19 □ A10
A1 □ 7 16K 18 □ $\overline{CE}$	A1 □ 7 32K 18 □ $\overline{CE}$
A0 □ 8 17 □ O7	A0 □ 8 17 □ O7
O0 □ 9 16 □ O6	O0 □ 9 16 □ O6
O1 □ 10 15 □ O5	O1 □ 10 15 □ O5
O2 □ 11 14 □ O4	O2 □ 11 14 □ O4
GND □ 12 13 □ O3	GND □ 12 13 □ O3

A_0–A_9	ADDRESSES
$\overline{CE}$/PGM	CHIP ENABLE/PROGRAM
$\overline{OE}$	OUTPUT ENABLE
O_0–O_7	OUTPUTS

Fig. 4-7. The pin configurations for the Intel 2716 and 2732 EPROMs.

READING INFORMATION FROM ROMS: THE PRINCIPLES

Now that we have some idea of the types of ROMs that are available for our use, we can begin to design them into a microcomputer system. As we saw in the last chapter, however, the ROM must be selected only when the appropriate address is on the address bus. Suppose that we have a microcomputer system that uses a single 1K × 8 ROM that is selected when addresses 00000000 00000000 through 00000011 11111111 are on the address bus. As you would expect, we can read information (instructions or data) from the ROM. What will happen if we mistakenly try to write information into the ROM? Of course, we know that no information can be written into the ROM. However, if we attempt to do this in the microcomputer, what will be on the microcomputer buses? Assume that we are trying to write information into memory location 00000001 11001111.

When the memory write operation is performed, a 16-bit address will be placed on the address bus (00000001 11001111) and *an 8-bit data value will be placed on the data bus by the microprocessor.* We also know that the ROM will be selected by this address, *so the 8-bit content of the addressed memory location will be placed on the data bus by the ROM. When this happens, two devices, the microprocessor and the ROM, will be placing data on the data bus simultaneously. This should never happen.*

What is the solution to this problem? We know that there are only five possible states that the microprocessor can be in: (1) reading from memory, (2) writing to memory, (3) reading from an I/O device, (4) writing to an I/O device, and (5) none of these (when the microprocessor is performing some internal operation). Based on these five possible states, when should a ROM place information on the data bus? *The ROM should only place information on the data bus (1) when the microprocessor is generating an address that represents a memory location contained within it and (2) when the microprocesor is performing a memory-read operation.* Only at this point should the ROM place the content of the selected memory location on the data bus. In Chapter 3 we simply used a decoder output or an address signal to select a ROM. As you now know, this is a very poor technique. We also know from Chapter 2 that by gating $\overline{RD}$ and $IO/\overline{M}$ together the signal $\overline{MEMR}$ is generated, which is only a logic zero when the microprocessor is reading from memory. Now, $\overline{MEMR}$ has to be gated with a decoded address to select a particular ROM.

READING INFORMATION FROM ROM: THE CIRCUITRY
Nonabsolute Decoding

The simplest example that we can use to demonstrate the chip select circuitry is a one-ROM system (Fig. 4-8). In this system the $\overline{MEMR}$

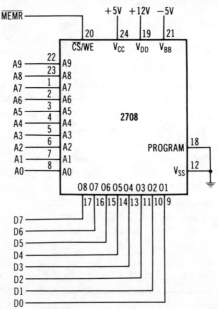

Fig. 4-8. Using $\overline{MEMR}$ to "chip select" a 1K × 8 2708 EPROM.

signal is used to select or enable the 1K × 8 ROM. Of course, this assumes that there are no other memory integrated circuits in the microcomputer system. Why? Because nonabsolute address decoding has been used. If the microprocessor tries to read information from another ROM, the ROM in Fig. 4-8 will be enabled by the $\overline{\text{MEMR}}$ signal and will place its information on the data bus.

A more reasonable system might be built using the circuitry shown in Fig. 4-9. In this figure the $\overline{\text{MEMR}}$ signal is used to enable the SN74SL42 decoder. Only when the $\overline{\text{MEMR}}$ signal is a logic zero can output 0 to 1 of the decoder go to a logic zero. If A10, A11, and A12 are in the proper states (000 or 001) and $\overline{\text{MEMR}}$ is a logic zero, the addressed ROM will place its information on the data bus. Even though nonabsolute address decoding has been used, how many 1K × 8 ROMs can be individually selected by the SN74LS42 decoder? Eight 1K × 8 ROMs (a total of 8192 memory locations) can be selected.

ROM-R/W Memory Problems

Let us assume that we now have a 1K × 8 R/W memory integrated circuit that we would like to add to the microcomputer system. This integrated circuit is very similar to the 1K × 8 ROM integrated circuits that we have used previously. Its block diagram and pin configuration are shown in Fig. 4-10. This type of integrated circuit will be discussed in detail in the next chapter. As you can see, the pin configuration for this integrated circuit is very similar to that of the 2708 EPROM (Fig. 4-5).

There are 10 address lines (A0–A9) which would be wired to address lines A0–A9 in the address bus and the eight data lines, I/O1–I/O8, would be wired to the 8 data bus lines. These data pins are labeled I/O because they are used both when data is read from R/W memory and when data is written into R/W memory. The $\overline{\text{CE}}$ input has the same function as the $\overline{\text{CS}}$ input of our ROMs. If the integrated circuit is selected ($\overline{\text{CE}} = 0$), the write enable ($\overline{\text{WE}}$) input determines if information is being read from memory ($\overline{\text{WE}} = 1$) or whether information is being written into memory ($\overline{\text{WE}} = 0$).

Suppose that $\overline{\text{MEMW}}$ is wired to the $\overline{\text{WE}}$ input and that output 2 (pin 3) of the decoder is wired to $\overline{\text{CE}}$ (Fig. 4-11). Will we be able to read information from, and write information into, the R/W memory integrated circuit? No, we will only be able to read information from it.

Suppose that we have to read a value from R/W memory. When a memory-read operation is performed, the $\overline{\text{MEMR}}$ signal will be a logic zero. If an address, where A10 = 0, A11 = 1, and A12 = 0, is placed on the address bus and $\overline{\text{MEMR}}$ is a logic zero, output 2 of the decoder will go to a logic zero. The R/W memory integrated circuit will then be selected. Since a memory-write operation is not being performed, $\overline{\text{MEMW}}$ will be a one, as will the $\overline{\text{WE}}$ input of the R/W memory inte-

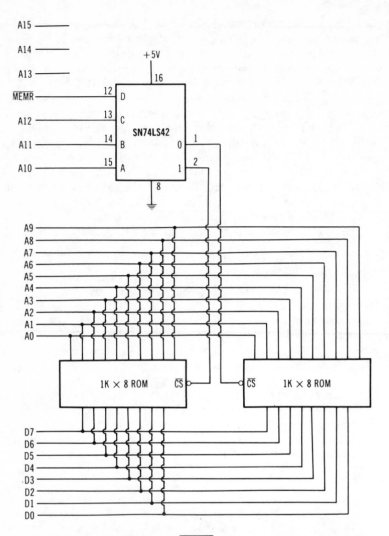

Fig. 4-9. Enabling ROMs with $\overline{\text{MEMR}}$ and a nonabsolutely decoded memory address.

grated circuit. Because of these two conditions ($\overline{\text{CE}} = 0$, $\overline{\text{WE}} = 1$), an 8-bit value will be read from R/W memory.

There is, of course, also the possibility that at some time we may have to write information into the R/W memory integrated circuit. Assume that we need to write information into memory location 00001000 11111111. As you would expect, the $\overline{\text{MEMW}}$ signal will be a logic zero, so a value should be written into memory. However, it will not be be-

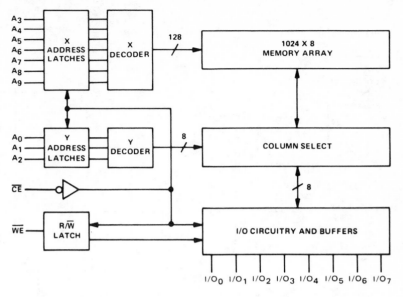

(A) Block diagram.

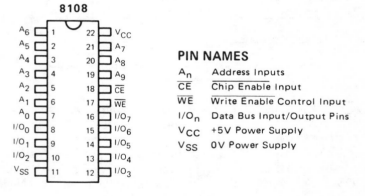

PIN NAMES

A_n	Address Inputs
$\overline{CE}$	Chip Enable Input
$\overline{WE}$	Write Enable Control Input
I/O_n	Data Bus Input/Output Pins
V_{CC}	+5V Power Supply
V_{SS}	0V Power Supply

(B) Pin configuration.

Courtesy EMM Semi, Inc.

Fig. 4-10. The block diagram and pin configuration for a 1K × 8 R/W memory.

cause the $\overline{CE}$ input is a logic one. Why? The $\overline{CE}$ input can only be a logic zero if a memory-read operation is taking place, since $\overline{MEMR}$ is used to enable the decoder. Because a memory-read and memory-write operation cannot occur at the same time, our circuit design permits us only to read information from read/write memory. No information can be written into read/write memory.

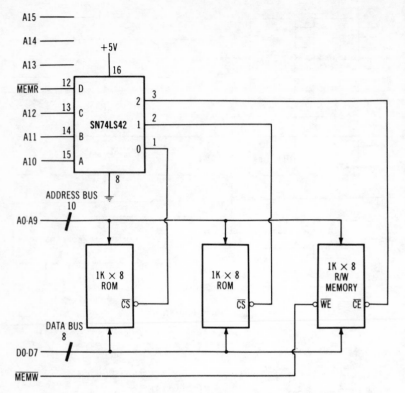

Fig. 4-11. Selecting a ROM or R/W memory with a nonabsolute decoded memory address.

You now know one of the limitations of decoders that are only enabled by the $\overline{MEMR}$ signal. The outputs of the decoder(s) can only be used to select ROMs. This will not be a problem if your microcomputer system is designed properly. Let us return to the problem of selecting ROMs with the $\overline{MEMR}$ signal. The problem of using R/W memory and ROM in the same system will be discussed again in the next chapter.

Absolute Decoding for ROMs

In Fig. 4-12 we can see how a memory address is absolutely decoded and how $\overline{MEMR}$ is used to enable the decoder. In Chapter 3 the same circuitry was used, except that the D input of the A decoder was wired to ground. In this new design the A decoder is enabled only if a memory-read operation is taking place. This means that *ROM 1 or ROM 2 will be selected only if (1) the microprocessor is reading from memory and (2) an appropriate address (00000000 00000000–00000111 11111111) is on the address bus.* Can another output of the B decoder

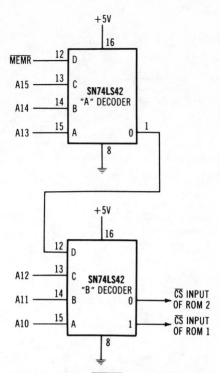

Fig. 4-12. Enabling ROMs with $\overline{\text{MEMR}}$ and an absolutely decoded
memory address.

be used to enable a R/W memory integrated circuit? No, because the
R/W memory would only be selected during a memory-read operation.
Could another output of the A decoder, for instance, output 4, be used
to enable another B decoder, whose outputs would be used to enable
R/W memories? No, this second B decoder would only be enabled dur-
ing a memory-read, since $\overline{\text{MEMR}}$ is used to enable the A decoder.

If you need a decoder that can be used with a larger number of
$1\text{K} \times 8$ ROMs, the decoder in Fig. 4-13 could be used. As you can see,
$\overline{\text{MEMR}}$ has not been used to enable either of the two decoders. Where
should the $\overline{\text{MEMR}}$ signal be wired to? It could be wired to (1) both the
C and D inputs of the SN74LS42, (2) to either the C or D input, with
the other input wired to ground, and (3) to the G2 input of the
SN74LS154, with the G1 input wired to the zero output of the
SN74LS42, or *vice versa*. All of these different combinations of signals
can be seen in Fig. 4-14. As you might guess, there is no reason why
$\overline{\text{MEMR}}$ should be wired to *both* decoders. Which method—enabling the
SN74LS42 or enabling the SN74LS154 with $\overline{\text{MEMR}}$—is better? Neither
method is better than the other; both work equally well.

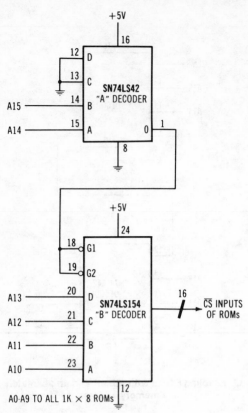

Fig. 4-13. Absolutely decoding the first 16K of the microprocessor address space into 1K blocks.

If $\overline{\text{MEMR}}$ enables the SN74LS42 decoder, the outputs of this decoder can only be used to enable other decoders that are used with ROMs. Of course, if R/W memory has to be used in the system, this will present problems. On the other hand, if large numbers of ROMs are to be used with the system, we will not have to wire each B decoder to $\overline{\text{MEMR}}$. We know from past experience that the SN74LS42 decoder (Fig. 4-13) can be used to enable four "16K" decoders. Therefore, if additional decoders are wired to the SN74LS42, they can only be used to enable ROMs.

If $\overline{\text{MEMR}}$ is used to enable the SN74LS154, its 16 outputs can only be used to enable ROMs. However, an output of the SN74LS42 could be used to enable *another SN74LS154,* which could be used to *enable R/W memories.* Personally, the authors prefer to enable the SN74LS154 decoder (Fig. 4-15). This means that the remaining decoded outputs of the SN74LS42 decoder can be used for other tasks and are not limited

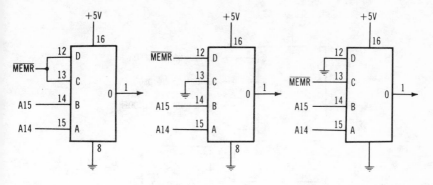

(A) SN74LS42 decoder.

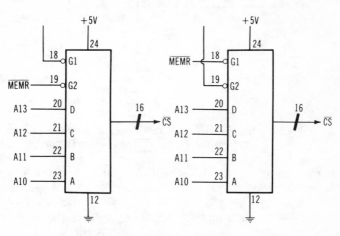

(B) SN74LS154 decoder.

Fig. 4-14. Different methods of enabling decoders with $\overline{MEMR}$.

to enabling ROM decoders. In Chapter 5 we will discuss different decoding methods that can be used with both ROMs and R/W memories.

ELECTRICAL CHARACTERISTICS OF ROMS

In Chapter 2 we discussed the electrical capabilities of the 8085A (0.45 V, 2 mA sink; 2.4 V, −400 μA source) along with the voltage and current requirements of peripheral circuitry, such as control signal decoders and address latches. In this section we will discuss the voltage and current requirements of ROMs. Typical electrical characteristics of ROMs are summarized in Appendix C.

From Appendix C we can make some interesting observations. As you can see, all of the mask ROMs and EPROMs have input current re-

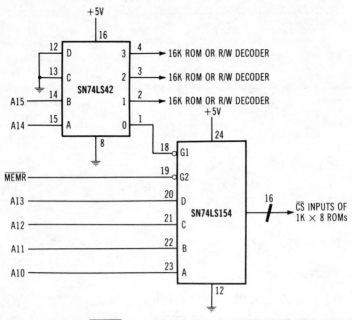

Fig. 4-15. Using $\overline{\text{MEMR}}$ to enable a decoder that decodes 16K of the microprocessor address space into 1K blocks.

quirements of between 1 and 10 μA (source or sink). Of course, only the *address* and *chip select* pins have *input current requirements.* Therefore, if required, an address pin of the microprocessor (0.45 V, 2 mA; 2.4 V, −400 μA) could drive more than 40 of the memory integrated circuits with these current requirements. Of course, the more significant address lines (A10 or A11 to A15) only have to drive a 74LS decoder or similar chip, rather than every memory integrated circuit. From our previous experience, there will be no drive problem here. Also, the 8 least significant bits of the address bus are *buffered* by the address latch, which drives the A0–A7 inputs of all memory integrated circuits. The only address signals that we would have to be concerned with would be A8 to A10, A11, or A12, because they may not be used in the chip select decoder design, and they are not buffered by the address latch. As an example, if 2K × 8 ROMs are used in the microcomputer system, A8, A9, and A10 are wired to the ROMs and A11 through A15 are used in the *absolute* address decoder design. Another area of concern is whether the memory integrated circuits can drive the data bus lines in the microcomputer system. This means that the 8085A microprocessor inputs must be at a potential of 2.0 V or greater for a logic one. At this potential the 8085A sinks 10 μA, which the ROM must be able to source. For a logic zero the microprocessor data pin must be at a potential of 0.8 V or less, and a source current of $-10\ \mu A$ will be generated by the 8085A which the ROM must be able to sink. Based on these requirements, all of the mask ROM and EPROMs listed in Tables 4-2, 4-3, and 4-4 can be used with the 8085A microprocessor. Don't forget, though, that you haven't considered any other TTL inputs (I/O ports, R/W memories) on the bus. These can "load" the bus significantly.

An Intel 2716 $2K \times 8$ EPROM is shown in Fig. 4-16 wired to the 8085A microprocessor. Included in this design is the address demultiplexer, a control signal decoder, and a memory address decoder. Some of the current sinks and sources that we must consider in this design are listed in Table 4-5.

Table 4-5. Signal Sources and Destinations in a Small 8085A-Based Microcomputer

Signal Source	Signal Destination
8085A AD0–AD7 Outputs	SN74LS373 A0–A7 Inputs
SN74LS373 A0–A7 Outputs	2716 A0–A7 Inputs
8085A A8–A10 Outputs	2716 A8–A10 Inputs
8085A A11–A13 Outputs	SN74LS42 A, B, and C Inputs
8085A RD, WR, and IO/M Outputs	SN74LS42 A, B, and C Inputs
8085A ALE Output	SN74LS373 Clock Input
SN74LS42 MEMR Output	SN74LS42 D Input
SN74LS42 Zero Output	2716 CS Input
2716 D0–D7 Outputs	8085A AD0–AD7 Inputs

All of the voltages and current drive capabilities and input requirements of these signals must be considered in order to determine if the microcomputer will operate as designed. We can determine very quickly that the system will work properly with a 2716-type EPROM (Intel or Texas Instruments, among others). The logic one and logic zero input requirements for both the address and CS inputs of the EPROM are 10 μA sink (2.4 minimum) and $-10\ \mu A$ source (0.8 V maximum). The logic zero and one outputs of the 2716 can sink 2.1 mA (0.45 V maximum) and source $-400\ \mu A$ (2.4 V minimum).

From these values we can see that the input requirements of the Intel 2716 EPROM (0.8 V maximum, 2.0 V minimum) are within the output capabilities of the 8085A (0.45 V, 2 mA sink maximum; 2.4 V, $-400\ \mu A$ source minimum) and that the input requirements of the 8085A (0.8 V, $-10\ \mu A$ source maximum; 2.0 V, 10 μA sink minimum) are within the output capabilities of the Intel 2716 EPROM. Therefore the 8085A can source more current that the 2716 EPROM sinks, and the 8085A sinks less current than the 2716 can source. The two devices are thus electrically compatible.

ROM Leakage Currents

Does a ROM or any other type of memory device place data on the data bus when it is not selected? No, if a device is not selected the mem-

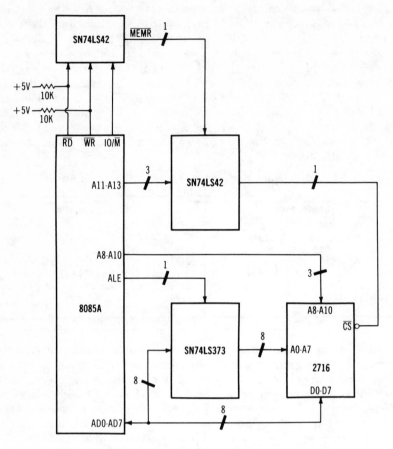

Fig. 4-16. A complete single ROM microcomputer system.

ory should not place any information on the data bus. This means that the outputs of ROMs and other memory and peripheral devices have three states. When selected, the device can place a logic one or a logic zero on the data bus (two possible states), and when not selected, the ROM places no information on the data bus (the third state). When a ROM of other memory device is not selected, it is said to be in the *third,* or *high-impedance, state.* When in this state the ROM, read/write memory, or peripheral device places no information on the data bus.

Unfortunately, none of the devices that are used in microcomputers are perfect. As an example, *even though a ROM is not selected, it will sink some current from, or source some current to, the data bus, even when it is in the high-impedance state.* This current is called the *leakage current* and can be seen in Table 4-6. In Table 4-6 the leakage current

Table 4-6. The Electrical Characteristics of the Intel 2316E 2K × 8 Mask ROM

$T_A = 0^\circ C$ to $+70^\circ C$, $V_{CC} = 5V \pm 10\%$, unless otherwise specified.

SYMBOL	PARAMETER	LIMITS			UNIT	TEST CONDITIONS
		MIN.	TYP.[1]	MAX.		
I_{LI}	Input Load Current (All Input Pins)			10	μA	$V_{IN} = 0$ to 5.25V
I_{LOH}	Output Leakage Current			10	μA	Chip Deselected, $V_{OUT} = 4.0V$
I_{LOL}	Output Leakage Current			–20	μA	Chip Deselected, $V_{OUT} = 0.4V$
I_{CC}	Power Supply Current		70	120	mA	All Inputs 5.25V Data Out Open
V_{IL}	Input "Low" Voltage	–0.5		0.8	V	
V_{IH}	Input "High" Voltage	2.4		$V_{CC}+1.0V$	V	
V_{OL}	Output "Low" Voltage			0.4	V	$I_{OL} = 2.1$ mA
V_{OH}	Output "High" Voltage	2.4			V	$I_{OH} = -400 \mu A$

NOTE: 1. Typical values for $T_A = 25^\circ C$ and nominal supply voltage.

Courtesy Intel Corp.

may be either 10 μA or -20 μA, depending on whether a logic one or a logic zero would be output if the chip were selected. If one data output of the ROM is a logic zero when the chip is selected, -20 μA will be sourced by the same output when the chip is not selected (high-impedance or third state). If a logic one is output when the chip is selected, 10 μA of current will be sunk by the same output when the chip is deselected or is in the third state. Therefore, in calculating the number of integrated circuits that the 8085A can "drive," the leakage currents of the integrated circuits that are not selected must also be taken into account.

USING ROMS WITH LONG ACCESS TIMES

In all of our previous examples we have assumed that the *access times* of the ROMs are short enough so that data will be output by the memory integrated circuit before the microprocessor actually gates it off of the data bus and into an internal register. How "fast" must a ROM be? To determine this the microprocessor timing diagram in Fig. 2-4 and the contents of Table 2-1 should be re-examined. The time that we are interested in is t_{AD} (Valid Address to Valid Data In). This is specified as a maximum of 575 ns for a 6.25-MHz 8085A and a maximum of 350 ns for a 10-MHz 8085A-2. If the microprocessor has a 2000-ns cycle time, what will the maximum permissible access time be? To determine this we can use the mathematical formula for the 8085A t_{AD} listed on the left in Table 4-7. We will assume that there are no wait states, so the maximum access time would be $2.5t_{CYC} - 225$ or 4775 ns. The longest access time that we know of for a commonly available ROM is 1700 ns

Table 4-7. Bus Timing Specifications of the 8085A and 8085A-2 as a Function of t_{CYC}

8085A				8085A-2 (Preliminary)			
t_{AL}	–	(1/2) T – 45	MIN	t_{AL}	–	(1/2) T – 50	MIN
t_{LA}	–	(1/2) T – 60	MIN	t_{LA}	–	(1/2) T – 50	MIN
t_{LL}	–	(1/2) T – 20	MIN	t_{LL}	–	(1/2) T – 20	MIN
t_{LCK}	–	(1/2) T – 60	MIN	t_{LCK}	–	(1/2) T – 50	MIN
t_{LC}	–	(1/2) T – 30	MIN	t_{LC}	–	(1/2) T – 40	MIN
t_{AD}	–	(5/2 + N) T – 225	MAX	t_{AD}	–	(5/2 + N) T – 150	MAX
t_{RD}	–	(3/2 + N) T – 180	MAX	t_{RD}	–	(3/2 + N) T – 150	MAX
t_{RAE}	–	(1/2) T – 10	MIN	t_{RAE}	–	(1/2) T – 10	MIN
t_{CA}	–	(1/2) T – 40	MIN	t_{CA}	–	(1/2) T – 40	MIN
t_{DW}	–	(3/2 + N) T – 60	MIN	t_{DW}	–	(3/2 + N) T – 70	MIN
t_{WD}	–	(1/2) T – 60	MIN	t_{WD}	–	(1/2) T – 40	MIN
t_{CC}	–	(3/2 + N) T – 80	MIN	t_{CC}	–	(3/2 + N) T – 70	MIN
t_{CL}	–	(1/2) T – 110	MIN	t_{CL}	–	(1/2) T – 75	MIN
t_{ARY}	–	(3/2) T – 260	MAX	t_{ARY}	–	(3/2) T – 200	MAX
t_{HACK}	–	(1/2) T – 50	MIN	t_{HACK}	–	(1/2) T – 60	MIN
t_{HABF}	–	(1/2) T + 50	MAX	t_{HABF}	–	(1/2) T + 50	MAX
t_{HABE}	–	(1/2) T + 50	MAX	t_{HABE}	–	(1/2) T + 50	MAX
t_{AC}	–	(2/2) T – 50	MIN	t_{AC}	–	(2/2) T – 85	MIN
t_1	–	(1/2) T – 80	MIN	t_1	–	(1/2) T – 60	MIN
t_2	–	(1/2) T – 40	MIN	t_2	–	(1/2) T – 30	MIN
t_{RV}	–	(3/2) T – 80	MIN	t_{RV}	–	(3/2) T – 80	MIN
t_{LDR}	–	(4/2) T – 180	MAX	t_{LDR}	–	(4/2) T – 130	MAX

NOTE: N is equal to the total WAIT states.

$T = t_{CYC}$.

NOTE: N is equal to the total WAIT states.

$T = t_{CYC}$.

Courtesy Intel Corp.

(Intel 4702). This ROM could be used in an 8085A-based microcomputer system with the appropriate clock. For use in an 8085A-2 based microcomputer system the t_{AD} formula on the right side of Table 4-7 would have to be used.

There are only two different methods that we can use so that ROMs or R/W memories with access times greater than 575 ns can be used with the 8085A microprocessor: (1) slow down the microprocessor clock or (2) use the microprocessor at "full speed" but insert *wait states* whenever the slow memory is accessed.

Adjusting the Microprocessor Cycle Time

As you might expect, the simplest method is to slow down the microprocessor clocks so that the microprocessor can be used with "slow" memories. What would the frequency of the quartz crystal have to be if the microprocessor has to access ROMs with access times of 1200 ns? To determine this, we would evaluate the expression:

$$t_{CYC} = \left(\frac{1200 + 225}{2.5}\right)$$

$$t_{CYC} = 570 \text{ ns}$$

The quartz crystal has to have a frequency whose period is one-half of this, or 285 ns. This means that its frequency is 3.51 MHz.

By slowing the microprocessor down, it can properly access the 1200-ns ROMs. What will happen if some memories with a 300-ns access time are later added to this system? Will they be accessed properly? Yes, they will. In fact, the microprocessor will read information from these memories 1200 ns after it generates an address, even though the memories have information ready at their outputs only 300 ns after the address is generated. Therefore, even though fast (300-ns) memories are used in the system, *the clock has to be slow enough so that the slowest memories are accessed properly.*

Inserting Wait States

Another method of slowing down the microprocessor is to insert *wait states* into the memory-read or memory-write machine cycle. To do this we apply a logic zero to the READY input on the microprocessor (pin 35; see Chapter 1, Additional 8085A Control Signals). The use of the READY input can be seen in Figs. 4-17 (memory-read) and 4-18 (memory-write). To determine the timing requirements of the READY input, refer to Table 4-7.

In Fig. 4-17 the 8085A has generated a 16-bit address during state T_1. The READY line is then brought to a logic zero by some external logic. The READY input is *sampled* by the microprocessor during this state. If the READY input is a logic zero, the microprocessor enters the T_{WAIT} state. The microprocessor will stay in the T_{WAIT} state until the READY lines goes back to a logic one. In Figs. 4-17 and 4-18 the READY input is in the logic zero state during T_2 just long enough to be sensed as a logic zero, but then returns to the logic one state. Because of this the microprocessor is in the T_{WAIT} state for only one clock cycle. How do wait states help the microprocessor to access memories with long access times? *While the microprocessor is "executing" wait states, the memory address is still on the address bus, the $\overline{RD}$ or $\overline{WR}$ signal is still in the logic zero state, and IO/$\overline{M}$ is in the logic zero state* (IO/$\overline{M}$ is not shown in Figs. 4-17 or 4-18). During the one wait state shown in Figs. 4-17 and 4-18 the memory being accessed has an additional 320 ns to 2000 ns (depending on t_{CYC}) to respond to the address and control signals and to place information on the data bus or to gate information off of the data bus. In fact, *a wait state can be inserted in any machine cycle.* In Fig. 4-19 the microprocessor is executing an instruction that requires four machine cycles, and wait states could be inserted between T_2 and T_3 of machine cycles M_1, M_2, M_3, and M_4.

The READY Input Timing Requirements

As we have seen in previous chapters, ROMs and, as we will see, R/W memories do not have an output signal that we can wire to the

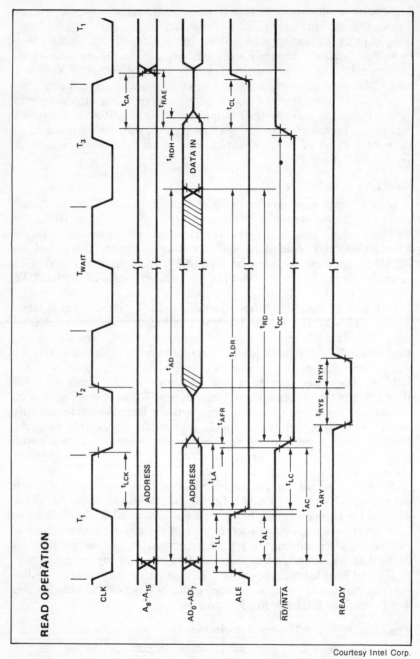

Courtesy Intel Corp.

Fig. 4-17. Adding a wait state to a memory-read cycle.

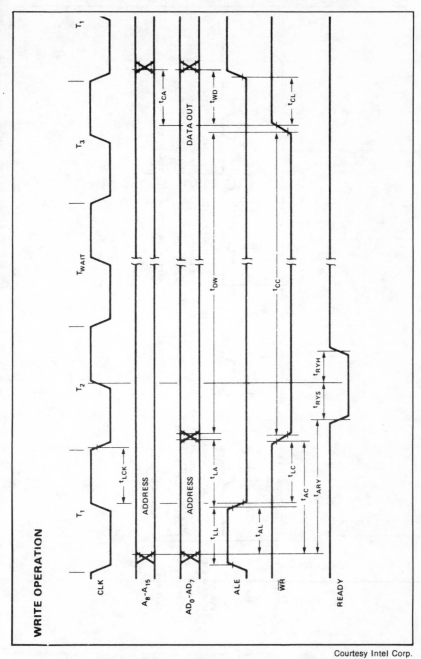

Courtesy Intel Corp.

Fig. 4-18. Adding a wait state to a memory-write cycle.

137

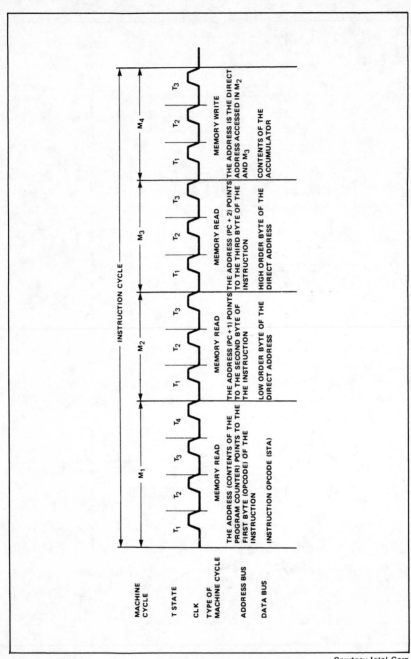

Courtesy Intel Corp.

Fig. 4-19. A typical instruction cycle.

Table 4-8. The Timing Requirements and Characteristics of the 8085A and 8085A-2

$T_A = 0°C$ to $70°C$; $V_{CC} = 5V \pm 5\%$; $V_{SS} = 0V$

Symbol	Parameter	8085A [2]		8085A-2 [2] (Preliminary)		Units
		Min.	Max.	Min.	Max.	
t_{CYC}	CLK Cycle Period	320	2000	200	2000	ns
t_1	CLK Low Time	80		40		ns
t_2	CLK High Time	120		70		ns
t_r, t_f	CLK Rise and Fall Time		30		30	ns
t_{XKR}	X_1 Rising to CLK Rising	30	120	30	100	ns
t_{XKF}	X_1 Rising to CLK Falling	30	150	30	110	ns
t_{AC}	A_{8-15} Valid to Leading Edge of Control [1]	270		115		ns
t_{ACL}	A_{0-7} Valid to Leading Edge of Control	240		115		ns
t_{AD}	A_{0-15} Valid to Valid Data In		575		350	ns
t_{AFR}	Address Float After Leading Edge of READ (INTA)		0		0	ns
t_{AL}	A_{8-15} Valid Before Trailing Edge of ALE [1]	115		50		ns
t_{ALL}	A_{0-7} Valid Before Trailing Edge of ALE	90		50		ns
t_{ARY}	READY Valid from Address Valid		220		100	ns
t_{CA}	Address (A_8-A_{15}) Valid After Control	120		60		ns
t_{CC}	Width of Control Low (RD, WR, INTA) Edge of ALE	400		230		ns
t_{CL}	Trailing Edge of Control to Leading Edge of ALE	50		25		ns
t_{DW}	Data Valid to Trailing Edge of WRITE	420		230		ns
t_{HABE}	HLDA to Bus Enable		210		150	ns
t_{HABF}	Bus Float After HLDA		210		150	ns
t_{HACK}	HLDA Valid to Trailing Edge of CLK	110		40		ns
t_{HDH}	HOLD Hold Time	0		0		ns
t_{HDS}	HOLD Setup Time to Trailing Edge of CLK	170		120		ns
t_{INH}	INTR Hold Time	0		0		ns
t_{INS}	INTR, RST, and TRAP Setup Time to Falling Edge of CLK	160		150		ns
t_{LA}	Address Hold Time After ALE	100		50		ns
t_{LC}	Trailing Edge of ALE to Leading Edge of Control	130		60		ns
t_{LCK}	ALE Low During CLK High	100		50		ns
t_{LDR}	ALE to Valid Data During Read		460		270	ns
t_{LDW}	ALE to Valid Data During Write		200		120	ns
t_{LL}	ALE Width	140		80		ns
t_{LRY}	ALE to READY Stable		110		30	ns
t_{RAE}	Trailing Edge of READ to Re-Enabling of Address	150		90		ns
t_{RD}	READ (or INTA) to Valid Data		300		150	ns
t_{RV}	Control Trailing Edge to Leading Edge of Next Control	400		220		ns
t_{RDH}	Data Hold Time After READ INTA [3]	0		0		ns
t_{RYH}	READY Hold Time	0		0		ns
t_{RYS}	READY Setup Time to Leading Edge of CLK	110		100		ns
t_{WD}	Data Valid After Trailing Edge of WRITE	100		60		ns
t_{WDL}	LEADING Edge of WRITE to Data Valid		40		20	ns

Notes:
1. A_8-A_{15} address Specs apply to IO/$\overline{M}$, S_0, and S_1 except A_8-A_{15} are undefined during T_4-T_6 OF OF cycle whereas IO/$\overline{M}$, S_0, and S_1 are stable.
2. Test conditions: $t_{CYC} = 320ns$ (8085A)/200ns (8085A-2); $C_L = 150pF$.
3. Data hold time is guaranteed under all loading conditions.

Courtesy Intel Corp.

READY input, so that wait states are automatically generated when these slow memories are accessed. Therefore external logic must be used. However, before this external logic can be designed, we must know the timing requirements of the READY input.

From Fig. 4-17 and Table 4-8 we can see that t_{RYS} is a minimum of 110 ns and t_{RYH} is a minimum of 0 ns for the 8085A. Also from Table 4-8 we see that t_1, the time the CLK is a logic zero, must be a minimum of 80 ns ($t_{CYC} = 320$ ns). This means that in some systems, because of the microprocessor clock source, the READY input must be brought to a logic zero *before* CLK goes to a logic zero in state T_2. Because of this possibility the only signals that we can use to clock or pulse this external logic are the ALE and CLK signals (during the T_1 state).

There are two different combinations of ALE and CLK that we could use to clock this external logic: (1) the positive edge of ALE and the positive edge of CLK during T_1 and (2) the negative edge of ALE and the positive edge of CLK during T_1. Our choice will be to use the positive edge of ALE and CLK. The negative edge of ALE may be too close to the positive edge of CLK during T_1, and by using two positive-edge signals our external logic can be very simple. In fact, a single integrated circuit can be used to insert a single wait state into *every* machine cycle (Fig. 4-20). The integrated circuit that can be used is the SN74LS74 (Fig. 4-21).

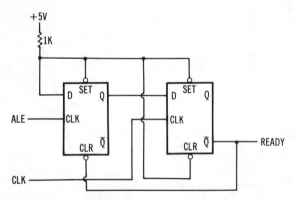

Fig. 4-20. Adding a single wait state to every machine cycle.

To understand the operation of the circuitry shown in Fig. 4-20 we will initially assume that the Q output of the left-hand flip-flop is a logic zero and that the $\bar{Q}$ (pronounced Q bar) output of the right-hand flip-flop is a logic one. This means that the READY input of the microprocessor is a logic one, so no wait states are inserted into any machine cycles. When the ALE signal is generated by the microprocessor in the next machine cycle, its positive edge clocks the logic one at the D input to the Q output of the left-hand flip-flop. The positive edge of the CLK signal during T_1 (after the positive edge of ALE) clocks the logic one into the right-hand flip-flop, so that $\overline{Q}$ output goes to a logic zero. The right-hand flip-flop is clocked in less than 40 ns after the positive edge of CLK. This is at least 80 ns before the microprocessor gets to the T_2 machine cycle. The READY input of the microprocessor is now a logic zero. The logic zero output of this flip-flop also clears the left-hand flip-flop, so the Q output of the left-hand flip-flop goes to a logic zero. This logic zero is clocked into the right-hand flip-flop by CLK, in the middle

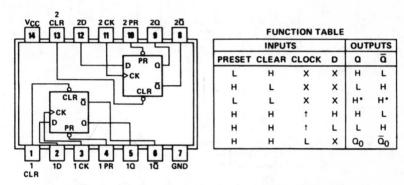

FUNCTION TABLE						
INPUTS					OUTPUTS	
PRESET	CLEAR	CLOCK	D		Q	$\overline{Q}$
L	H	X	X		H	L
H	L	X	X		L	H
L	L	X	X		H*	H*
H	H	↑	H		H	L
H	H	↑	L		L	H
H	H	L	X		Q_0	$\overline{Q}_0$

Courtesy Texas Instruments, Inc.

Fig. 4-21. The pin configuration and truth table for the SN74LS74 dual-D positive-edge-triggered flip-flop with preset and clear inputs.

of T_2. This means that the READY input of the microprocessor is a logic zero during the last half of T_1 and the first half of T_2. As you can see from Fig. 4-17 and Table 4-8 the READY input hold time (t_{RYH}) is specified as 0 ns. This means that the READY input can go to a logic one at the same time that CLK goes to a logic one during T_2. Our circuitry works with the READY input as specified by Intel. The timing of this external logic, with respect to ALE and CLK, is shown in Fig. 4-22.

If a wait state is inserted in every machine cycle, why don't we just slow the microprocessor down with a slower clock, rather than add external logic that slows the microprocessor down using the READY input? There *is* a difference between the two methods. *If we use a slower clock, every T state is longer. By inserting wait states, only the T_2 state is longer.*

In a previous section of this chapter we saw that to use the microprocessor with a 1200-ns ROM a cycle time of 570 ns was required. This means that to execute an instruction that requires four clock cycles (one machine cycle), 2280 ns (4×570 ns) are required. Instead of lengthening every T state we can lengthen only the memory-reference (T_2) state. This means that the microprocessor can still access the 1200-ns ROM, but the four-cycle instruction will be executed in less time!

From Fig. 4-17 we know that the memory address generated by the microprocessor is present on the address bus during part of T_1 and all of T_2. If the microprocessor has a cycle time of 320 ns and the maximum access time of memory can be 575 ns, the address must be present of the address bus for 255 ns during T_1 and 320 ns during T_2. For the ROM with an access time of 1200 ns, the address must be on the address bus for an additional 625 ns. This means that if two wait states (2×320 ns $= 640$ ns) are inserted, the address will be on the bus for 1215 ns. For

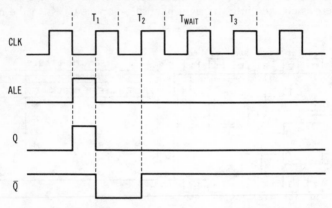

Fig. 4-22. The timing of the dual-D flip-flop (see Fig. 4-20).

a margin of safety, we might insert three wait states, so that the address is on the address bus for 1535 ns. This is more than enough time for the ROM to respond to the address. The time required to execute the four-cycle instruction is now $T_1 + T_2 + (3 \times T_{WAIT}) + T_4$, or 6×320 ns (1920 ns). Although the savings is only 320 ns, the time saved by using wait states, rather than slowing the clock down, will be greater because most of the microprocessor instructions require more than four clock cycles to be executed.

Wait State Problems

In Appendix A all of the 8085A instructions are listed along with the number of clock cycles required to execute each instruction. The number of clock cycles is important, because it means that we can calculate the amount of time required to execute each instruction, knowing the cycle time of the microprocessor. Suppose that we have calculated (using Appendix A) that a particular program will require 10 minutes to be executed, assuming that the microprocessor has a 320-ns cycle time. What will happen if this program is stored in a ROM that has a 700-ns access time and this program is used with a microprocessor with a 320-ns cycle time? How much time will be required to execute this program? Of course, the program will require more than 10 minutes to be executed, because when the microprocessor accesses the ROM a single wait state *has to be* inserted between T_2 and T_3.

There is also the possibility that the program was developed and debugged in R/W memory that required one or two wait states. If this program is later executed in a microcomputer system using memory with an access time of less than 575 ns, no wait states are required (8085A only). This means that the program will be executed faster than planned. In fact, in some microcomputer systems different sections of memory have different access times, because different memory integrated circuits have been used. Sophisticated hardware can be used so that a different number of wait states will be inserted, depending on which section of memory is being accessed.

Avoiding Wait States

As you can see, the use of wait states can cause many problems; the microprocessor/microcomputer hardware becomes more complex, as does determining the amount of time required to execute a program or sequence of instructions. There are two very simple ways of avoiding wait states: (1) Use memories that have access times less than 575 ns/ 320 ns (8085A/8085A-2), or (2) if slow memories must be used, slow down the microprocessor clock. Most of the memory integrated circuits used with microprocessors (ROM or R/W) have access times of 450 ns or less, so no wait states are required. If memories that have access times greater than 575 ns must be used, slow down the microprocessor clock. By doing this you can easily predict *exactly* how much time will be required to execute each instruction in a program. You can calculate the amount of time required to execute an instruction if wait states are used, but it is more difficult.

PRELIMINARY ROM DECODER USE/DESIGN

Now that we have discussed the different ways that ROMs are used in microcomputer system, you will have the opportunity to test your knowledge of ROM decoders and how ROMs are used with microprocessors and microcomputers. In this chapter a number of different ROMs have been described, including their access times, power supply requirements, electrical characteristics, and storage capabilities (number of words). The application of the $\overline{\text{MEMR}}$ signal to ROMs and decoders has also been described.

Preliminary Design No. 1

Using a single SN74LS42 decoder, nonabsolutely decode the first 5K of the microprocessor address space. Using any additional integrated circuits that you require, generate a chip select signal for a Texas Instruments TMS 4732 ROM and an Intel 2708 EPROM. Assume that the address/data bus demultiplexing latch and control signal decoder have already been designed. The TMS 4732 should contain memory location zero.

From Table 4-2 you should determine that the Texas Instruments TMS 4732 is a 4K×8 ROM, and from Table 4-3 that the Intel 2708 is a 1K×8 EPROM. Both ROMs have access times of 450 ns (Tables 4-2 and 4-3). Therefore no wait states have to be generated. To design the decoder you might try to decode two 4K blocks of the microprocessor address space, and then further decode one 4K address block into four 1K address blocks. However, since no additional decoders are available for your design, this would be difficult. Instead, the SN74LS42 should be wired as shown in Fig. 4-23.

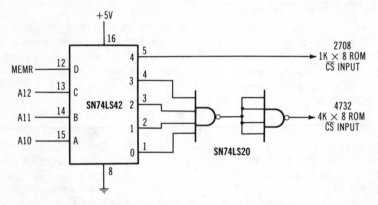

Fig. 4-23. Decoding a 4K and a 1K block of the microprocessor address space with one decoder.

Some design points that you should look for in your own design include:

1. Has the D input of the decoder been wired to $\overline{\text{MEMR}}$?
2. Have the address signals A10, A11, and A12 been wired to the A, B, and C inputs of the decoder?
3. Have A0 through A9 been wired to the 2708, and A0 through A11 been wired to the 4732?
4. Have outputs 0 through 3 been gated together to generate the chip select for the 4732?
5. Has output 4 of the decoder been used as the chip select for the 2708?

The difficult design point in this problem is to realize that the first four consecutive outputs (0–3) of the SN74LS42 decoder, the "1K chip selects," have to be gated together to generate the chip select for the

4K×8 TMS 4732. The gating design must be based on the following truth table:

0	1	2	3	Chip Select
0	1	1	1	0
1	0	1	1	0
1	1	0	1	0
1	1	1	0	0
1	1	1	1	1

Note that there are only five possible input states for this logic, because no two outputs of the decoder can be in the logic zero state at the same time. Readers with a "logic design" background probably realize that we need a four-input AND gate. To build a four-input AND gate we will use two four-input NAND gates (SN74LS20). Since two of these gates are contained in one integrated circuit, the design is simple and low-cost. The pin configuration and truth table for this integrated circuit are shown in Fig. 4-24.

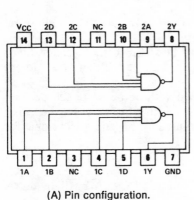

(A) Pin configuration.

	INPUTS			OUTPUT
A	B	C	D	Y
0	0	0	0	1
0	0	0	1	1
0	0	1	0	1
0	0	1	1	1
0	1	0	0	1
0	1	0	1	1
0	1	1	0	1
0	1	1	1	1
1	0	0	0	1
1	0	0	1	1
1	0	1	0	1
1	0	1	1	1
1	1	0	0	1
1	1	0	1	1
1	1	1	0	1
1	1	1	1	0

(B) Truth table.

Courtesy Texas Instruments, Inc.

Fig. 4-24. The pin configuration and truth table for the SN74LS20 dual 4-input positive-logic NAND gate.

Preliminary Design No. 2

Using a single SN74LS42 decoder, nonabsolutely decode the microprocessor address space, starting at memory location zero, for an Intel 2716 EPROM, a Texas Instruments TMS 2732 ROM, and a *2K×8 R/W memory integrated circuit*. The 2716 should occupy the first 2K of memory, followed by the 2K R/W memory, followed by the 4K×8

ROM. Show only the circuitry required to generate the chip select signals. Do not be concerned with any additional control signals required by the R/W memory. You can use any additional gate-type integrated circuits (Fig. 2-10) that you need in your design.

A design that meets these requirements is shown in Fig. 4-25. Some of the design points that you should check for in your design include:

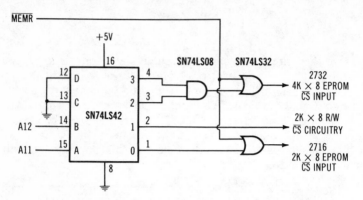

Fig. 4-25. Selecting a ROM or R/W memory with the same decoder.

1. $\overline{\text{MEMR}}$ must not be wired to the SN74LS42, due to the chip select requirements of the R/W memory.
2. Address lines A11 and A12 must be wired to the decoder. Since nonabsolute addressing has been used, A13, A14, and A15 do not have to be used.
3. Has the $\overline{\text{MEMR}}$ signal been gated with output 0 of the decoder with an OR gate, and the output used as the chip select for the 2716?
4. Has output 1 of the decoder been used as the chip select signal for the 2K×8 R/W memory?
5. Has an AND gate (Fig. 2-10) been used to gate outputs 2 and 3 of the decoder together?
6. Has the output of the AND gate been gated with $\overline{\text{MEMR}}$ by an OR gate?
7. Has the output of the OR gate been used to select the 2732?

Do you think that an SN74LS155 decoder could be used to simplify this design? It can, but the authors leave it up to you to prove that it can be used to simplify the design.

Preliminary Design No. 3

You have two different 2K×8 ROMs. One has an access time of 400 ns and the other has an access time of 700 ns. You want to design an 8085A-based microcomputer system that has a cycle time of 320 ns, but both ROMs must be used in the system. This means that wait states must be inserted in the machine cycles of the microprocessor. In fact, you only want wait states to be inserted when the 700-ns ROM is accessed. When the microprocessor accesses the 400-ns ROM, *no* wait states must be inserted.

You may use any integrated circuits and any 4K block of the microprocessor address space in your design. Assume that the address latch and control signal decoder have already been designed.

A design that meets these requirements is shown in Fig. 4-26. Some design points that you should look for in your design include:

1. At the very least, has A11 been used to select one or the other ROM? Of course, any combination of address lines, between A11 and A15, could be used.
2. Has $\overline{\text{MEMR}}$ been used with other signals in the design to select one or the other ROM?
3. Has a single wait state been generated only when the microprocessor accesses the 700-ns ROM?

To keep the design simple, absolute address decoding has been used. Whenever the address 00000XXX XXXXXXXX is present, the 700 ns ROM will be accessed, and a wait state will be inserted. In this particular design, note how the Q output of the left-hand flip-flop is gated with the decoder output, and the result is clocked into the right-hand flip-flop.

One important limitation of this design is that a wait state will be inserted whenever the address 00000XXX is present on A15-A8. Thus, a wait state will be inserted when the 8085 addresses I/O devices 00000XXX. You should also realize that because of timing constraints, memory and I/O control signals cannot be used in wait state circuit designs. These signals are generated during T2, which is when the READY input is sampled (Figs. 4-17, 4-18).

CONCLUSION

In this chapter we have discussed a number of different ROMs and their features. Some of the important features include the type of ROM (mask, programmable, erasable and programmable), word size and number of words, power supply requirements, access time, and the electrical characteristics of the ROM inputs and outputs. As you have seen, regardless of the ROM used, *the $\overline{\text{MEMR}}$ signal must always be used in the decoding scheme so that the ROM is only selected when a memory-read is being performed.* We have also seen two different methods that can be used when the 8085A (8085A-2) microprocessor has to access ROMs that have access times greater than 575 ns (350 ns). By using a lower clock frequency the microprocessor gives the memory more time to respond to an address, but all other states are also slower. By inserting

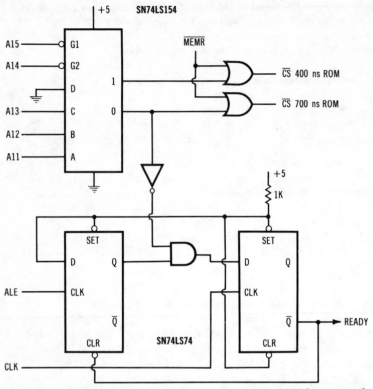

Fig. 4-26. Generating a wait state when the 700-ns ROM is accessed.

wait states the microprocessor is only slowed down when it has to access memory, and, as we just saw, the microprocessor may only have to slow down when a certain section of memory is being accessed. If wait states are used, however, it is difficult to calculate just how much time the microprocessor will require to execute a program.

PROBLEMS

4-1. In a 10-MHz (200-ns cycle time) 8085A-2 based microcomputer, what is the maximum access time that memories in this microcomputer can have (ignoring the possibility of wait states)?

4-2. List the advantages and disadvantages of using mask ROMs, PROMs, and EPROMs in a microcomputer design.

4-3. What are the differences between a 2708 and a TMS 2716? What are the differences between a 2708 and an Intel 2716?

4-4. When should a ROM place information on the data bus? What conditions must be present for this to occur?

4-5. What control signal is used to control the flow of information between a ROM and the microprocessor?

4-6. How many wait states are required if a 1200-ns ROM is used with an 8085A that has a 450-ns cycle time?

4-7. What is leakage current and when is it present on the data bus?

4-8. What is the maximum access time of a ROM that can be used with an 8085A-based microcomputer, assuming that no wait states are used?

4-9. How many different 1K × 8 R/W memories can be used with the absolute memory address decoder shown in Fig. 4-13? State why this type of memory can or cannot be used with this decoder design.

4-10. Design a "universal" EPROM socket for use in a microcomputer system. Either a 2708 or a TMS 2716 may be plugged into this socket. By adding or removing a few jumpers or by setting a switch in one of two possible positions, either 1K or 2K of the microprocessor address space will be absolutely decoded. For the 2708, addresses 10000000 00000000 through 10000011 11111111 will be decoded. Addresses 10000000 00000000 through 10000111 11111111 will be decoded for the TMS 2716.

4-11. A single 2716 must contain two independent assembly language programs. Each program is 1K or less in length. By setting a single switch in one of two positions and resetting the microprocessor, either one or the other program will be executed. The starting address of each program is zero. However, one program is stored in the EPROM starting at location 000000000000 and the other is stored in the EPROM starting at memory location 100000000000. Design the circuitry required so that this EPROM can be used with the microprocessor.

4-12. Assume that a microprocessor design must include a 4K × 8 mask ROM that has three chip select inputs. For the ROM to be selected, all three chip select inputs must be at the logic zero state. Design an absolute address decoder so that this ROM occupies addresses 11010000 00000000 through 11011111 11111111 in the microprocessor address space. No decoded control signals ($\overline{\text{MEMR}}$ or $\overline{\text{MEMW}}$) are available for use in this design. Only $\overline{\text{RD}}$, $\overline{\text{WR}}$, and IO/$\overline{\text{M}}$ are available.

4-13. Design a memory address decoder for a 2708 EPROM using either absolute or nonabsolute address decoding. The addresses for the EPROM should be from 00010000 00000000 through 00010011 11110000. Whenever the microprocessor generates the addresses 0010011 11110001 through 0010011 11111111, the ROM is not selected. This unused portion of the ROM address space could be used by peripheral devices or R/W memory in some microcomputer designs.

4-14. Assume that a microcomputer system has been designed that uses 4K × 8 mask ROMs and a small amount of R/W memory. Since one mistake in a mask ROM can make hundreds of these expensive devices worthless, it was decided to build a 4K × 8 mask ROM simulator, using 2708s. This means that the microcomputer software is developed in inexpensive EPROM, and, when all the bugs have been worked out, the less expensive mask ROMs can be used. Design the simulator, which would be plugged into the 4K × 8 ROM socket, so that one of the four 2708s is selected whenever the 8085A reads from memory locations 00110000 00000000 through 00111111 11111111.

4-15. To erase any type of EPROM, it must be exposed to ultraviolet light. Depending on the intensity of this light the EPROM may be erased in from 5 to 60 minutes. Think of one way in which you could determine how long it takes to erase an EPROM. Assume that when the EPROM is erased, *every* memory location contains 11111111. This is not a "hardware" design problem.

CHAPTER 5

Read/Write Memories

Read/write memories, like ROMs, are used in most microcomputer systems. This type of memory can be used to store data as it is input from a keyboard, paper tape reader, audio cassette, or analog-to-digital converter. Read/write memory is also used when a program is being *developed* (edited, assembled, and debugged). This means that if an error is found in a program, it can be fixed by changing one or more instructions or data values stored in memory. This is done by writing new values into R/W memory. If a program is developed using EPROMs, we would have to program a new EPROM and erase the old one each time the program is changed. By using R/W memory during program development, we can make many changes very quickly.

Quite often the term *random-access memory* (RAM) is used instead of the term read/write memory or R/W memory. "Random access" means that it takes the same amount of time to access any one of a number of memory locations. Instead of RAM we might have sequential-access memory, or SAM. Typical SAMs include shift registers, bubble memory, CCD memory, audio cassettes, and floppy disks. This means that *both* ROM and R/W memory are RAM. Unfortunately, most people incorrectly use the term RAM to mean R/W memory.

Read/write memories are similar to ROMs in many respects. Both types of devices have address lines, data lines, power lines, and one or more CS lines. The only real difference is the fact that R/W memories have a control line, which determines whether information will be read from, or written into, the selected memory location. Like ROMs, R/W memories also have timing requirements that are specified by the manufacturers. A typical timing diagram is shown in Fig. 5-1, and the associated times are listed in Table 5-1.

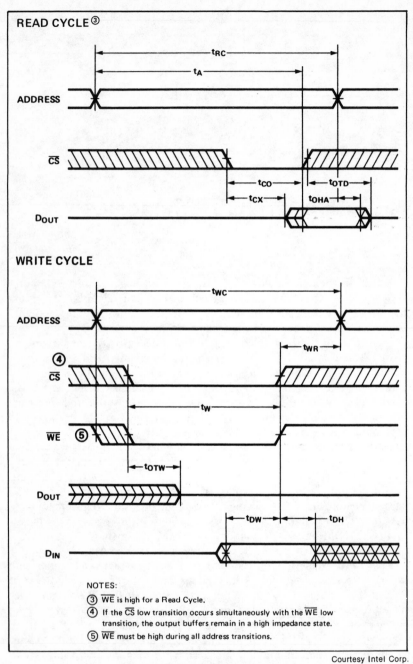

Courtesy Intel Corp.

Fig. 5-1. Typical R/W memory timing.

Table 5-1. The Timing Characteristics of the Intel 1K × 4 2114 Static R/W Memory Integrated Circuit

A.C. CHARACTERISTICS $T_A = 0°C$ to $70°C$, $V_{CC} = 5V \pm 5\%$, unless otherwise noted.

READ CYCLE [1]

SYMBOL	PARAMETER	2114-2, 2114L2 Min.	2114-2, 2114L2 Max.	2114-3, 2114L3 Min.	2114-3, 2114L3 Max.	2114, 2114L Min.	2114, 2114L Max.	UNIT
t_{RC}	Read Cycle Time	200		300		450		ns
t_A	Access Time		200		300		450	ns
t_{CO}	Chip Selection to Output Valid		70		100		120	ns
t_{CX}	Chip Selection to Output Active	20		20		20		ns
t_{OTD}	Output 3-state from Deselection		60		80		100	ns
t_{OHA}	Output Hold from Address Change	50		50		50		ns

WRITE CYCLE [2]

SYMBOL	PARAMETER	2114-2, 2114L2 Min.	2114-2, 2114L2 Max.	2114-3, 2114L3 Min.	2114-3, 2114L3 Max.	2114, 2114L Min.	2114, 2114L Max.	UNIT
t_{WC}	Write Cycle Time	200		300		450		ns
t_W	Write Time	120		150		200		ns
t_{WR}	Write Release Time	0		0		0		ns
t_{OTW}	Output 3-state from Write		60		80		100	ns
t_{DW}	Data to Write Time Overlap	120		150		200		ns
t_{DH}	Data Hold From Write Time	0		0		0		ns

NOTES:
1. A Read occurs during the overlap of a low $\overline{CS}$ and a high $\overline{WE}$.
2. A Write occurs during the overlap of a low $\overline{CS}$ and a low $\overline{WE}$.

Courtesy Intel Corp.

As you can see from Fig. 5-1 a memory-read operation for an R/W memory is the same as for a ROM. For example, an address is placed on the device address inputs, and the $\overline{CS}$ input is taken to ground. After a short period (the access time), information appears on the output or outputs of the device. This information will remain there as long as the address remains the same and the integrated circuit is selected.

A write operation is very similar to a read operation, only the write enable ($\overline{WE}$) input of the R/W memory integrated circuit must be a logic zero in order to write the information present on the data lines into the integrated circuit. As you can see, the only difference between a memory-read and a memory-write operation is that during a memory-write the $\overline{WE}$ input must be at logic zero. *This means that during a memory read, the $\overline{WE}$ input must be a logic one,* although this is not shown in Fig. 5-1.

TYPICAL READ/WRITE MEMORIES

There are many, many different types of R/W memories that can be used in microcomputer systems. Like ROMs, however, there are only a

Table 5-2. Typical R/W Memory Configurations and Their Manufacturers

	EMM/SEMI	Intel	Mostek	National	TI	Fairchild	Motorola	NEC
128 × 8						S	S	
256 × 4		S		S	S			S
256 × 8	S					S		
1024 × 1		S	S	S	S	S	S	S
1024 × 4	S	S	S	S	S	S	S	S
1024 × 8	S	S	S					
2048 × 8				S	Q			
4096 × 1	S	D/S	D/S	D	D/S	D	D/S	D/S
16,384 × 1		D	D	D	D	D	D	S

S = Static Memory
D = Dynamic Memory
Q = Quasi-Static Memory
D/S = Dynamic and Static Memory Available

few popular configurations. These are summarized in Table 5-2. The most popular configurations, as indicated by the number of manufacturers, are 1K×1, 1K×4, and 4K×1. Also in Table 5-2 you can see that there are static, quasi-static, and dynamic R/W memories.

The differences between these three different types of R/W memories have to do with their internal design and construction. Basically the static R/W memories will retain information as long as power is applied. The quasi-static and dynamic R/W memories will retain information only if (1) power is applied and (2) the memory integrated circuit is periodically accessed or refreshed. In general, each memory location in a dynamic R/W memory must be refreshed at least once every 2 ms. Fortunately we can refresh at least 64 memory locations at once, so only 64 refresh operations have to be performed every 2 ms. Quite often external logic is required to perform the refresh function. The Intel Corporation even has a single-chip refresh controller, the 8202. In fact, the Z-80 8-bit microprocessor has much of the required refresh logic built into it. If a microprocessor such as this is used, dynamic R/W memories can be used just as easily as static R/W memories.

The design of refresh logic can be very complex and we will not discuss it in this book. If you are interested in this type of memory, refer to Reference 1. Information about dynamic memories can also be found in many of the references in the bibliography at the end of this chapter. Additional refresh circuitry can also be found in Intel's *Memory Design Handbook*.

Perhaps the two most popular static R/W memories are configured as 1K×1 and 1K×4. The *de facto* standard pin configurations for these two types of R/W memory are shown in Figs. 5-2 and 5-3. Often these memory integrated circuits are called 2102-type (1K×1) and 2114-type (1K×4) R/W memories. The manufacturers of these two types of devices are extensive, and their names along with the names of their products are summarized in Table 5-3. Typical electrical characteristics for

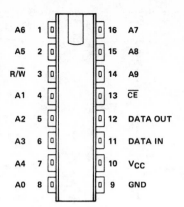

$A6$	1			16	$A7$
$A5$	2			15	$A8$
$R/\overline{W}$	3			14	$A9$
$A1$	4			13	$\overline{CE}$
$A2$	5			12	DATA OUT
$A3$	6			11	DATA IN
$A4$	7			10	V_{CC}
$A0$	8			9	GND

(A) 16-pin ceramic and plastic dual-in-line packages (top view).

$\overline{CE}$	$R/\overline{W}$	D_{in}	D_{out}	MODE
H	X	X	HIGH Z	NOT SELECTED
L	L	L	L	WRITE "0"
L	L	H	H	WRITE "1"
L	H	X	D_{out}	READ

(B) Truth table.

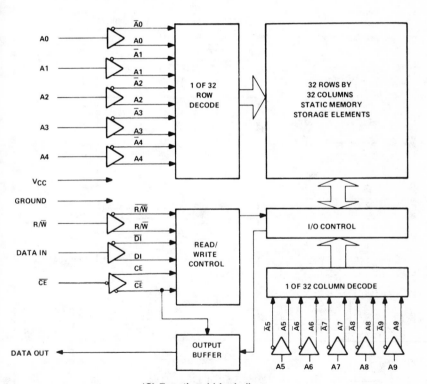

(C) Functional block diagram.

Courtesy Texas Instruments, Inc.

Fig. 5-2. The *de facto* standard pinout, truth table, and block diagram for the 2102-type 1K × 1 R/W memory.

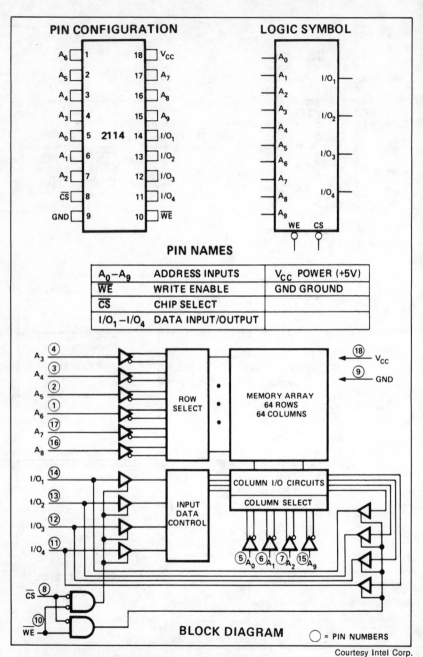

PIN CONFIGURATION

2114

A_6	1	18	V_{CC}
A_5	2	17	A_7
A_4	3	16	A_8
A_3	4	15	A_9
A_0	5	14	I/O_1
A_1	6	13	I/O_2
A_2	7	12	I/O_3
$\overline{CS}$	8	11	I/O_4
GND	9	10	$\overline{WE}$

LOGIC SYMBOL

PIN NAMES

$A_0 - A_9$	ADDRESS INPUTS	V_{CC} POWER (+5V)
$\overline{WE}$	WRITE ENABLE	GND GROUND
$\overline{CS}$	CHIP SELECT	
$I/O_1 - I/O_4$	DATA INPUT/OUTPUT	

BLOCK DIAGRAM ◯ = PIN NUMBERS

Courtesy Intel Corp.

Fig. 5-3. The *de facto* standard pinout and block diagram for the 2114-type 1K × 4 R/W memory.

**Table 5-3. The Manufacturers of 2102-Type and 2114-Type
Read/Write Memories and Their Part Numbers**

Manufacturer	2102 Type	2114 Type
Advanced Micro Devices	Am2102	Am9114
AMI		S2114
Fairchild		2114
Fujitsu		MB8114
Hitachi		HM472114
Intel	2102	2114
Intersil		D2114
Mostek	MK4102N	MK4114
National	MM2102	MM2114
NEC		μPD2114
Motorola		MCM2114
Signetics		2614
Synertek		SY2114
Texas Instruments	TMS 4033	TMS 4045

these devices are tabulated in Tables 5-4 (2102 type) and 5-5 (2114
type). As you can see, the input and output voltages and currents of
these two devices are very similar to those of the ROMs that we discussed in the previous chapter.

The 2102

The 2102-type R/W memory contains 1024 1-bit words (Fig. 5-2),
so eight of these integrated circuits are required to make a 1024×8 memory. This means that all eight of the $\overline{\text{CE}}$ (chip enable bar: the same as
$\overline{\text{CS}}$) signals would be wired together to the output of a memory address
decoder or other chip select circuitry. Also, A0 through A9 of the address bus would have to be wired to the appropriately labeled inputs of
each integrated circuit along with +5 V (pin 10, V_{CC}) and ground
(pin 9, GND).

At first glance you might wire both D_{IN} and D_{OUT} to the microprocessor bidirectional data bus. However, by examining the truth table in Fig.
5-2 you can see that problems will occur during a memory-write operation. During a memory-write operation the microprocessor is placing
information on the data bus, and an address on the address bus. The
$\overline{\text{MEMW}}$ signal is also generated. During this time a logic one or logic
zero is written into the 2102-type memory, *but this same information is
also output on the D_{OUT} pin*. This means that the 2102 is both gating
information off of the data bus, and placing information onto the data
bus *at the same time*. To avoid this problem a buffer is often placed between the D_{OUT} pins and the data bus. This buffer is only enabled when
(1) the 2102 is enabled or selected and (2) a memory-read operation is
being performed. When these two conditions are met, the logic one or
logic zero on the D_{OUT} pin is gated on to the data bus. Although this
requires some external circuitry the 2102 is the most popular static R/W

memory today. It is popular because it is easy to use and it is low in cost (less than $1.00 each).

The 2114

The 2114 is very similar to the 2102. It has ten address inputs (A0–A9), a chip select input ($\overline{CS}$), a memory-write input ($\overline{WE}$), and power and ground inputs. Because the 2114 contains 1024 4-bit words, there are four data input/output pins (pins 11, 12, 13, and 14). Thus the 2114 is an 18-pin integrated circuit (Fig. 5-3). Since the 2114 does have these four *bidirectional inputs and outputs* they can be wired directly to the microcomputer data bus. As you would expect, two of these integrated circuits are required to form a 1024×8 memory (Fig. 5-4).

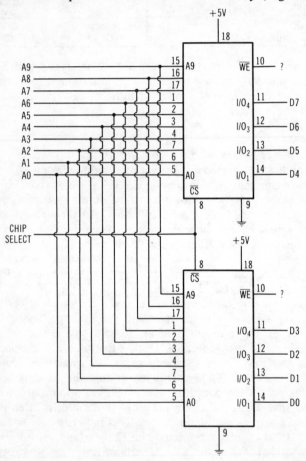

Fig. 5-4 Using two 2114-type 1024 × 4-word R/W memories to form 1024 8-bit words.

READING AND WRITING WITH R/W
MEMORY: THE PRINCIPLES

Reading from R/W Memory

To read information from an R/W memory, (1) an address must be on the address bus, (2) the memory integrated circuits must be selected (both of the 2114s or all eight of the 2102s), and (3) the R/$\overline{W}$ (2102) or $\overline{WE}$ (2114) input must be a logic one. We already know that an address is generated each time the microcomputer accesses memory, so ten lines of the address bus can be wired directly to the memory integrated circuits. By absolutely or nonabsolutely decoding A10–A15 we can decode part or all of the microprocessor 64K of address space into 1K blocks. A logic zero, which is generated by this logic, can then be used to select eight 2102s or two 2114s (Fig. 5-4), which make up 1K×8 of the microcomputer memory.

What signal will be wired to the R/$\overline{W}$ or $\overline{WE}$ input of the memory integrated circuits? During a memory read, $\overline{MEMR}$ is a logic zero and $\overline{MEMW}$ is a logic one, so $\overline{MEMW}$ could be wired to these inputs. Once the memory integrated circuits are enabled and the access time of the integrated circuits has passed, information will be placed on the data bus, where it will be gated into the microprocessor. This is very similar to the operations performed when the microprocessor reads information from ROMs. In fact, the microprocessor has no way of knowing whether it is reading information from ROM or R/W memory! You are the one who decides which type of memory will be read from, when the microcomputer is programmed.

Writing to R/W Memory

Writing information into R/W memory is just as easy as reading information from R/W memory. When the microprocessor executes a memory-write instruction, a memory-write operation is performed. A 16-bit address is placed on the address bus, 8 bits of information are placed on the data bus, and the $\overline{MEMW}$ signal is generated. By appropriate decoding logic the R/W memories are selected and the $\overline{MEMW}$ signal writes the contents of the data bus into the appropriate memory location.

If 2114-type memories are being used, we know that two integrated circuits have to be selected, as shown in Fig. 5-4. As you can see, one of the integrated circuits is wired to D0–D3 and the other is wired to D4–D7 of the data bus. If 2102-type R/W memories are used, eight integrated circuits have to be selected. This means that each one of the eight 2102s gates data off of (memory write) or gates data on to (memory read) a different bit in the data bus. *No two memory integrated circuits must be enabled (selected) that are wired to the same data bit(s) of the data bus.* We saw this in Chapter 4. However, since each ROM

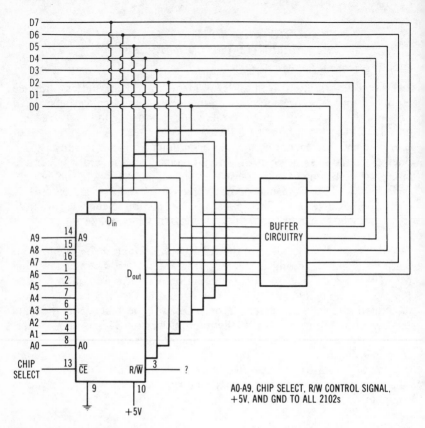

Fig. 5-5. Using eight 2102-type R/W memories to form 1024 × 8 words of memory.

used all 8 bits of the data bus, only one ROM was selected at a time. By using 2114s, only two R/W memory integrated circuits are selected at a time. With 2102s each device is wired to a single bit in the data bus, so eight of this type of R/W memory must be enabled at the same time.

In Fig. 5-5 eight of the 2102s have been used. The address bus wired to each individual integrated circuit has not been shown. Rather, all of the memory integrated circuits are shown stacked side by side, with the appropriate address signals wired to the first integrated circuit. This is a common type of diagram that is often found in manufacturer's literature. Each individual signal (D_{IN} or D_{OUT}) has been shown going to each individual integrated circuit. How signals such as $\overline{\text{MEMR}}$ and $\overline{\text{MEMW}}$ are used is not shown, and a design for the D_{OUT} buffer circuitry is not shown. Note that the chip select signal is wired to all eight of the memory integrated circuits. *None of the memory integrated circuits in Fig. 5-5 are wired to the same data bus lines.*

162

The problem that we must avoid is shown in Fig. 5-6. To keep this drawing as simple as possible, two 2114s have been used, rather than eight 2102s. If the circuitry in this figure is actually used in a microcomputer, the chip select signal will cause both 2114s to be enabled or selected. Most of the time this is what you would consider to be normal,

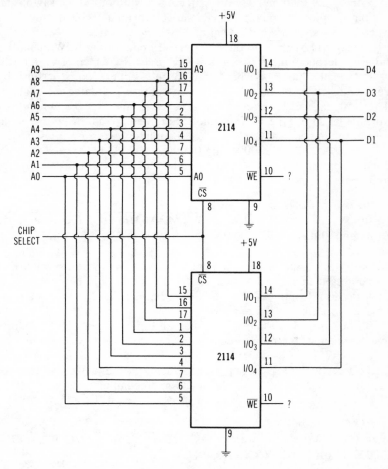

Fig. 5-6. Improperly selecting R/W memory integrated circuits that are wired to the data and address buses.

because two 2114s must be used to form 8-bit memory locations. However, the four data ouputs of one 2114 in Fig. 5-6 are wired to the data outputs of the other 2114. Since they are both enabled at the *same* time, we have no way of knowing what will be gated on the four LSBs of the data bus. This type of design must not be used.

R/W Memory Problems

Suppose that we simply wire the R/$\overline{W}$ or $\overline{WE}$ inputs of the memory integrated circuits to $\overline{MEMW}$ and that the memories are selected by means of an absolute or nonabsolute decoder. Will these memories operate properly all the time? Unfortunately they will not. As we saw in the previous chapter we could not enable a ROM with a decoded "address." Instead, we had to use a decoded address *and* $\overline{MEMR}$.

If we do wire $\overline{MEMW}$ to the R/$\overline{W}$ or $\overline{WE}$ input of the R/W memories and use a decoder output to select or enable the R/W memory, what will the state of the buses be when a memory-read operation is performed? We know that the buses will contain an address and data, and that the $\overline{MEMR}$ signal will be a logic zero. Let us assume that the contents of two parallel 2114-type R/W memories are being read. They are wired to an absolute decoder, so that 1K of the microprocessor address space, between 01000000 00000000 and 01000011 11111111, represents one of the addresses of the 2114. For an address of 01000011 00111101, we would have:

High Address	Low Address	Data	$\overline{MEMR}$	$\overline{MEMW}$	$\overline{I/O\ R}$	$\overline{I/O\ W}$
01000011	00111101	11000011	0	1	1	1

on the buses during a memory-read operation. We have assumed that the addressed memory location contains 11000011. Since $\overline{MEMW}$ is wired to the $\overline{WE}$ input of the memories, the fact that $\overline{MEMR}$ is a logic zero has no effect on the memories.

From Chapter 1 we know that when an input/output (I/O) instruction is executed, the microprocessor places the 8-bit device address on both A0–A7 and A8–A15 of the address bus. At the same time either the $\overline{I/O\ R}$ or $\overline{I/O\ W}$ signal is generated. For a device address of 01000011, what would the state of the microcomputer buses be? If an IN (I/O read) instruction is executed, the buses will contain:

High Address	Low Address	Data	$\overline{MEMR}$	$\overline{MEMW}$	$\overline{I/O\ R}$	$\overline{I/O\ W}$
01000011	01000011	XXXXXXXX	1	1	0	1

Even though we are "reading" information from a peripheral, we are also reading information from the 2114 R/W memories (memory location 01000011 01000011)! Note that during a memory read, $\overline{MEMW}$, which is wired to the $\overline{WE}$ inputs of the 2114s, is a logic one. As we can see, $\overline{MEMW}$ is also a logic one when an IN instruction is executed. Just as we cannot read from or write to two memory locations at the same time, we cannot read from a memory location and a peripheral at the same time. *Therefore the decoded chip select signal, $\overline{MEMR}$, and*

$\overline{MEMW}$ must be gated together, so that the R/W memories are only selected when the proper address is generated by the microprocessor, and a memory-read or a memory-write operation is taking place. As we saw in Chapter 4, since we can only read from ROMs, $\overline{MEMR}$ was gated with a decoded memory address.

READING AND WRITING WITH R/W
MEMORY: THE CIRCUITRY

Nonabsolute Decoding

As one would expect, we can use both nonabsolute and absolute decoding with R/W memory, just as we did with ROMs. Therefore one of the simplest decoding methods that we try to use is shown in Fig. 5-7. This circuitry will select the 2114s if any one of the first 1024 memory addresses, starting at zero, is placed on the address bus and if either $\overline{MEMR}$ or $\overline{MEMW}$ is a logic zero.

If a memory-read operation is taking place, the 2114s will be selected, but the $\overline{MEMW}$ signal will be a logic one, so information will be read from memory. If a memory-write operation is taking place, the 2114s will be selected, but $\overline{MEMW}$ will be a logic zero, so the content of the data bus will be written into the selected memory location. What will happen if an IN or OUT instruction is executed? *The 2114s will not be selected,* because both $\overline{MEMR}$ and $\overline{MEMW}$ are in the logic one state. Of course, the circuit shown in Fig. 5-7 is not very practical. Do you know why?

When the microprocessor is reset, it executes the instruction stored in memory location zero. This, however, is an R/W memory location. When power is first applied to the microcomputer system, random values are stored in R/W memory. Also, when power is turned off, any values stored in R/W memory are lost. Unfortunately we do not have a program in R/W memory, starting at memory location zero. You might think that we could use a keyboard, paper tape reader, or audio cassette to load a program into R/W memory, but, to do so, the microcomputer must be executing a program that reads information from these peripheraps and stores the information in memory. Since a program can only be started at memory location zero by resetting the microprocessor, we must have a program in R/W memory in order to load a program into R/W memory. There is no easy way to do this. There are microcomputer designs that do have R/W memory at location zero, but they are complex and are beyond the scope of this book.[2] Of course the solution to this is to use the first few "K" of the microprocessor address space for ROM, and the remainder for R/W memory. A program stored in ROM could then be used to load a program into R/W memory. In Fig. 5-8 a nonabsolute decoder for R/W memory, starting at 01000000 00000000, is shown.

165

Since nonabsolute decoding has been used in Fig. 5-8, how much of the microprocessor address space has been "used up" by this 1K of memory? For the R/W memory to be selected A14 must be a logic one. Therefore 32K of the microprocessor address space has been used.

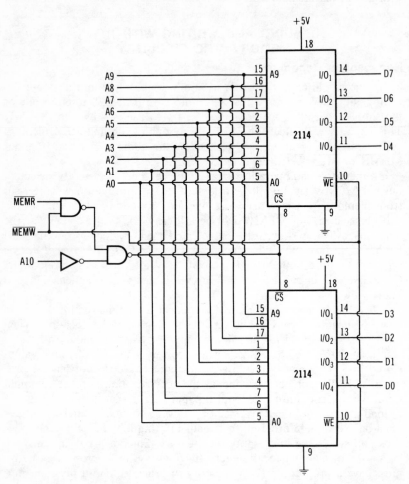

Fig. 5-7. Nonabsolutely decoding the first 1K of the microprocessor address space for two 2114 (1K × 4) R/W memories.

What do the two NAND gates in Fig. 5-8 do? If either $\overline{\text{MEMR}}$ or $\overline{\text{MEMW}}$ is a logic zero, the output of the left-hand NAND gate will be a logic one. This is gated with A14, and if A14 is also a logic one, the output of the right-hand NAND gate is a logic zero. Therefore the 2114s will be enabled when one of the two conditions:

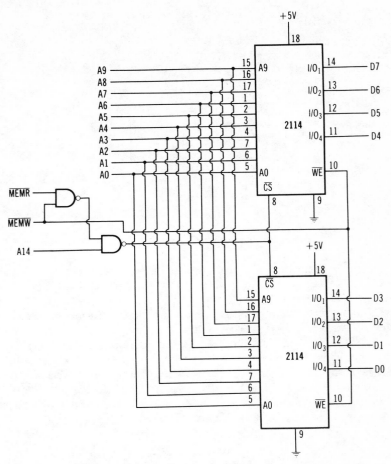

Fig. 5-8. One of the methods for nonabsolutely decoding 1K of the microprocessor address space for R/W memory.

(1) $\overline{\text{MEMR}} = 0$ and A14 = 1

or

(2) $\overline{\text{MEMW}} = 0$ and A14 = 1

is met.

Suppose that we need 8K of R/W memory, starting at address 01000000 00000000 up to 01011111 11111111. Could the nonabsolute decoder in Fig. 5-9 be used? No, it could not. *The G1 and G2 inputs of the SN74LS154 must both be logic zeroes for the decoder to be enabled.* This is not possible if $\overline{\text{MEMR}}$ and $\overline{\text{MEMW}}$ are wired to these inputs. However, by slightly modifying this circuitry we can successfully design a nonabsolute decoder for 8K of R/W memory (Fig. 5-10).

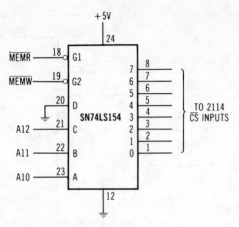

Fig. 5-9. A nonabsolute decoder "design" for 8K of R/W memory.

In Fig. 5-10 the output of the NAND gate is a logic one whenever either $\overline{\text{MEMR}}$ or $\overline{\text{MEMW}}$ is a logic zero. Therefore outputs 8 through 15 of the decoder are used to select the R/W memories. If A10, A11, and A12 are logic zeroes and the D input is a logic one (a memory read or memory write is taking place), output 8 of the decoder will be a logic zero. If these three address lines are logic ones and the D input is a logic one, output 15 will be a logic zero. Which output of the decoder will be a logic zero when an IN or OUT instruction is executed? We know that outputs 8–15 will be logic ones, because neither $\overline{\text{MEMR}}$ or $\overline{\text{MEMW}}$ is a logic zero. Any of the other outputs of the SN74LS154 (0–7) may be a logic zero, depending on the device address on the address bus.

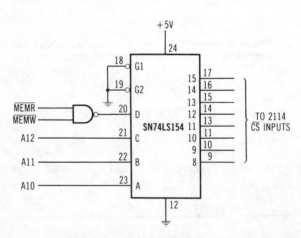

Fig. 5-10. An improved nonabsolute decoder design for 8K of R/W memory.

Could the decoder shown in Fig. 5-10 be used with 2102s ($1K \times 1$) or any other type of R/W memory? Yes, these outputs could be used to enable 2102s or many other different types of R/W memories that contain 1024 words. Of course, if 2102s are used, each output would have to be wired to the chip select inputs of *eight* 2102s, since eight of them are required to form 1024 words of 8 bits each.

Absolute Decoding

In one of the examples in Chapter 4 two decoders were used for absolute decoding: an SN74LS42 that decoded A14 and A15 and enabled an SN74LS154, which decoded A10, A11, A12, and A13. Since these decoders were used to select ROMs, we had the choice of enabling either the SN74LS42 or SN74LS154 with the $\overline{\text{MEMR}}$ signal. We choose to enable the SN74LS154 with $\overline{\text{MEMR}}$ (Fig. 4-15). In this section we will add another decoder to this circuitry. Fig. 5-11 shows the decoders used to do this.

As you can see in Fig. 5-11 $\overline{\text{MEMR}}$ is still used to enable a decoder that is used exclusively to select ROMs. By gating $\overline{\text{MEMR}}$ and $\overline{\text{MEMW}}$ together with an AND gate, the G2 input of the B decoder will be a logic zero only if either $\overline{\text{MEMR}}$ or $\overline{\text{MEMW}}$ is a logic zero. By wiring the AND gate output to the G2 input rather than the D input, the SN74LS154 can be used to absolutely decode a 16K block of the microprocessor address space into 1K blocks. This decoder design also meets a very important design requirement. That is, ROM starts at memory location zero. What are the addresses for the 16K block of R/W memory? Read/write memory will only be addressed when output 1 of the SN74LS42 decoder is a logic zero. This means that A15 must be a logic zero and A14 must be a logic one. Therefore all of the address lines between A12 and A0 can assume any combination of values, so the 16K block of R/W memory has the addresses between 01000000 00000000 and 01111111 11111111.

Suppose you have eight $4K \times 2$ static R/W memory chips. What would an absolute decoder for 8K of R/W memory, starting at 11000000 00000000, look like? Because these are $4K \times 2$ chips, we know that A0–A11 will be wired directly to them. Therefore the decoder must use address lines A12, A13, A14, and A15. If the first R/W memory location has the address 11000000 00000000, then 1100 will be present on the four most significant address lines. One absolute decoder design that could be used with these chips is shown in Fig. 5-12. Of course, because $4K \times 2$ chips are used, each of the appropriate outputs of the decoder (12 and 13) must be wired to four of these chips. Outputs 12 and 13 were used because A15, A14, A13, and A12 can be in the logic states 1100 or 1101. Not shown in this figure is the connection of the address and data buses to the memory integrated circuits, and also not shown is how $\overline{\text{MEMW}}$ is connected to these chips.

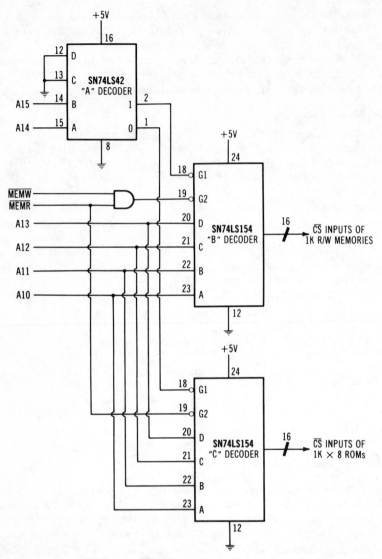

Fig. 5-11. Using $\overline{MEMR}$ and $\overline{MEMW}$ with decoders to absolutely address R/W and read-only memories.

ELECTRICAL CHARACTERISTICS OF R/W MEMORIES

Drive Capability

In general, R/W memories have electrical characteristics that are very similar to those of the ROMs that we discussed in Chapter 4. Typical

170

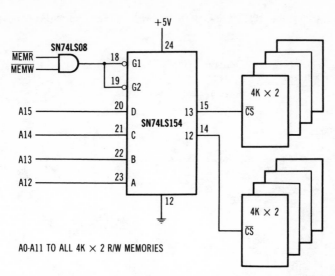

Fig. 5-12. An absolute decoder for 8K of 4K×2 R/W memories, starting at address 11000000 00000000.

R/W memory electrical characteristics are summarized in Tables 5-4 and 5-5. There really isn't anything unusual about these characteristics. Note that the I/O leakage current of the 2114 (Table 5-5) is a current that can be sourced or sunk by the data input/output pin(s) *when the chip is not selected.* Because current can flow in either direction the *ab-*

Table 5-4. Typical 2102-type R/W Memory Electrical Characteristics

D. C. and Operating Characteristics

$T_A = 0°C$ to $70°C$, $V_{CC} = 5V$ ±5% unless otherwise specified.

Symbol	Parameter	2102A, 2102A-4 2102AL, 2102AL-4 Limits Min.	Typ.[1]	Max.	2102A-2, 2102AL-2 Limits Min.	Typ.[1]	Max.	2102A-6 Limits Min.	Typ.[1]	Max.	Unit	Test Conditions
I_{LI}	Input Load Current		1	10		1	10		1	10	μA	$V_{IN} = 0$ to 5.25V
I_{LOH}	Output Leakage Current		1	5		1	5		1	5	μA	$\overline{CE} = 2.0V$, $V_{OUT} = V_{OH}$
I_{LOL}	Output Leakage Current		-1	-10		-1	-10		-1	-10	μA	$\overline{CE} = 2.0V$, $V_{OUT} = 0.4V$
I_{CC}	Power Supply Current		33	Note 2		45	65		33	55	mA	All Inputs = 5.25V, Data Out Open, $T_A = 0°C$
V_{IL}	Input Low Voltage	-0.5		0.8	-0.5		0.8	-0.5		0.65	V	
V_{IH}	Input High Voltage	2.0		V_{CC}	2.0		V_{CC}	2.2		V_{CC}	V	
V_{OL}	Output Low Voltage			0.4			0.4			0.45	V	$I_{OL} = 2.1mA$
V_{OH}	Output High Voltage	2.4			2.4			2.2			V	$I_{OH} = -100μA$

Notes: 1. Typical values are for $T_A = 25°C$ and nominal supply voltage.
2. The maximum I_{CC} value is 55mA for the 2102A and 2102A-4, and 33mA for the 2102AL and 2102AL-4.

Courtesy Intel Corp.

171

Table 5-5. Typical 2114-type R/W Memory Electrical Characteristics

D.C. AND OPERATING CHARACTERISTICS
$T_A = 0°C$ to $70°C$, $V_{CC} = 5V \pm 5\%$, unless otherwise noted.

SYMBOL	PARAMETER	2114-2, 2114-3, 2114 Min. Typ.[1] Max.			2114L2, 2114L3, 2114L Min. Typ.[1] Max.			UNIT	CONDITIONS
I_{LI}	Input Load Current (All Input Pins)			10			10	μA	$V_{IN} = 0$ to 5.25V
I_{LO}	I/O Leakage Current			10			10	μA	$\overline{CS} = 2.4V$, $V_{I/O} = 0.4V$ to V_{CC}
I_{CC1}	Power Supply Current		80	95			65	mA	$V_{IN} = 5.25V$, $I_{I/O} = 0$ mA, $T_A = 25°C$
I_{CC2}	Power Supply Current			100			70	mA	$V_{IN} = 5.25V$, $I_{I/O} = 0$ mA, $T_A = 0°C$
V_{IL}	Input Low Voltage	-0.5		0.8	-0.5		0.8	V	
V_{IH}	Input High Voltage	2.0		6.0	2.0		6.0	V	
I_{OL}	Output Low Current	2.1	6.0		2.1	6.0		mA	$V_{OL} = 0.4V$
I_{OH}	Output High Current	-1.0	-1.4		-1.0	-1.4		mA	$V_{OH} = 2.4V$
I_{OS}[2]	Output Short Circuit Current			40			40	mA	

NOTE: 1. Typical values are for $T_A = 25°C$ and $V_{CC} = 5.0V$.
2. Duration not to exceed 30 seconds.

Courtesy Intel Corp.

solute value of the current is specified. Of course, if the integrated circuit were "perfect," no current should leak into or out of the device when it is not selected.

Note that the leakage current of the 2102 (Table 5-4) is determined by the bit of information that *would be* output if the chip were selected. If the bit of information that would be output if the chip were selected is a logic zero, the D_{OUT} pin will source current ($-10~\mu A$). If the bit of information is a logic one, the D_{OUT} pin will sink current ($10~\mu A$). Unfortunately, because of the internal structure of the 2114 we cannot determine when one of the bidirectional data pins will sink or source leakage current. Table 5-6 contains the voltage and current characteristics of the 8085A. As you can see, these R/W memories are directly compatible with the 8085A.

Leakage Currents

As was just mentioned, R/W memories (and ROMs) are not perfect devices. Therefore, even though one of these memories is not selected, it will still sink/source current from/to the data bus. For a 2114-type memory this is called the *I/O leakage current*. Since the 2012-type memory has separate D_{IN} and D_{OUT} pins, the leakage current is called *output leakage current* (from D_{OUT}). This type of memory integrated circuit typically sinks 5 μA (logic one) and sources $-10~\mu A$ (logic zero) when it is not selected. Remember, "logic ones" and "logic zeroes" are not

Table 5-6. The Electrical Characteristics of the 8085A and 8085A-2 Microprocessors

(T_A = 0°C to 70°C; V_{CC} = 5V ±5%; V_{SS} = 0V; unless otherwise specified)

Symbol	Parameter	Min.	Max.	Units	Test Conditions
V_{IL}	Input Low Voltage	-0.5	+0.8	V	
V_{IH}	Input High Voltage	2.0	V_{CC} +0.5	V	
V_{OL}	Output Low Voltage		0.45	V	I_{OL} = 2mA
V_{OH}	Output High Voltage	2.4		V	I_{OH} = -400μA
I_{CC}	Power Supply Current		170	mA	
I_{IL}	Input Leakage		±10	μA	V_{in} = V_{CC}
I_{LO}	Output Leakage		±10	μA	0.45V ≤ V_{out} ≤ V_{CC}
V_{ILR}	Input Low Level, RESET	-0.5	+0.8	V	
V_{IHR}	Input High Level, RESET	2.4	V_{CC} +0.5	V	
V_{HY}	Hysteresis, RESET	0.25		V	

Courtesy Intel Corp.

"output" on the data bus, but they do influence the current on the data bus.

Suppose that we have four 2102-type memories that are all wired to D0. Of course, each memory has its *own* unique chip select signal. If the microprocessor is reading a logic zero from one of the 2102s, which of the remaining memory integrated circuits will influence the amount of current on the D0 line? All of the integrated circuits wired to D0 (the four 2102s and the 8085A) will, as shown in Fig. 5-13. As you can see, the determination of current can be very complex, because the amount of current that is sourced or sunk is dependent on the logic levels that *would* be output by the memories if they *were* selected. From Fig. 5-13 you can see that two of the 2102s are sourcing −10 μA (due to logic zeroes) and the other unselected 2102 is sinking 5 μA. The 8085A is even sourcing −10 μA to the D0 line of the bus. The selected 2102 can sink 2.1 mA and still keep the D0 line of the data bus at 0.4 V or less. Therefore the 8085A reads the data value as a logic zero.

What is the worst possible combination of leakage currents? Our first guess would be that it would occur when all of the unselected memories

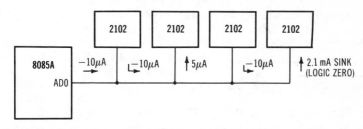

Fig. 5-13. The current sources and current sinks on the data bus when four 2102-type memories are used with the 8085A.

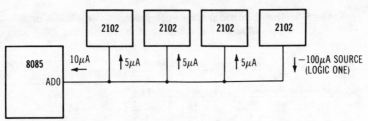

Fig. 5-14. One 2102 sourcing current while all the other devices are sinking current.

are sourcing current (due to logic zeroes) and the selected memory integrated circuit is sinking current. Since 2.1 mA = 2100 μA, however, 200 2102s could be sourcing leakage current on the same data line, and the one selected memory could still sink all of this leakage current *and* maintain a logic zero (0.4 V or less) on the data line. It is doubtful that you would have this number of 2102s wired to the same data line. This case infers that you could have 200K of R/W memory in the microcomputer system, yet the microprocessor can only address 64K.

The "other" worst case situation, which is shown in Fig. 5-14, is when the selected 2102 is sourcing current and all of the unselected 2102s are sinking current (due to logic ones). In Fig. 5-14 the unselected 2102s are sinking 5 μA and the microprocessor is also sinking 10 μA. The selected 2102 is placing a logic one on the data line, so it can source a maximum of −100 μA to the data line to maintain a minimum voltage of 2.4 V on the data line. There is the very real possibility that we might have 18 or more 2102s wired to the same data bus line. This is only 18K of R/W memory. If this occurs, the logic one from the selected 2102 may not be read into the microprocessor correctly. It may appear as a logic zero. All is not lost, however. *Remember that we must buffer the D_{OUT} outputs of the 2102s if 2102s are to be used in the microcomputer system.* Therefore we only have to worry about the leakage currents due to other memory integrated circuits that are wired to the same buffer. We do not have to worry about the leakage current contributions of the microprocessor.

It is impossible to easily determine all possible combinations of currents, simply because the data values in R/W memory may change and these changes will affect the amount of leakage current and its direction. In fact, many designers ignore the influence of these currents in small microcomputer systems. In large systems the data inputs and outputs of the memory integrated circuits are buffered by additional logic, so the leakage currents on the data bus become negligible.

Input and Output Capacitance

In general, all integrated-circuit pins have a capacitance associated with them. For the memory and microprocessor integrated circuits that we have been working with, these capacitances are within the range of 5 to 15 pF. Quite often an output of an integrated circuit is specified as being capable of driving a specific resistive and capacitive load. As an example, Intel, Texas Instruments, Motorola, and NEC use a load of one 7400-series TTL device and 100 pF when determining the access times of their 2114-type 1K×4 R/W memories. This can be seen in the data sheets for the Motorola MCM 2114 and the NEC μPD 2114 shown in Appendix D.

In previous chapters the electrical characteristics of the 8085A have been summarized in tables. These timing values, however, are valid only if the 8085A is driving a *capacitive load* of less than 150 pF. If memory and peripheral integrated circuits have an input capacitance of 5 pF, the 8085A *may* be able to drive 30 of these chips, as long as it has the current capability. In some designs the current required by memory and peripheral chips will limit the number of chips that can be driven directly by the 8085A. In other systems the capacitance of these integrated circuits may limit the number of chips that can be driven by the 8085A, even though the 8085A is not sinking 2 mA or sourcing -400 μA of current. Therefore in large systems (15 or more chips) both the current and capacitance capabilities and limitations of the 8085A must be considered.

USING R/W MEMORIES WITH LONG ACCESS TIMES

Like ROMs, R/W memories can be obtained with access times of between 250 and 1000 ns. As long as the R/W memory has an access time of 575 ns (350 ns) or less they can be used directly with the 8085A (8085A-2) with no wait states. If the access times are longer than this, the cycle time of the microprocessor can be lengthened or wait states can be inserted. We have discussed both techniques, so little would be gained by repeating that information here. As far as the authors know, all 2114-type 1K×4 R/W memories have access times of 450 ns or less, so they are easy to use in 8085A-based microcomputer designs. The 2102-type memories have access times up to 1000 ns. Since the 2114 can store four times as much information as a 2102, it would probably be easier to use 2114s. Currently 2114s are about six times more expensive than 2102s, but each 2114 is equal to four 2102s.

MEMORY BUFFERING

As we have seen, the input requirements (both address and chip select) of memories are very reasonable; they require very little current. The outputs, when the chips are selected, have reasonable drive capabilities. When the chips are not selected, some current does leak onto the data bus or is drawn off of the data bus, but in small systems this is not a problem. Even though the 8085A microprocessor can sink 2 mA (0.45 V) and source -400 μA (2.4 V), it is easy to see that we may have so many memory integrated circuits wired to the microcomputer buses, that large sink and source currents are required. In fact, we must remember that not only are memory chips wired to the buses, but peripheral devices also use the address bus (to decode a device address) and the data bus (to transfer information). For these reasons the data and address buses are often *buffered*. This means that the sink and source current capability is increased, while a maximum logic zero voltage and a minimum logic one voltage are maintained.

Surprisingly enough, we have already buffered part of one of the microcomputer buses in many of our designs. Do you know which part of what bus was buffered? By demultiplexing the address/data bus with an SN74LS373, 8212, or two SN74LS75s, we buffered the low address bus (A0–A7). By using these devices, how much have the current capabilities of these address lines been increased? We know that the 8085A can sink 2 mA (0.45 V) and source -400 μA (2.4 V). From Table 2-5 we can find the current capabilities of the SN74LS373 and the 8212. For instance, the SN74LS373 can source -2.6 mA (2.4 V minimum) and sink 12 mA (0.4 V maximum). This means that the SN74LS373 is capable of 6.5 times more source current and 6 times more sink current. As we have seen, memories generally require input currents of 10 μA and have leakage currents of ± 10 μA. Therefore the SN74LS373 can "drive" a tremendous number of address pins (A0–A7). The 8212 is even a better buffer because it can source more current (-16 mA at 2.4 V minimum) and sink more current (15 mA at 0.45 V maximum).

Buffering the High Address Bus

Even though A14 and A15 may only drive two or three decoders, A8, A9, and possibly A10 and A11 are wired directly to *all* memory integrated circuits. For this reason you may wish to buffer the high address bus: the eight most significant address lines. You would save very little time, effort, and money by buffering only A8, A9, A10, and A11. Therefore we will assume in our discussion that all 8 address lines (A8–A15) must be buffered. Have we already seen integrated circuits that can be used to buffer these signals? Yes, the SN74LS373 and the 8212 could be used.

Typical circuitry using the SN74LS373 is shown in Fig. 5-15, and the buffer circuitry using the 8212 shown in Fig. 5-16. As you can see, it is very easy to use these devices as buffers. Note that the three-state outputs of these devices are always enabled. This means that pin 1 of the SN74LS373 is wired to ground and that pin 2 of the 8212 is wired to +5 V. The latches are also always enabled (pin 11 of the SN74LS373 to +5 V; pin 1 of the 8212 to ground, pin 13 to +5 V). Of course, there are many other devices that can be used to buffer this part of the address

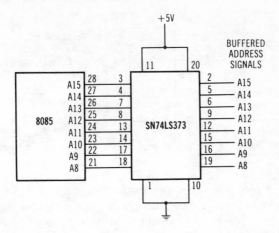

Fig. 5-15. Buffering A8 through A15 with an SN74LS373 octal D-type
transparent latch.

bus. Latches do not have to be used and the devices do not have to have
three-state capability.

Buffering the Data Bus

Buffering the data bus is more difficult than buffering the address bus.
This is because we have to buffer the data outputs of the microprocessor
during a memory write or I/O write, and the data inputs during a memory read, I/O read, and interrupt acknowledge. (See Fig. 5-17.) At
what other times does the microprocessor place information on the data

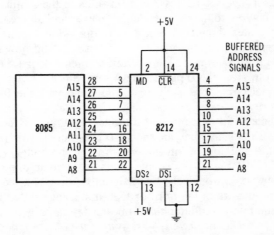

Fig. 5-16. Buffering A8 through A15 with an 8212 8-bit input/output port.

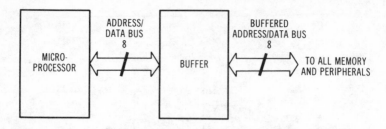

Fig. 5-17. Buffering the flow of data in both directions on the data bus.

bus? The data bus is also used by the microprocessor to output the 8 low-order address bits. This information must also be buffered. Note that we could buffer the data bus in only one direction; for example, only the information that is output by the microprocessor could be buffered. However, it costs very little to buffer the bus in both directions.

Both 4- and 8-bit buffers are available, and typical devices are shown in Fig. 5-18. Of the two buffers, the SN74LS245 is the easier to use. If we do use the 8216 to buffer the data bus, we would need two of them.

The SN74LS245

Since information may be placed on the bus or may be gated off of the bus, by the microprocessor, we have a bidirectional data bus. Therefore the bus really should be buffered in both directions. As you can see from the pin configuration of the SN74LS245, it has a DIR or direction pin (pin 1). If this pin is taken to ground, information will flow from the B inputs to the A outputs. If the DIR pin is taken to +5 V, information will flow from the A inputs to the B outputs. This means that we could wire the microprocessor address/data bus pins to the A pins, and the B pins would be wired to the address demultiplexer and all the memory and interface integrated circuits. When a write operation (memory, I/O, or address) operation is taking place, information should flow from the A pins to the B pins. During a read operation (memory or I/O), information should flow from the B pins to the A pins. Since the A and B buffers in the integrated circuit are equivalent, you could wire the B pins to the microprocessor integrated circuits and wire the A pins to the address demultiplexer and all memory and interface integrated circuits.

The SN74LS245 also has an enable ($\overline{G}$) input. If this pin is at the logic zero state, the flow of information through the buffer will be determined by the DIR pin. If the enable pin is at the logic one state, no information can flow through the buffer in either direction, because all of the buffer outputs are in the third or high-impedance state. This feature is useful if the microcomputer that you are designing will be used with direct memory access devices. *If your system uses these types of devices, the enable ($\overline{G}$) pin should be wired to the hold acknowledge (HLDA)* *output pin of the 8085A*. Otherwise, pin $\overline{G}$ can be wired to ground.

From the data sheet for this integrated circuit in Appendix B, you should be able to determine its electrical characteristics. You should determine that this device can sink 24 mA (0.5 V maximum) and source −15 mA (2.0 V minimum). The inputs of the SN74LS245 will sink 20 μA at 2.7 V when a logic one is placed on the input, and they will source −0.2 mA at 0.4 V when a logic zero is placed on the input. This means that the 8085A has to source more than −20 μA (logic one) and sink more than 0.2 mA (logic zero). Since the 8085A can source −400 μA (2.4 V) and sink 2 mA (0.45 V), the address/data pins will have no trouble driving either the A or B inputs of the SN74LS245 buffer. Remember, the multiplexed address/data bus pins are wired only to this buffer. The outputs of the buffer are wired to *all* memory and interface integrated circuits and the address demultiplexer latch.

What signal or combination of signals would we use to control the direction of data flow through the buffers? We know that $\overline{MEMW}$ and $\overline{I/O\ W}$ will be a logic zero when the microprocessor places data on the data bus, and that $\overline{MEMR}$ and $\overline{I/O\ R}$ will be logic zeros when the microprocessor is reading data off of the bus. We also know that the ALE signal will be a logic one when the microprocessor places an address on the data bus. This situation can be slightly simplified, because the $\overline{RD}$ signal will be a logic zero only when a read operation (memory or I/O) is taking place and $\overline{WR}$ will be a logic zero when a write (memory or I/O) operation is taking place. Of course, neither of these two signals is related to ALE, so a combination of ALE and $\overline{WR}$ could be used to determine the direction of data flow, or ALE and $\overline{RD}$ could be used. If the A pins are wired to the microprocessor and the B pins are wired to the data bus, it will be easier to wire the direction pin to $\overline{RD}$ (Fig. 5-19).

The 8216

The 8216 (Fig. 5-18A) is not as versatile as the SN74LS245, because it can really only be wired one way to the microprocessor integrated circuit. The DB pins have the largest sink and source current capabilities, so they are wired to the data bus in the microcomputer. The DI and DO pins have less current capability, so they are wired to the microprocessor integrated circuit. As an example, the DI_1 and DO_1 pins are both wired to AD0 on the microprocessor (Fig. 5-20). The $\overline{CS}$ pin (Fig. 5-18A) has the same function as the enable ($\overline{G}$) input of the SN74LS245. It is wired to ground in non-dma systems, and to hold acknowledge (HLDA) in systems that do use dma. The $\overline{DIEN}$ input, like the DIR input of the SN74LS245, determines the direction of data flow through the buffer. If the $\overline{DIEN}$ input is a logic zero, data flows from the DI pins to the DB pins. If $\overline{DIEN}$ is a logic one, data flows from the DB pins to the DO pins. Of course, by wiring the appropriate DI and DO pins together, we create a bidirectional buffer. Since information is only read off of the bus by the microprocessor when $\overline{RD}$ is a logic zero, this signal should be used to control the direction of data flow through the buffers. However, for information to flow from the DB pins to the DO pins, $\overline{DIEN}$ must be a logic one. Therefore the $\overline{RD}$ signal must be inverted before it is used to control the $\overline{DIEN}$ pin of the 8216 buffers. Remember, we cannot arbitrarily use either the DB pin or the DI/DO pins with either the microprocessor or the data bus. Because of the design of the 8216 the DB pins should be wired to the bus, and the DI and DO pins should be wired to the microprocessor. Therefore the $\overline{RD}$ signal has to be used to control the 8216s, and it has to be inverted. Of course, this means that we have to use an SN74LS04-type inverter in our design.

NOTE: It was mentioned that the data bus buffers must be in the "read" state when the 8085A acknowledges an interrupt. This is really only true if the INTR interrupt input is used. The 8085A has four other interrupt inputs that you can use, which should be more than sufficient for most applications. If you must use the INTR input, $\overline{RD}$ and $\overline{INTA}$

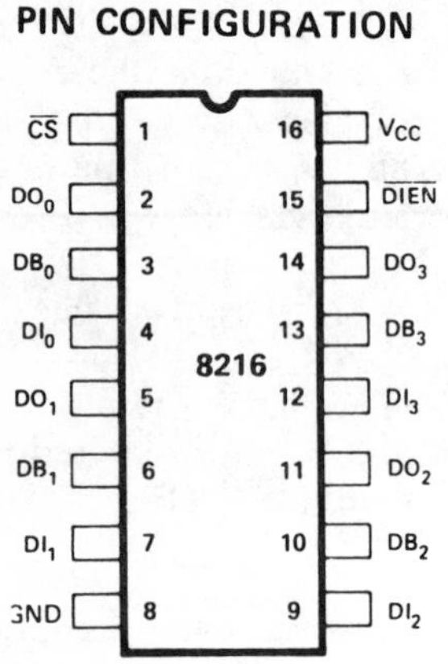

PIN CONFIGURATION

LOGIC DIAGRAM 8216

PIN NAMES

DB_0-DB_3	DATA BUS BI-DIRECTIONAL
DI_0-DI_3	DATA INPUT
DO_0-DO_3	DATA OUTPUT
$\overline{DIEN}$	DATA IN ENABLE DIRECTION CONTROL
$\overline{CS}$	CHIP SELECT

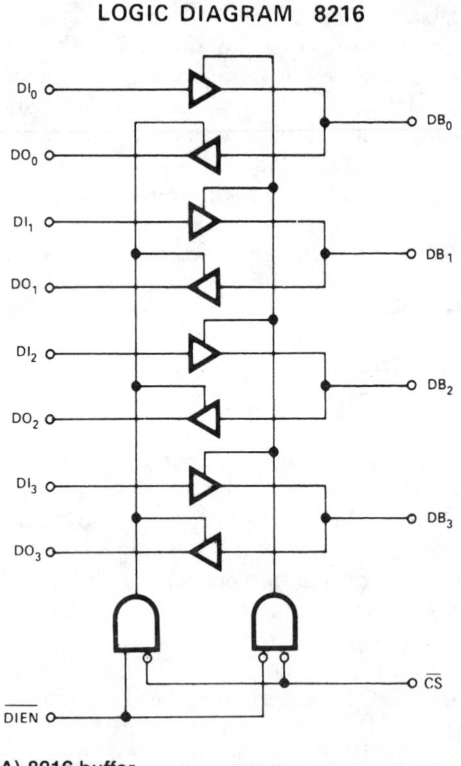

(A) 8216 buffer.

Courtesy Intel Corp.

Fig. 5-18. Typical buffers that can be used

should be ANDed and the signal wired to the DIR pin of the SN74LS245. If 8216s are used, these signals should be NANDed and wired to the $\overline{\text{DIEN}}$ pins.

Buffer Time Delays

All of the decoders, demultiplexers, and buffers that we have wired to the microprocessor require a known amount of time to react to a change on an input. The SN74LS245 and 8216 buffers that we have just discussed are no exception. In fact, the SN74LS245 may require a maximum of 40 ns to react to a change in a logic level. However, this really will not have much effect on the performance of the microprocessor. Remember, the $\overline{\text{RD}}$ signal is a logic zero for a minimum of 400 ns (6.25-MHz clock). Therefore as long as the buffers can "turn around" in less time than this, we will have no trouble using them. Of course, once the read operation has been performed, the buffers have to "turn around" again, back to their normal state, when information from the microprocessor is placed on the bus. The buffers have at least one clock cycle to

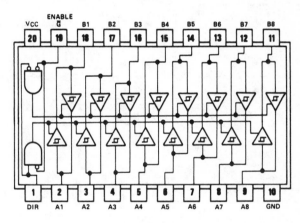

FUNCTION TABLE

ENABLE $\overline{\text{G}}$	DIRECTION CONTROL DIR	OPERATION
L	L	B data to A bus
L	H	A data to B bus
H	X	Isolation

H = high level, L = low level, X = irrelevant

(B) SN74LS245 buffer.

Courtesy Texas Instruments, Inc.

with the microprocessor bidirectional data bus.

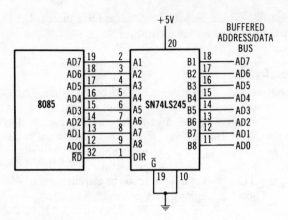

Fig. 5-19. Buffering the microprocessor address/data bus with an SN74LS245 octal bus transceiver with three-state outputs.

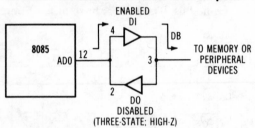

(A) Memory write, I/O write, or address out.

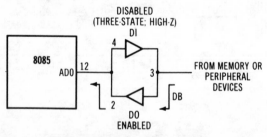

(B) Memory read or I/O read (IN).

Fig. 5-20. Buffering 1 bit of the bidirectional data bus.

do this (320 ns, minimum), so again there is no timing problem. A number of the problems associated with buffer timing, drive requirements, and system design are discussed in Appendix 1 of Reference 3.

PRELIMINARY DESIGN USING R/W MEMORIES

We have now discussed R/W memories and how they are used in a microcomputer system. Both absolute and nonabsolute decoding can be used to enable these devices, and wait states can be used if their access times are greater than 575 ns for the 8085A or 350 ns for the 8085A-2. We have also discussed the use of both $\overline{\text{MEMW}}$ and $\overline{\text{MEMR}}$, the electrical characteristics of the commonly available memory integrated circuits, and the use of data and address bus buffers.

Now, in the following sections you will have the opportunity to design R/W memory decoders, to design the circuitry required so that R/W memories can be wired to the microcomputer buses, and to design data bus buffers.

Preliminary R/W Memory Design No. 1

Using any combination of gates or decoders that you want, decode 1K of the microprocessor address space, starting at 01110000 00000000, for 1K of R/W memory. For R/W memories, use eight 2102s, Your design may use either absolute or nonabsolute decoding. Since 2102s have separate D_{IN} and D_{OUT} pins you will have to design the appropriate buffer circuitry.

A design that meets all of the design requirements is shown in Fig. 5-21. Some of the design points that you should look for in your design include:

1. Has some combination of A10, A11, A12, A13, A14, and A15 been used, along with *both* $\overline{\text{MEMR}}$ and $\overline{\text{MEMW}}$, to generate a chip select signal?
2. Has the data bus been wired directly to the D_{IN} inputs of all eight of the 2102s?
3. Has a *three-state buffer,* such as an SN74LS373 or 8212, been used to buffer the *data outputs* of all eight 2102s?
4. Is the three-state buffer enabled *only* when both $\overline{\text{CS}}$ and $\overline{\text{MEMR}}$ are logic zeros?

Although absolute decoding has been used in Fig. 5-21, it does not have to be used. As you will remember from the description of the 2102, the D_{OUT} pin is in the three-state condition only when the chip is not selected. Therefore during both a memory read and a memory write the D_{OUT} pin outputs data. By using a three-state buffer the data from the 2102s is placed on the data bus only when the microprocessor is reading from these devices (the combination of $\overline{\text{CS}}$ and $\overline{\text{MEMR}}$). At all other times the outputs of the three-state buffer are "disconnected" from the bus or are in the high-impedance state. Therefore the $\overline{\text{CS}}$ and $\overline{\text{MEMR}}$ signals are gated together with an OR gate (SN74LS32), and the output of this gate is used to control the output state of the SN74LS373. As we have already seen, there are a number of three-state devices that we could have used, including the 8212 latch, two 8216 buffers, or the SN74LS245 buffer.

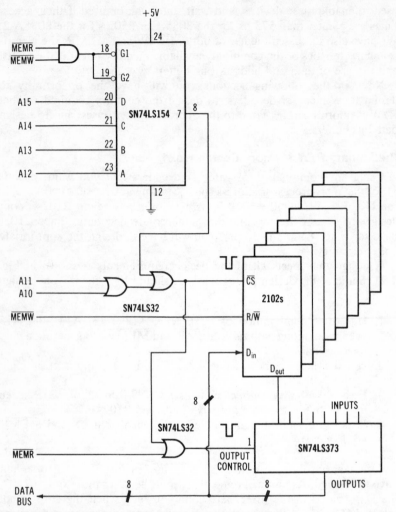

Fig. 5-21. Designing the data bus buffers and decoding logic required for use by
2102 1K × 1 R/W memories.

Preliminary R/W Memory Design No. 2

Using SN74LS373 octal D-type transparent latches, buffer the microprocessor bidirectional data bus (both ways). Also include in your
design an address demultiplexer using another SN74LS373. You may
use any additional integrated circuits that you require. In your design
you only need to show the data bus, the buffers, and the address demultiplexer.

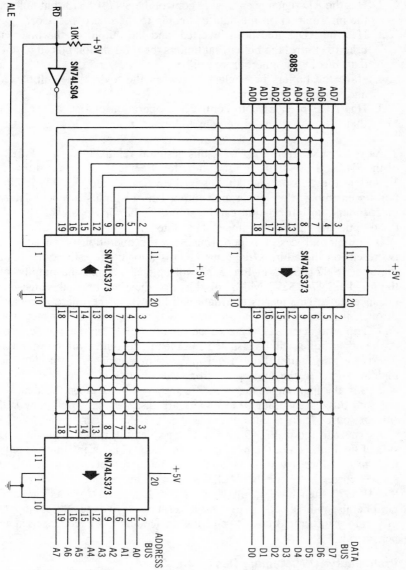

Fig. 5-22. Buffering the bidirectional data bus with SN74LS373s.

A design that meets these requirements is shown in Fig. 5-22. Some of the design points that you should check for in your design include:

1. Has pin 11 of the SN74LS373s (just the data bus buffers) been wired to +5 V?

2. Has the $\overline{RD}$ signal been used to control the SN74LS373 that buffers the information on the data bus going to the microprocessor?
3. Has the $\overline{RD}$ signal been inverted, and the output of the inverter used to control the buffer that buffers the information placed on the data bus by the microprocessor?
4. Have the buffers been placed between the address demultiplexer and the microprocessor?
5. Has ALE been used to control the operation of the SN74LS373 that is used to demultiplex the address/data bus?

As you can see from Fig. 5-22, this design is relatively simple. Pin 11 of the SN74LS373s that are used to buffer the bus must be wired to +5 V, so that the data on the data bus is always gated into the D-type flip-flops. Remember, the enable and output control inputs are completely independent, so information can be stored in the flip-flops even though the outputs are in the high-impedance state.

If the microprocessor is performing a write operation or an address is present on the address/data bus ($\overline{RD}$ is a logic one), the outputs of the upper SN74LS373 in Fig. 5-22 will be enabled and the outputs of the middle SN74LS373 will be disabled, or they will be in the high-impedance state. This means that data will flow from the microprocessor, through the upper buffer, to the address demultiplexer latch, memory, and peripheral devices. During a read operation $\overline{RD}$ will be a logic zero, so the upper buffer will be disabled and the middle buffer will be enabled. Therefore information flows from memory or peripherals, through the middle buffer, to the microprocessor. The outputs of the upper buffer will be in the high-impedance state, so they will not change the data on the data bus. Even though the buffers are disabled, however, they still sink or source leakage currents.

As you can see in Fig. 5-22 the address demultiplexer is on the bus side of the buffers, not the microprocessor side. This means that we only have to be concerned with the ability of the microprocessor to sink and source currents to one SN74LS373 latch. The outputs of the upper SN74LS373 then have to drive all of the data inputs of memory and peripherals, and the address demultiplexer has to drive the address inputs of memory integrated circuits and the device address decoders used in peripherals.

Preliminary R/W Memory Design No. 3

The design shown in Fig. 5-23 was used to wire two 2114s to the microcomputer buses. Assuming that an absolutely decoded 1K chip select, which is only generated during a memory-read or memory-write operation, is wired to these two memory integrated circuits, will the microprocessor be able to read information from, and write information to, these memories?

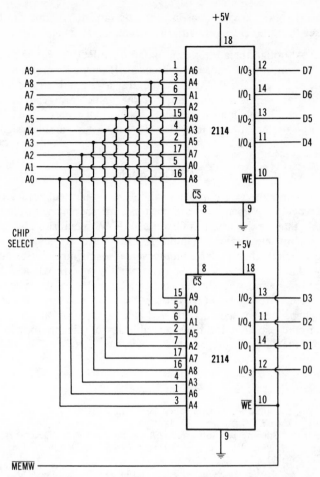

Fig. 5-23. Using two 2114 1K × 4 R/W memories with the 8085A.

Yes, it will, even though the address and data inputs are "mixed up." When the microprocessor generates a memory address for the 2114s and writes a value into one of their memory locations, it does not matter where the information is actually written inside the integrated circuit. When the microprocessor wants to read the same information from memory, it will generate the *same* memory address, and the same memory location inside of the integrated circuits will be selected and the proper information will be placed on the data bus. The only reason that a design such as this should be used is if a printed-circuit board is being designed, where it would be extremely difficult, if not impossible, to connect address line A9 to the A9 input, A8 to A8, etc. Although this design is perfectly correct, it might be difficult for someone else to "debug" a system using this design. The only reason that a design such as this can be used is the fact that the 2114s are *random-access* R/W memory.

NOTE: Although the address and data bus to ROMs can be "scrambled," the authors do not recommend it. If they are scrambled, you will have to send the ROM manufacturer a "scrambled" version of the program or data values so that the values are read correctly when used in the microcomputer system. Of course, this ROM would be useless in a system that did not have scrambled signals.

CONCLUSION

You have now seen a number of different design techniques that can be used when R/W memories are used in a microcomputer system. Like the ROMs that we discussed in Chapter 4, R/W memories have address, data, and chip select signals. Unlike ROMs, however, an R/W memory must be selected when either a memory-read *or* memory-write operation is taking place. As you have seen, a combination of $\overline{MEMR}$ and $\overline{MEMW}$ is used in this memory selection circuitry. Regardless of the type of memory integrated circuits used (R/W or ROM) you also must determine, as best you can, the leakage currents and capacitances of the memory integrated circuits, so that the drive capabilities of the microprocessor or buffer circuitry are not exceeded.

REFERENCES

1. Volk, A. "Dynamic RAM Controller Performance/Cost Tradeoffs." *Computer Design,* March 1979, pages 127–136.
2. Titus, J. A. "Starting μP Software." *Electronic Design* 25, December 6, 1976, pages 74–77. See also "Across the Desk." *Electronic Design* 26, December 20, 1976, page 11.
3. *MCS-85 User's Manual, September 1978,* Intel Corp. Santa Clara, CA 95051.

BIBLIOGRAPHY

1. Franson, P. "Semiconductor Memories—Technology Advances Spur New Products; Manufacturers Strive for Standardization." *EDN,* June 20, 1977, pages 46–58.
2. "Semiconductor Memories Mature." *Electronic Business,* July 1977, pages 90–91.
3. Hackmeister, D. "Focus on Semiconductor RAMs." *Electronic Design* 17, August 16, 1977, pages 56–62.
4. Hnatek, E. R. "Current Semiconductor Memories." *Computer Design,* April 1978, pages 115–126.
5. Wallace, C. "Electrically Erasable Memory Behaves Like a Fast, Nonvolatile RAM." *Electronics,* May 10, 1979, pages 128–131.
6. Jones, F. "Pseudostatic RAM Offers Dynamic Density Plus Easy Interfacing with Popular μPs." *Electronic Design* (18), September 1, 1979, pages 94–97.

PROBLEMS

5-1. Using only comparators and NAND gates, absolutely decode 1K of the microprocessor address space, from 00000100 00000000 through 00000111 11111111, for 2114 R/W memories. No other type of integrated circuit may be used.

5-2. What is the difference between R/W memory and read-only memory? What control signals are used to control these two different types of memory?

5-3. If an R/W memory has an access time of 660 ns, what is the shortest cycle time that can be used with the 8085A so that no wait states are required when this memory is accessed? What must the quartz crystal frequency be to obtain this cycle time?

5-4. What are some of the advantages of using 2114s, rather than 2102s, in a microcomputer design?

5-5. If 5K of R/W memory must be added to a microcomputer system, which is less expensive to use: 2102s that cost $1.09 or 2114s that cost $6.05?

5-6. Integrated circuits such as the SN74LS373 and the 8212 can be used to buffer the high address bus (A8 through A15). During the design of a particular microcomputer system, however, these devices were not available. Show how the high address bus can be buffered using only SN74LS04 inverters.

5-7. Buffer the 8085A bidirectional data bus using 8216s. Use any additional integrated circuits that you require.

5-8. Design the circuitry so that 4K of a possible 8K of R/W memory can be "write protected." The 8K of memory should have addresses 01000000 00000000 through 01011111 11111111. The 4K of R/W memory that can be write protected should have addresses 01000000 00000000 through 01001111 11111111. When write protected the microprocessor can only read information from R/W memory; it cannot write any information into R/W memory. To write protect the 4K of R/W memory a switch should be placed in one of two positions. In the other position the R/W memory acts as normal R/W memory.

5-9. Using a single decoder integrated circuit and any additional integrated circuits required, design a memory decoder so that 8K of the microprocessor address space is decoded into two 4K blocks, one for R/W memory and one for ROM. Any 8K block of the microprocessor address space may be used, as may either absolute or nonabsolute address decoding.

5-10. A microcomputer system contains 2K of R/W memory. The access time of 1K of this memory is 450 ns and the access time of the other 1K of RW memory is 1250 ns. Design the circuitry so that wait states are inserted into the microprocessor timing only when the 1K of 1250-ns memory is accessed. In this design any 2K of the microprocessor address space may be used. Absolute address decoding should also be used.

5-11. A number of "ROM simulators" are currently available for use with microcomputers. These devices are plugged into a ROM socket so that the microcomputer appears to be addressing ROM. However, the microcomputer often addresses R/W memory contained in the ROM simulator. Design a ROM simulator for a 2708 EPROM using 2114 R/W memories. Remember the 2114s must get their control signals from the 2708 EPROM socket. Label all of the signals coming from the 2708 socket with the appropriate pin number and signal name. Since the MEMR and MEMW signals are not present at the 2708 socket assume that these signals are obtained from some other point in the microcomputer.

5-12. Most of the control signal decoders that have been designed have generated the $\overline{\text{MEMR}}$ and $\overline{\text{MEMW}}$ signals along with the I/O control signals. There are, however, only two different types of memory that are used in a microcomputer: ROM and R/W memory. There is no write-only memory. Therefore design a decoder that generates the $\overline{\text{ROM}}$ and $\overline{\text{R/WMEM}}$ signals. The $\overline{\text{ROM}}$ signal is only a logic zero when a memory-read operation takes place and the $\overline{\text{R/WMEM}}$ is only a logic zero when *either* a memory-read or memory-write operation takes place.

5-13. Design the decoding logic for 1K of R/W memory (based on 2114s) and 1K of EPROM (2708) so that, by placing a switch in one of two positions, either the R/W memory or EPROM contains memory location zero. If the R/W memory or ROM is "selected," it will contain memory location zero, along with the next consecutive 1023 memory locations.

5-14. List the advantages and disadvantages of storing a program in R/W memory, mask ROM, PROM, and EPROM.

5-15. What must the access time of R/W memory be if it is to be used in a 10-MHz 8085A-2 (200-ns cycle time) microcomputer? Assume that no wait states can be used.

CHAPTER 6

Microcomputer Interfacing

In previous chapters we have discussed the different methods that can be used to connect ROMs and R/W memories to the microprocessor address bus, data bus, and control signals. Even though we can design and build a fully operational microcomputer based on these devices, the microcomputer would not be very useful. This is simply because we could not get any information into the microcomputer from a peripheral device, such as a keyboard, or get information out of the microcomputer to a peripheral device, such as a printer. To use these types of devices with a microcomputer or any other type of computer we have to have an *interface,* which is composed of integrated circuits, so that the computer can communicate with the peripheral device.

Some peripheral devices do not transfer information to the microcomputer or receive information from the microcomputer. Instead, the microcomputer is used to *control* the operation of the peripheral device. To perform this control function the microcomputer generates short pulses that can be used to clear counters, increment counters, or reset a peripheral device (to a known state). In fact, these same pulses can be used, if required, to cause information or data to be transferred between the microcomputer and a peripheral device. In another section of this chapter we will see how these pulses are generated.

I/O OPERATION

There are two different input/output techniques that we can use to interface the 8085A to peripheral devices: *accumulator I/O* and *memory-mapped I/O.* In accumulator I/O the IN and OUT instructions are used to transfer data between the *A register* or *accumulator* and a peripheral. In memory-mapped I/O the peripheral appears as a memory location(s) to the microprocessor. By using this technique the 8085A can transfer data between *any* of the general-purpose registers (A, B, C, D, E, H, or L) and a peripheral.

From Chapters 1 and 2 we know that the $\overline{\text{IN}}$ and $\overline{\text{OUT}}$ control signals are generated by gating IO/$\overline{\text{M}}$ with $\overline{\text{RD}}$ and $\overline{\text{WR}}$ (Figs. 2-20 and 2-21). When the 8085A executes an IN instruction, the $\overline{\text{IN}}$ signal is generated by the decoder, and the peripheral address (the device address), which is contained in the second byte of the instruction, is placed on address lines A0 through A7 and also on A8 through A15. In the interface the decoded device address is gated with $\overline{\text{IN}}$ and the resulting logic one or logic zero pulse is used by the peripheral device. This signal can be used to reset the peripheral or increment a count (control functions) or it can be used to gate data on to the data bus and into the A register of the 8085A (a data-transfer function). If the IN instruction is used for the transfer of data, the *input port* must be designed using *three-state devices*. Only when the appropriate control signal is generated should the input port place data on the data bus. At all other times the data outputs of the input port (which are wired to the data bus) should be in the third (high-impedance) state. Note that the operation of an input port is very similar to that of a ROM. Only when the ROM is selected does it place data on the data bus. At all other times the outputs of the ROM are in the third state.

When an OUT instruction is executed, the device address contained in the second byte of the instruction is placed on address lines A0 through A7 and on A8 through A15. The $\overline{\text{OUT}}$ signal is also generated, and the content of the A register is placed on the data bus. In the interface of the peripheral the decoded device address is gated with $\overline{\text{OUT}}$, and the resulting signal is used to latch the content of the A register off of the data bus, or it can be used for a control function. A latch or latch-type device must be used in output port designs because the content of the A register is only on the data bus for 300–400 ns. In fact, an output port operates much like R/W memory. During a memory-write operation the R/W memory has to gate information off of the data bus and store it for later use.

ACCUMULATOR I/O DECODERS

In previous chapters the logic used to select one of many memory integrated circuits was designed. In general, decoders were used for this. Depending on the number of words in each memory integrated circuit, from 2 to 8 bits of the 16-bit memory address were decoded. With accumulator I/O ports an 8-bit device address is generated by the microprocessor, and all 8 bits of this address are normally decoded. This means that there can be up to 256 input ports and 256 output ports in a microcomputer system. Although the *same* device address is placed on

A0 through A7 and A8 through A15 when the 8085A executes an accumulator I/O instruction, address lines A0 through A7 are normally used in accumulator I/O decoder designs. However, A8 through A15 can be used just as easily.

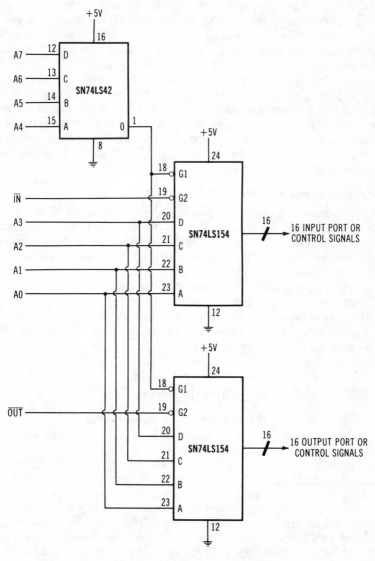

Fig. 6-1. An absolute accumulator I/O device address decoder.

Device Address Decoders

You have already seen a number of different decoders and decoding techniques, so you should be able to understand the operation of the device address decoder shown in Fig. 6-1 with little effort. It should not surprise you to see that $\overline{IN}$ and $\overline{OUT}$ have been used to enable the SN74LS154 decoders. By using this decoder design the output port and input port addresses from 00000000 through 00001111 have been absolutely decoded. Of course, the logic zero output pulse generated by the decoder that is enabled with $\overline{OUT}$ would be used with output (latch-type) devices. The outputs of the decoder that is enabled by $\overline{IN}$ would be used with input (three-state) devices. The logic zero outputs of *either* decoder can be used to reset, pulse, or control peripheral devices. The outputs of either decoder can be used, because the pulses are not being used to gate data on to, or gate data off of, the data bus. In some complex peripherals, such as floppy disks, data must be transferred (read a sector, write a sector) *and* the peripheral has to be controlled (step the head, load the head).

Nonabsolute Accumulator I/O Decoders

Just as absolute accumulator I/O decoders can be used in the design of interfaces, nonabsolute accumulator I/O decoders can also be used. Of course, as was the case when nonabsolute memory address decoders were discussed, nonabsolute accumulator I/O decoders would only be used in small, low-cost microcomputers where no expansion is foreseen. By modifying the previous absolute decoder design a nonabsolute decoder can be designed (Fig. 6-2). By eliminating the decoder that is wired to A4 through A7, the remaining circuitry decodes only the address present on A0 through A3. There are hundreds of additional absolute and nonabsolute accumulator I/O decoder designs that can be used in interfaces.

OUTPUT PORTS

In many situations the microprocessor has to output information to a peripheral device. This information might be an ASCII character for a crt terminal, a track and sector number for a floppy disk, or a seven-segment code for a seven-segment light-emitting diode (LED) display. However, when the 8085A executes an OUT instruction, *the content of the A accumulator is placed on the data bus for only a very short period.*

A very simple 8-bit output port design is shown in Fig. 6-3. In this design $\overline{OUT}$ is inverted and is gated with A6. The logic one output of the AND gate (SN74LS08) is used to enable the eight flip-flops contained in the SN74LS373 octal latch. The content of the data bus will be gated into the latch only when $\overline{OUT}$ is a logic zero and A6 is a logic one. For

196

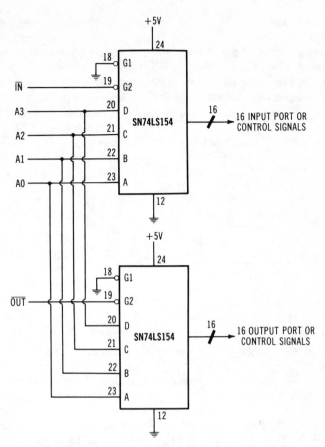

Fig. 6-2. A nonabsolute accumulator I/O device address decoder.

$\overline{\text{OUT}}$ to be a logic zero the 8085A must execute an OUT instruction. What address or addresses will cause A6 to be a logic one? Address line A6 will be a logic one when any of the addresses between 01000000 and 01111111 or between 11000000 through 11111111 are present on the low address bus. This means that there are 128 different accumulator I/O device addresses that will cause the latch to be enabled, so that the content of the data bus is latched. Of course, this is one of the disadvantages of nonabsolute device address decoding. One of its advantages is the fact that the decoding logic can be very simple when there are only a few peripherals in the microcomputer system.

The output port in Fig. 6-3 latches the content of the data bus when an OUT instruction containing the appropriate device address is executed by the 8085A. If a memory-read or memory-write instruction is executed, the $\overline{\text{OUT}}$ signal will remain in the logic one state, so no information will be latched by the SN74LS373. What will happen if the latch is enabled only when A6 is a logic one? This means that the latch could be enabled when either a memory-read or memory-write operation is performed. There is also the possibility that the latch would be enabled during the execution of an IN instruction. *Therefore in all decoder designs for input and output ports the decoder must be enabled by either $\overline{IN}$ or $\overline{OUT}$, or the decoder outputs must be gated with either $\overline{IN}$ or $\overline{OUT}$.*

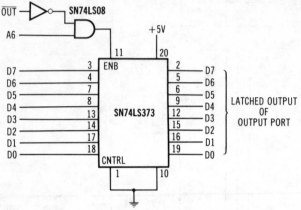

Fig. 6-3. A nonabsolutely decoded output port.

An output port that uses absolute device address decoding is shown in Fig. 6-4. This output port will be enabled only when one out of a possible 256 device addresses is present on the address bus and $\overline{OUT}$ is a logic zero. The decoder design in this interface uses two decoders: an SN74LS42 and an SN74LS154. Neither of these two decoders is enabled by $\overline{OUT}$. This means that output 0 of the SN74LS154 will be a logic zero whenever the address 00000000 is present on A0 through A7, regardless of whether a memory location or I/O device is being addressed. However, the output port has been properly designed, because the latch will not be enabled until (1) an address of 00000000 is present on A0 through A7 *and* (2) the $\overline{OUT}$ signal is a logic zero. These two logic zeroes are gated together with a NOR gate and the resulting logic one pulse enables the 4-bit latch so that the content of the accumulator is gated off of the data bus.

Even though this interface latches only the four least significant bits (LSBs) of the data bus, the microprocessor still places the entire 8-bit content of the accumulator on the data bus. The microprocessor does not know which peripheral the data are going to or how many bits of the 8-bit word are being latched. It simply outputs the content of the accumulator on the data bus, places the device address on the address bus, and generates the proper control signals. In one microcomputer system the microprocessor might be using this address to communicate with a floppy disk, and, in another, a crt.

Since the decoder shown in Fig. 6-4 is not enabled by $\overline{\text{OUT}}$, the output of the decoder has to be gated with $\overline{\text{OUT}}$, and the resulting signal is used to enable the latch. Another possible design could be used, where output 0 of the SN74LS42 is wired to input G1, and $\overline{\text{OUT}}$ is wired to input G2 of the SN74LS154 (Fig. 6-5). Can output 0 of the SN74LS154

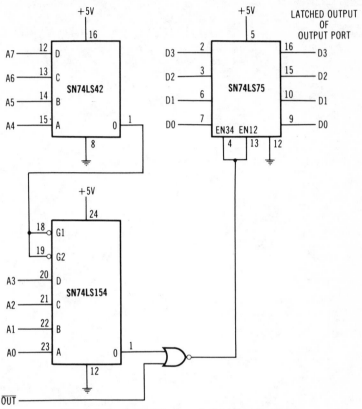

Fig. 6-4. An absolutely decoded 4-bit output port.

be wired directly to the enable input of the latch? No, output 0 of the SN74LS154 must be inverted first. If, however, there are output devices that *do* require logic zero pulses for control, the decoder outputs could be used directly.

One limitation of this type of design is the fact that the 16 outputs of the SN74LS154 can be used only with output ports or for control. If there are any input ports in the microcomputer system, another decoder would have to be used.

Output ports are rather easy to design. Most parallel-in logic devices with internal latch capabilities can be used. Examples of devices that can be used as latches are the SN74LS193 synchronous 4-bit up/down

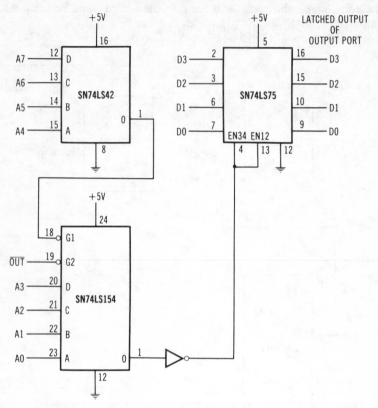

Fig. 6-5. Using $\overline{OUT}$ to enable a decoder for a 4-bit output port.

counter, the SN74LS194A universal shift register, and the SN74LS198 8-bit shift register.

Electrical Characteristics of Output Ports

Typical latch integrated circuits, such as the SN74LS75, SN74LS373, and the 8212, can be used as output ports. All three of these devices are much "faster" than the microprocessor, so they will have no trouble latching the data off of the data bus at the appropriate time. However, these devices do source and sink different amounts of current. The input current requirements of these three integrated circuits are summarized in Table 6-1.

As you can see from this table the SN74LS75 and the SN74LS373 have the largest input current requirements and the 8212 has the smallest. If these output ports are used in a small, unbuffered 8085A microcomputer system (-400 μA at 2.4 V minimum, -2 mA at 0.8 B maximum), the SN74LS75 or SN74LS373 will use 20 percent of the 8085A data bus sink current (-0.4 mA vs. 2 mA). Remember, the data bus is also wired to all of the memory integrated circuits in the system, which also have source, sink, and leakage current requirements. In a buffered system where an SN74LS245 is used to buffer the data bus, only 2 percent of the SN74LS245 sink current will be used (-0.4 mA vs. 24 mA). If an 8212 is used as an output port, even less of the data bus sink current and source current will be used.

Table 6-1. The Input Current Requirements of Typical Chips Used in Output Port Designs

Input	SN74LS75	SN74LS373	8212
Logic Zero	-0.4 mA/0.4 V	-0.4 mA/0.4 V	-0.25 mA/0.45 V
Logic One	20 μA/2.7 V	20 μA/2.7 V	10 μA/2.0 V

One unusual feature of output ports is the fact that they will always source current to, and sink current from, the data bus. Unlike the data input and outputs of memory integrated circuits (such as the 2114), the data inputs of output ports are always enabled. In memories the data inputs only sink current or source current when the chip is selected (ignoring the small amount of leakage current for the moment). In an output port the data is only *latched* when the chip is "selected." *Therefore the inputs of output ports either sink/source current from/to the data bus at all times.* You should keep this in mind when determining the current requirements of data bus buffers and the like.

INPUT PORTS

Input ports are used with I/O devices so that they can *transfer information to the microcomputer.* Unlike output ports, which must be able to accept and latch data at a specific time and which are continuously connected to the data bus, input ports must place information on the data bus at specific times and at all other times their outputs must be in the "third state." Input ports must pass information (logic ones and logic zeroes) to the data bus, and they must also have the ability to be configured so that they do not interfere with the use of the data bus when they are not selected. Therefore input ports must have "three-state" capability, just as do the ROM and R/W memories that were discussed in the last two chapters. Like a ROM an input port must only place information on the data bus when it is selected, and at all other times it must be in the third state.

Input ports are readily constructed using standard three-state integrated circuits. There are many "chips" that can be used in the design of input ports, but only a few of them are general-purpose enough to warrant our consideration. Two three-state integrated circuits that will be used in our designs are the SN74LS365 and the SN74LS244. The pin configurations for these two chips are shown in Fig. 6-6.

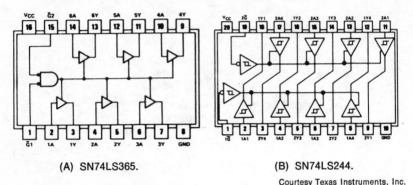

(A) SN74LS365.

(B) SN74LS244.

Courtesy Texas Instruments, Inc.

Fig. 6-6. The pin configurations for the SN74LS365 and SN74LS244 three-state buffers.

There are, of course, a number of differences between these two chips. For instance, the SN74LS365 contains six buffers, while the SN74LS244 contains eight buffers. Also, the SN74LS365 contains a NOR gate (an AND gate with inverters on its inputs is equivalent to a NOR gate), and the output of this gate is used to control the state of *all* the buffers in the chip. The SN74LS244 also has two control inputs, but they are not gated together within the chip. Instead, each of these control inputs controls four of the eight buffers independently of the other group of four. From this description you should realize that one SN74LS244 or two SN74LS365s will be required in the design of an 8-bit input port. An input port design based on the SN74LS244 is shown in Fig. 6-7 and an input port design based on the SN74LS365 is shown in Fig. 6-8.

In Fig. 6-7 a single SN74LS244 has been used. Since the three-state buffers are divided into two groups of four, the two enable inputs are wired together to the output of an OR gate (SN74LS32). This gate is used to gate $\overline{\text{IN}}$ and a decoded device address ($\overline{00111000}$). The notation for the decoded device address indicates the address that is decoded ($\overline{00111000}$ = A7 through A0) and that this decoded address causes a logic zero to be generated by the decoding logic (the bar over the device address).

In Fig. 6-8 two SN74LS365s have been used in the 8-bit input port design. Remember, each SN74LS365 contains six buffers, so there are

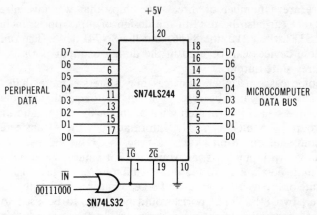

Fig. 6-7. Using the SN74LS244 8-bit octal buffer in an input port design.

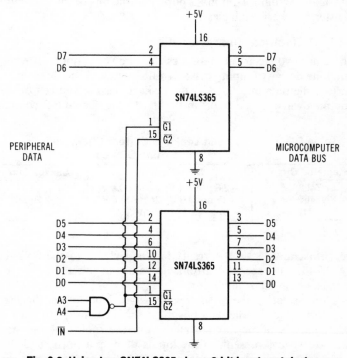

Fig. 6-8. Using two SN74LS365s in an 8-bit input port design.

four buffers that are wasted in one of the chips. Unfortunately they cannot be used as part of another input port, *because all six buffers in the chip have a single, common enable line.*

There are a number of three-state chips that we have already discussed that can also be used in the design of input ports, including the SN74LS373, the 8212, the 8216, and the SN74LS245. The *only* reason that these devices can be used in the design of input ports is that they have three-state outputs.

In some cases peripheral devices may generate more than 8 bits of information that must be read or input by the microcomputer. When more than 8 bits of information must be input, the information is divided into groups of 8 bits each. The information is then transferred to the microcomputer one 8-bit byte at a time. A 16-bit value would require the use of two input ports, as would a 9-bit value. When not all 8 bits in an input port are used, the unused bits are often placed in the logic zero state or are wired to ground. To keep hardware costs to a minimum, however, two 8-bit input ports would not have to be used to transfer 9 bits of information to the microcomputer. Instead, an 8-bit and a 1-bit input port might be designed. However, when the 8085A inputs 8 bits of information from a 1-bit input port, 7 of the bits of information in the A register will be meaningless.

Input Port Electrical Characteristics

There are two electrical quantities that are very important when considering the design of input ports: (1) the ability of the three-state chips to "drive" the data bus and (2) the leakage current sourced or sunk by the outputs when the device is in the third state. Table 6-2 contains the

Table 6-2. The Drive and Leakage Current Characteristics of Typical Three-State Buffers

Integrated Circuit	Drive Current	Leakage Current
SN74LS365	− 2.6 mA/2.4 V; 12 mA/0.4 V	± 20 μA
SN74LS244	− 15 mA/2.0 V; 24 mA/0.4 V	± 20 μA
8212	− 16 mA/2.4 V; 15 mA/0.45 V	± 20 μA

source, sink, and leakage currents for the outputs of the SN74LS365, SN74LS244, and the 8212. From the values in this table any of these devices can be used as input ports.

When considering the drive capabilities of input ports, the load that output ports place on the data bus must also be considered. Remember, the data bus is never disconnected from the inputs of output ports. Values are always present on the inputs of output ports, and these inputs are either sinking current from the data bus or are sourcing current to the data bus. Only when an OUT instruction is executed will these values be latched into the output port. The data bus for a simple, unbuffered microcomputer system is shown in Figs. 6-9 and 6-10, along with current sinks and sources.

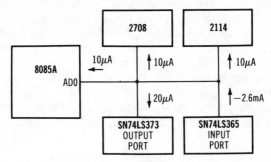

Fig. 6-9. Possible current sinks when an input port is enabled.

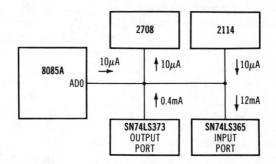

Fig. 6-10. Possible current sources when an input port is enabled.

In these figures you can see that the SN74LS373 output port sinks and sources more current than either of the two memory chips when the input port drives the data bus. At some other point in time the microprocessor, ROM, or R/W memory may be placing information on the data bus, and these chips will have to sink or source enough current not only for the other chips on the data bus but also for the output port. Therefore the current requirements of both input and output ports must be considered very carefully when designing large microcomputer systems.

We have now seen the design of both input and output ports. As always, there is an endless variety of gates, decoders, latches, and three-state devices that can be used in an interface. In previous sections of this chapter we limited our discussion to interfaces that are based on accumulator I/O, where the IN and OUT instructions are used for control or data transfer. Unfortunately, one limitation of this type of I/O is that the content of the accumulator is either gated onto the data bus (OUT) or the content of the data bus is gated into the accumulator (IN). Since the 8085A microprocessor only has one accumulator, it can be very inconvenient at times to save the content of the accumulator in another register (Fig. 1-10) or in memory, before an IN instruction is executed. Of course, if we forget to save the content of the accumulator *before* the IN instruction is executed, the IN instruction will cause the content of the accumulator to be altered. A new and probably different 8-bit word will be stored in the accumulator. Likewise, before a data value can be output to a peripheral, it has to be moved *to* the accumulator. As you might guess, the accumulator can be a bottleneck when values have to be input from or output to peripherals. Unfortunately, if IN and OUT instructions are executed, the accumulator must be used.

MEMORY-MAPPED I/O

If memory-mapped I/O is used instead of accumulator I/O, the 8085A can be programmed so that information is transferred between any of the general-purpose registers (A, B, C, D, E, H, or L) and the memory-mapped I/O device. At times this makes the microcomputer software simpler. However, to use these registers and a large number of memory-reference assembly language instructions, *each input and output port must "look like" a memory location.* This means that the microprocessor must generate a 16-bit memory address and one of the memory control signals, $\overline{\text{MEMR}}$ or $\overline{\text{MEMW}}$, to control the memory-mapped I/O ports. The microprocessor "assumes" that it is communicating with a memory location when, in fact, it is communicating with a peripheral device. Using memory-mapped I/O, data can be transferred *to* the peripheral device, data can be transferred *from* the peripheral device, and control pulses can be generated that are used solely for the control of peripherals.

Memory-Mapped I/O Device Address Decoders

One difficulty with using memory-mapped I/O is that a 16-bit address, present on A0 through A15, must often be decoded. This will require a considerable number of gates, decoders, or comparators. Remember, the decoders used with memory integrated circuits are not as complex, because memory chips contain from 256 to 16,384 memory locations, so only 2 to 8 bits of the memory address have to be decoded. Unfortunately a single latch or three-state buffer represents only a single "memory location," so the decoder must decode all 16 bits of the memory address for absolute decoding.

Some microcomputer designers and manufacturers get around this problem by segmenting the microprocessor 64K of address space into two 32K blocks. One block is reserved for use by memory and the other block is reserved for use by peripherals. One reason that 32K blocks are used is that A15 will be a logic zero for one block and a logic one for the other block. Since the microprocessor will fetch the first instruction to be executed from memory location zero when it is reset, A15 is a logic zero when memory is addressed and a logic one when peripherals are addressed. Of course, within the 32K block allocated for peripherals, either nonabsolute or absolute decoding can be used.

One possibility for a nonabsolute memory-mapped I/O device address decoder is shown in Fig. 6-11. In this design A15 is inverted and the resulting signal is used to enable two SN74LS154 decoders. Only when A15 is a logic one (a peripheral is being addressed) will the decoders be enabled. In this design we assume that the upper 32K of the

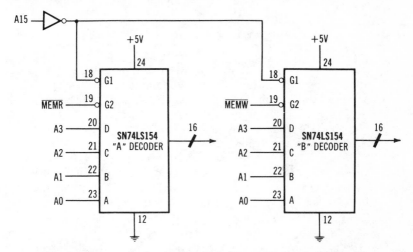

Fig 6-11. A nonabsolutely decoded, memory-mapped, I/O device address decoder.

microprocessor address space has been allocated to peripheral devices. Of course, with the appropriate design *any section of the microprocessor address space can be allocated to memory-mapped I/O devices.* The decoder contained in Fig. 6-11 is not an absolute decoder, because A4 through A14 have not been used in the decoder design.

Which of the decoders would be used with memory-mapped input ports and which would be used with memory-mapped output ports? The A decoder would be used with the memory-mapped input ports, because it is enabled by A15 and $\overline{\text{MEMR}}$. The B decoder would be used with memory-mapped output ports, because it is enabled by A15 and $\overline{\text{MEMW}}$. The actual input ports are still designed with three-state devices (SN74LS365, SN74LS244) and the output ports are still designed with latches (SN74LS75, SN74LS373). The decoder design determines whether the I/O port is a memory-mapped or accumulator I/O port.

Which memory addresses will be decoded by the decoders in Fig. 6-11? Addresses 1XXXXXXX XXXX0000 through 1XXXXXXX XXXX1111 will be decoded. In these addresses an X can be either a logic zero or a logic one. As an example, output 0 of the A decoder will go to a logic zero when the microprocessor *reads* information from any of the "memory locations" listed in Chart 6-1. In fact, there are 2^{11} or

Chart 6-1. Addresses That Cause Output 0 of the Decoder To Go to a Logic Zero (See Fig. 6-11)

10000000	00000000
11011011	10000000
10010111	10110000
11111111	11110000
11001100	01100000
10000000	00010000

2048 different memory addresses that will cause output 0 of the A decoder to go to logic zero when a memory-read operation takes place.

A complete, absolute memory-mapped I/O device address decoder is shown in Fig. 6-12. This design can be used if 16 absolutely decoded, memory-mapped output ports and 16 absolutely decoded, memory-mapped input ports are required.

With memory-mapped I/O, just as with accumulator I/O, either absolute or nonabsolute decoding may be used. Absolute decoding would probably be used if the microcomputer contains 40K of R/W memory, 15K of ROM, and 50 to 60 I/O devices. Although absolute decoding would not have to be used, it would be recommended in this case. With such a large system, additional memory or I/O devices might have to be added. If absolute memory-mapped device address decoding is used in this system, additional memory or I/O devices can be added to the system easily. In small, low-cost systems, nonabsolute decoding would be preferable. In many of these systems no expansion is expected, so the I/O devices can use as much of the microprocessor address space as required.

Memory-Mapped I/O Assembly Language Instructions

There are over 40 assembly language memory-reference instructions, which all can be used by the 8085A to communicate with a memory-mapped peripheral device. Chart 6-2 contains a number of these instruc-

Chart 6-2. Memory-Reference Instructions That Can Be Used With Memory-Mapped I/O Ports

MOVCM	ADDM	MOVME	MVIM

tions. The MOVCM instruction loads the C register with the content of memory. You might expect the C register to be loaded with the content of a specific memory location, but which one? The memory location *referenced* is the memory location addressed by the content of the

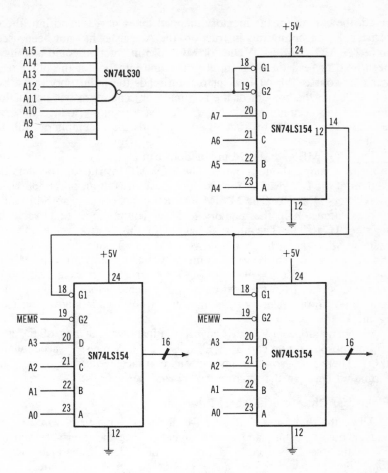

Fig. 6-12. An absolutely decoded, memory-mapped, I/O device address decoder.

H (high byte) and L (low byte) registers. When the MOVCM instruction is executed, the 16-bit number contained in the H and L registers is placed on the address bus, and then the 8085A reads the content of this memory location into the C register.

The ADDM instruction causes the content of the memory location addressed by the content of the H and L registers to be added to the content of the accumulator. The result of the addition is left in the accumulator. If either the MOVCM or ADDM instruction is used with a memory-mapped I/O peripheral device, the 16-bit address of the memory-mapped I/O port would first have to be loaded into the H and L registers. There are a number of other simple assembly language instructions that can be used to do this. When the MOVCM instruction is executed, the content of the memory-mapped input port is read into the C register. By executing this instruction, the A register has not been used. In fact, a MOVBM, MOVDM, or MOVEM instruction could also have been used to read the 8-bit input port value into one of the other registers. Of course, the ADDM instruction reads the input port value, but it is added to the content of the accumulator. Therefore this instruction does use the accumulator, but the value is not simply loaded into the accumulator. The IN instruction simply loads the accumulator with an 8-bit value.

The MOVME and MVIM instructions can be used to write values out to memory-mapped output ports. The MOVME instruction transfers the content of the E register to the memory location (output port) addressed by registers H and L. The MVIM instruction also causes an 8-bit value to be written out to the memory location (output port) addressed by registers H and L. The unusual feature of this instruction is the fact that the 8-bit value that is output is not stored in any register! Instead, the value to be output is stored in memory, immediately after the MVIM instruction. Therefore, when the MVIM instruction is executed, the 8-bit value is read from the next consecutive memory location and is then written out to the memory location (output port) addressed by registers H and L.

Memory-mapped I/O does have the advantage that any of the general-purpose registers can be used, not just the A register (accumulator I/O). There are also more instructions that can be used to transfer information between the microprocessor and peripherals.

Electrical Characteristics of Interfaces

All of the interfaces that we have discussed have been wired to the address bus, data bus, and control signals. Since the interfaces and decoders that were designed used a number of different integrated circuits, some interfaces will require more or less current from the buses than other interfaces.

Even though the input current requirements of the chips in these interfaces can be determined, it would be impossible to determine if the microprocessor has enough "drive." The microprocessor or microcomputer buses may or may not be buffered and we do not know how many memory integrated circuits or decoders have been used. To really analyze the current and voltage requirements and capabilities of the microprocessor/microcomputer, we would have to have a complete schematic of the *entire* microcomputer system.

With input ports the drive current capabilities and leakage currents of the three-state outputs have to be considered. In general, these devices can sink and source a considerable amount of current. This means that they can be used in microcomputer systems that have large numbers of chips wired to the data bus. Remember in particular that output ports are wired to the data bus and always sink or source current from/to the data bus. Of course, the greater the sink and source current capabilities of the bus, the smaller the effect of leakage currents from memories, buffers, three-state input ports, and the microprocessor chip.

COMPLEX PERIPHERAL INTEGRATED CIRCUITS

Most microcomputer manufacturers make not only microprocessors and memories, but also complex peripheral integrated circuits that can be used to interface floppy disks, keyboards, crt displays, and printers to the microcomputer. There are also peripheral integrated circuits that are general purpose in nature so that they can be used in a number of different applications. Two typical devices are the 8255A programmable peripheral interface (PPI) chip and the 8251A universal synchronous/asynchronous receiver/transmitter (USART) chip. These are powerful chips that make interfacing peripherals to the microcomputer very easy.

The 8255A Programmable Peripheral Interface (PPI)

The 8255A PPI chip actually contains four 8-bit I/O devices. One of these devices is always an output device, and the 8-bit value that is output to this device determines the internal operation and configuration of the other three ports. For instance, the three general-purpose I/O ports can be programmed, under software control, to be output ports, input ports, or any combination of input and output ports! The pin configuration and block diagram for this versatile integrated circuit are shown in Fig. 6-13. The internal control logic of the 8255A is shown on the left-hand side of the block diagram and the general-purpose I/O ports (A, B, and C) are shown on the right-hand side.

From the block diagram you can see that only +5 V is required by this device. Since we have 8-bit ports in this device, it must be wired to all eight data bus lines. The 8255A also has two inputs labeled $\overline{RD}$ and $\overline{WR}$. These signals are used so that information can be read from, and be written into, the 8255A. If the PPI chip is interfaced to the microcomputer as an accumulator I/O device, these two control inputs would be wired to $\overline{IN}$ and $\overline{OUT}$. The 8255A can also be used as a memory-mapped I/O device and, when it is, $\overline{RD}$ and $\overline{WR}$ are wired to $\overline{MEMR}$ and $\overline{MEMW}$.

How is one port distinguished from another port within the 8255A? The 8255A has two address inputs, A0 and A1, which are internally decoded so that one of four possible ports is selected during a read or write operation. These two inputs are normally wired to the A0 and A1 signals in the address bus. The 8255A has two additional inputs: RESET and $\overline{CS}$. The RESET input is very similar to the RESET input of the 8085A. A logic one on this input of the 8255A resets internal logic so that all three general-purpose ports (A, B, and C) are con-

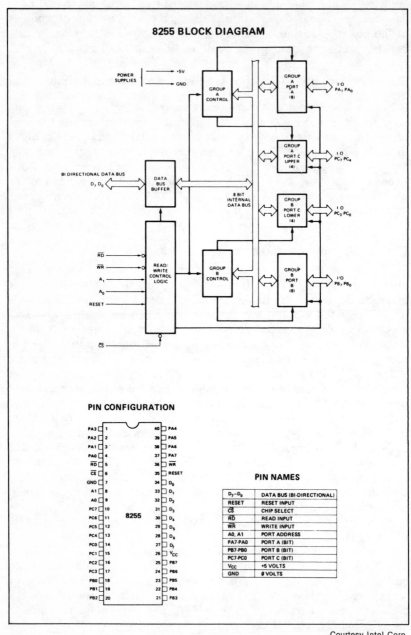

Courtesy Intel Corp.

Fig. 6-13. The pin configuration and block diagram for the 8255A programmable peripheral interface (PPI) chip.

figured as input ports. This input is normally wired to the RESET OUT output of the 8085A microprocessor integrated circuit. Once the 8255A is reset, software instructions can be executed so that one or more ports are programmed as output ports.

The $\overline{CS}$ input functions just like the chip select inputs of ROMs or R/W memories. When the $\overline{CS}$ input is a logic zero, the address on the A0 and A1 inputs is decoded so that one of the ports is addressed. The states of the $\overline{RD}$ and $\overline{WR}$ inputs determine whether the microprocessor is writing data out to an output port or reading data from an input port. The truth table for the A0, A1, $\overline{RD}$, $\overline{WR}$, and $\overline{CS}$ inputs is shown in Table 6-3. From Table 6-3 you can see that once an 8-bit control word

Table 6-3. A Truth Table for the 8255A PPI Chip

A1	A0	$\overline{RD}$	$\overline{WR}$	$\overline{CS}$	Action
0	0	0	1	0	Read the State of Port A
0	1	0	1	0	Read the State of Port B
1	0	0	1	0	Read the State of Port C
1	1	0	1	0	***Illegal Operation***
0	0	1	0	0	Write Information to Port A
0	1	1	0	0	Write Information to Port B
1	0	1	0	0	Write Information to Port C
1	1	1	0	0	Write the Mode Control Word to the Control Word Register
X	X	X	X	1	The 8255A Is Not Selected

has been written out to the control word register (A1 = 1, A0 = 1, $\overline{RD}$ = 1, $\overline{WR}$ = 0, $\overline{CS}$ = 0) it cannot be read back into the microprocessor. This is not a significant limitation of the 8255A PPI chip.

Not only can the PPI chip be used for simple input and output, but individual bits in port C can be set to logic ones or reset to logic zeroes (if port C is an output port). The ports can also be used for *handshaking* and *strobed I/O* operation. Within the control word are two bits that control the *mode* of operation of the 8255A. The mode that is most often used is Mode 0, which means that the PPI chip is used as latched output ports and three-state input ports. The format for the mode word or mode control word is shown in Fig. 6-14.

Interfacing the 8255A PPI Chip

A typical accumulator I/O interface for the 8255A PPI chip is shown in Fig. 6-15. What are the addresses for the mode control register and the A, B, and C ports if this interface is used? The addresses for these four I/O devices would be from 00111100 through 00111111. For output 3 of the decoder wired to A7, A6, A5, and A4 to go to a logic zero, 0011 has to be present on these four address lines. For output 3 of the other decoder to go to a logic zero, A3 and A2 would have to be in the

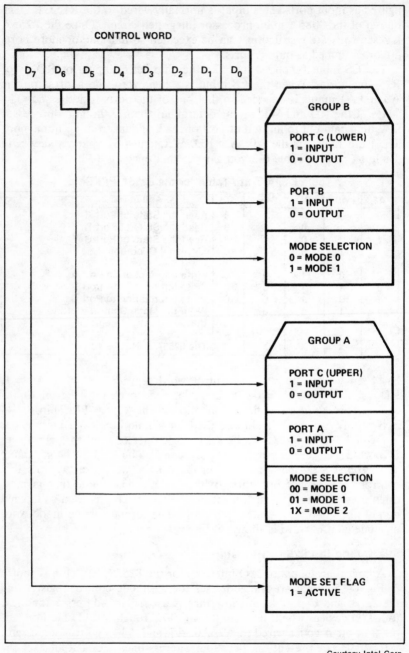

Courtesy Intel Corp.

Fig. 6-14. The format of the mode control word for the 8255 PPI chip.

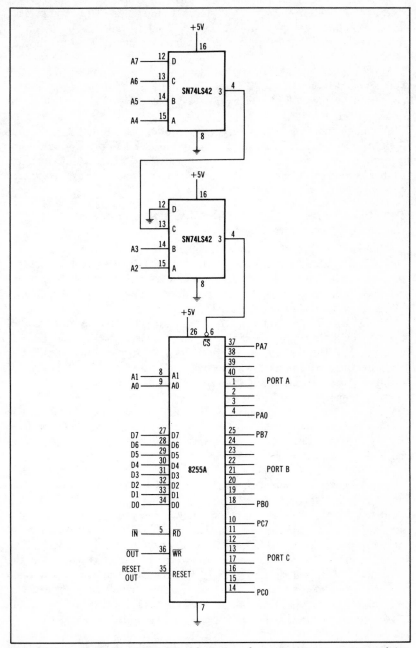

Fig. 6-15. Interfacing the 8255A PPI chip to the microcomputer as an accumulator I/O device.

states 11. Therefore the 8255A is selected only when 001111 is present on address lines A7 through A2. The A1 and A0 address lines can be in either the logic one or logic zero state so that one of the four devices is selected.

Since accumulator I/O has been used, $\overline{\text{OUT}}$ and $\overline{\text{IN}}$ are wired to the $\overline{\text{WR}}$ and $\overline{\text{RD}}$ inputs of the 8255A. Also, the RESET OUT signal that is generated by the 8085A microprocessor is wired to the RESET input of the 8155A.

Although the PPI chip is large and contains a number of powerful features, it can still be thought of as three 8-bit I/O ports: either input, output, or both. If you are interested in using the PPI chip and you want to learn more about the hardware and software, refer to *Microcomputer Interfacing with the 8255 PPI Chip.*[1]

The 8251A Universal Synchronous/Asynchronous Receiver/Transmitter (USART)

The 8251A USART is similar to the 8255A PPI chip in many respects. The 8251A contains a number of I/O devices, and it must be programmed, using software, before it can be used to perform I/O operations. The pin configuration and block diagram for the 8251A USART chip are shown in Fig. 6-16.

This particular integrated circuit is used to simplify the interface between a cathode-ray tube (crt) terminal or teletypewriter and the microcomputer. Because the 8251A was designed to perform a number of additional control functions it also has some control signals that are not ordinarily used. There are, however, also a number of signals that you should recognize. Pins D0 through D7 represent the pins over which information is transferred between the 8085A and the USART. The 8251A also has $\overline{\text{RD}}$, $\overline{\text{WR}}$, and $\overline{\text{CS}}$ inputs, which are used to control the chip and the flow of data to and from the chip. The 8251A also has to be supplied with power (+5 V) and ground.

The 8251A USART has three clock inputs ($\overline{\text{TxC}}$, $\overline{\text{RxC}}$, and CLK), which are used to control internal logic and the speed at which information is sent to or received from the peripheral. The CLK input is used for internal USART functions and *is not* related to the speed at which data is transferred between the USART and the *serial* peripheral device (crt or teletypewriter). This pin can be wired to the CLK (OUT) output of the 8085A. The frequency of the clock that is applied to the $\overline{\text{TxC}}$ and $\overline{\text{RxC}}$ inputs of the USART *will* determine the transmission and reception rate of the USART. As an example, a clock frequency of 110 Hz, 1760 Hz, or 7040 Hz can be used to clock the USART $\overline{\text{TxC}}$ and $\overline{\text{RxC}}$ inputs, if the USART is communicating with a peripheral at the rate of 110 bits per second. Once one of these clock frequencies is chosen, the user programs the USART by executing software instructions so that the proper *bit rate* is used.

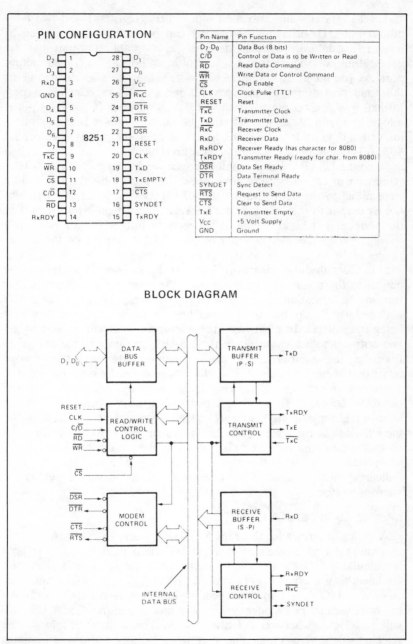

PIN CONFIGURATION

Pin Name	Pin Function
D_7–D_0	Data Bus (8 bits)
C/$\overline{D}$	Control or Data is to be Written or Read
$\overline{RD}$	Read Data Command
$\overline{WR}$	Write Data or Control Command
$\overline{CS}$	Chip Enable
CLK	Clock Pulse (TTL)
RESET	Reset
$\overline{TxC}$	Transmitter Clock
TxD	Transmitter Data
$\overline{RxC}$	Receiver Clock
RxD	Receiver Data
RxRDY	Receiver Ready (has character for 8080)
TxRDY	Transmitter Ready (ready for char. from 8080)
$\overline{DSR}$	Data Set Ready
$\overline{DTR}$	Data Terminal Ready
SYNDET	Sync Detect
$\overline{RTS}$	Request to Send Data
$\overline{CTS}$	Clear to Send Data
TxE	Transmitter Empty
V_{CC}	+5 Volt Supply
GND	Ground

BLOCK DIAGRAM

Courtesy Intel Corp.

Fig. 6-16. The pin configuration and block diagram for the 8251A universal synchronous/asynchronous receiver/transmitter (USART).

217

The 8251A contains two 8-bit input ports (registers) and two 8-bit output ports (registers). These ports can be further characterized as being either data or control ports. There is one data input port and one data output port. There is also a control input port and a control output port. As you might expect, there has to be some way of selecting one or the other port during a read or write operation. This selection is performed by the $C/\overline{D}$ pin when the 8251A is *selected*. If the C/D pin is a logic zero and the chip is selected, the microcomputer is communicating with a data port; and if it is a logic one when the chip is selected, the 8085A is communicating with a control register.

Since the USART can transmit and receive characters to/from a teletypewriter or crt, the information that is output to the data port will be transmitted to the peripheral by the USART. As soon as this information is output to the USART, the USART automatically transmits it to the peripheral, 1 bit at a time. If the receiver in the USART receives a character from the teletypewriter or crt, it can be input into the microprocessor by reading the content of the data port.

How does the microprocessor know when another character can be output to the transmitter or input from the receiver? If the transmitter transmits information at the rate of 110 bits per second, the transmitter may be busy for up to 110 ms, depending on the amount of information being transmitted. In most cases the microprocessor will be able to get and output another character to the USART in far less time than this. Likewise, the microprocessor can also input data from the receiver faster than it can be received. *Therefore there has to be some way of synchronizing the transfer of information between the microprocessor and the 8251 USART.* To do this, 2 bits within the control input port or control register indicate the *status* of the transmitter and receiver within the USART. These 2 status bits can be tested with software instructions so that a new character is only output to the transmitter once it has completed transmitting the previous character. The receiver status bit indicates when a character has been received and can be input by the microprocessor.

Interfacing the 8251A USART

A typical interface for the 8251A USART is shown in Fig. 6-17. Has accumulator I/O or memory-mapped I/O been used in this interface? Accumulator I/O has been used, because the control signals $\overline{OUT}$ and $\overline{IN}$ have been used to control the 8251A. Of course, nonabsolute accumulator I/O device address decoding has been used because only A7 has been used in the decoder design. This means that the 8251A USART will be selected whenever A7 is a logic one. Note that the chip will be selected when A7 is a logic one in either a memory address or accumulator I/O address. However, no information will be transferred unless either $\overline{IN}$ or $\overline{OUT}$ is generated by the microprocessor control circuitry.

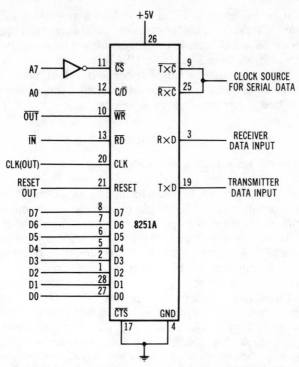

Fig. 6-17. Interfacing the 8251A USART to the microcomputer as an accumulator I/O device.

As you would expect, the RESET and CLK inputs of the 8251A are wired to the RESET OUT and CLK (OUT) outputs of the 8085A chip. To select either the control or data ports, A0 is wired to the C/$\overline{\text{D}}$ input of the 8251A. Based on this interface a truth can be generated (Table

Table 6-4. A Truth Table for the 8251A USART Interface (Fig. 6-17)

A7 ($\overline{\text{CS}}$)	A0 (C/$\overline{\text{D}}$)	$\overline{\text{WR}}$	$\overline{\text{RD}}$	Action
1	0	1	0	Read Data From the Receiver
1	0	0	1	Write Data to the Transmitter
1	1	1	0	Read the Status Flags of the USART
1	1	0	1	Write the Mode Word to the USART
0	X	X	X	The 8251A USART Is Not Selected

6-4) so that we know which register is accessed when the microprocessor generates an address during the execution of an IN or OUT instruction.

Unfortunately, we cannot wire the TTL-compatible output of the USART directly to most crt's and teletypewriters. Instead, the TTL signal must be converted to either 20 mA or a voltage between +15 V and −15 V (RS-232C). This "conversion" hardware is not complex, but it will not be discussed here. If you are interested in using USARTs and UARTs, which are very similar to USARTs, refer to *Interfacing and Scientific Data Communications Experiments*.[2] This book contains a considerable amount of useful circuitry, along with experiments that you can actually perform with these devices.

SERIAL I/O USING THE 8085A

In Chapter 1 we saw that the 8085A integrated circuit has two I/O pins, SID and SOD, that can be controlled using software. The serial input data (SID) pin can be used to input a single bit of information and the serial output data (SOD) pin can be used to output a single bit of information. These pins might be used so that a logic level generated by a switch could be input, and, based on this logic level, a logic one or logic zero could be output so that a light is turned on or a fan is turned off. These I/O pins can also be used to transmit serial data to a peripheral device such as a crt, teletypewriter, or audio cassette and to receive serial data from these same types of peripheral devices. This means that the microcomputer must be programmed so that it simulates the operation of a USART or UART, using the SID and SOD pins. The software required to do this is long and complex and can be found in *8080/8085 Software Design, Book 2: Asynchronous Communications, Interrupt, and Data Structure Software for 8080- and 8085-Based Microcomputers*.[3]

How is the state of the SID pin sensed? The 8085A will read the state of the SID pin into bit D7 of the accumulator when a RIM instruction is executed. Once this instruction has been executed, additional software instructions can be executed so that the microprocessor performs one task if a logic one was read, and performs another task if a logic zero was read. The 8085A also reads information about possible interrupts into the other bits of the accumulator when the RIM instruction is executed. Interrupts will be discussed in the next section. Therefore the RIM instruction reads 8 bits of information into the A register, and bit D7 represents the state of the SID pin.

Writing a logic one or a logic zero out to the SOD pin is a little more complex. To do this the SIM instruction must be executed in a program. If bit *D6* of the A register is a *logic one, bit D7 will be transferred to the SOD pin* when a SIM instruction is executed. If bit *D6* of the A register is a *logic zero* when the SIM instruction is executed, *the state of the SOD pin will remain unchanged*.

Based on this description, if the A register contains 01000000 when a SIM instruction is executed, a logic zero will be written out to the SOD pin. If the A register contains 10000000 and a SIM instruction is exe-

Table 6-5. The States of D6 and D7 in the A Register When the SIM Instruction is Executed

D7	D6	Effect on the SOD Pin
0	0	No Effect
0	1	Set the SOD Pin to a Logic Zero
1	0	No Effect
1	1	Set the SOD Pin to a Logic One

cuted, the logic level output by the SOD pin will remain unchanged. As you would expect, a logic one will be written out to the SOD pin if the A register contains 11000000 when the SIM instruction is executed. The other six bits of the A register cause other actions to take place when the SIM instruction is executed. These actions will be discussed in the next section. In Table 6-5 the different states of bits D6 and D7 in the A register, and their effect on the SOD pin when the SIM instruction is executed, have been summarized.

INTERRUPTS

In a previous section of this chapter an 8251A USART was interfaced to the 8085A. Since the 8085A can output information much faster than the 8251A USART can transmit it, and can input information much faster than the 8251A USART can receive it, the 8085A monitors the status of the transmitter and receiver within the USART by reading the content of the control port or control register. One of the bits within this 8-bit control word is used to indicate whether the transmitter is transmitting a character or not. Another bit in the control word is used by the receiver of the USART to indicate whether a character has been received by the USART and therefore can be input by the microprocessor.

In some situations, it may not be possible to program the microprocessor so that it can sense these *flags* with software. In general, this situation occurs when the microprocessor is *extremely* busy, that is, performing one or more tasks *continuously*. If we add instructions to this task, which cause the microprocessor to periodically check the UART flags, we may slow the microprocessor down enough so that the original task is not performed effectively, or not at all. For this reason peripherals are often wired to hardware interfaces that generate *interrupts*. This means that a peripheral interrupts the microprocessor, regardless of what the microprocessor is doing, so that the peripheral can be serviced (data input or output, control pulses generated, etc.). The microprocessor no longer has to monitor the flags of the peripheral, because the peripheral requests service only when it needs it. If a USART is wired to the interrupt of the microprocessor, the microprocessor could be interrupted when a character is received by the receiver, when the transmitter needs another character to transmit, or both. Once the interrupt signal is generated by the interface, the microprocessor needs only 5 or 10 μs before it starts to service the peripheral (input the USART character or output a character to the USART).

To service the peripheral the microprocessor has to execute a sequence of instructions that are specifically stored in memory for that device. If there are five or ten peripherals wired to the interrupt, there would have to be *five or ten interrupt service subroutines.* Of course, there has to be some way of associating each peripheral with its appropriate interrupt service subroutine. Some microprocessors, such as the 8085A, use hardware to do this, and others, such as the 6800 and 6502, use software. In an 8085A-based microcomputer the peripheral generating the interrupt can place a special instruction on the data bus once the microprocessor generates the interrupt acknowledge ($\overline{\text{INTA}}$) signal. This instruction causes the microprocessor to begin executing the interrupt service subroutine that is stored in memory, starting at a specific, unalterable memory address. There are eight of these special instructions, so up to eight peripherals can have their own *vector* or *vector instruction.* For the 8085A it is also possible to use a special interrupt controller chip, so that up to 64 peripherals can use the interrupt of the 8085A. As you will see, if there are only four or five peripherals that need to interrupt the operation of the microprocessor, no external hardware (expect possibly an inverter or two) will be needed.

Interrupting devices can also be assigned a *priority.* This means that if two devices try to interrupt the microprocessor at exactly the same time, the higher-priority device is serviced first. Suppose that two switches are wired to the microprocessor interrupt. One of the them is a high-temperature switch in a chemical reactor and the other switch is wired to the door of a cleaning equipment storeroom. If both of these switches generate an interrupt at the same time, it would probably be better for the microprocessor to find out what the problem is with the chemical reactor, rather than find out who is in the storeroom.

Suppose that the microprocessor is now servicing the *high-priority* chemical reactor. Do we want the *low-priority* storeroom door to interrupt the microprocessor while it is servicing the chemical reactor? No, we want the microprocessor to ignore any additional interrupts until it finds and corrects the problem with the reactor. Most microprocessors, including the 8085A, can disable the interrupt while it is servicing an interrupt and can then enable the interrupt once the peripheral device has been serviced. The EI instruction enables the interrupt and the DI instruction disables the interrupt. In addition, the 8085A disables the interrupt once an interrupt has been received. This prevents a peripheral from interrupting the microprocessor while it is servicing another. The user therefore has to program the microcomputer so that the interrupt is enabled once the peripheral has been serviced.

To do this the EI instruction would be added to the end of the interrupt service subroutine. We should note that when the 8085A is reset the interrupt is automatically disabled. This means that if interrupts are used in a microcomputer system an EI instruction must be executed before the microprocessor can be interrupted.

There is also the possibility that we have programmed the microprocessor to execute a *time-sensitive task*. During this task no interrupts must occur. If this type of situation exists, a DI instruction would be executed at the beginning of the task and an EI instruction would be executed once the time-sensitive task has been accomplished.

8085A Interrupts

The 8085A has five interrupt inputs called TRAP, RST 7.5, RST 6.5, RST 5.5, and INTR. There is also the $\overline{\text{INTA}}$ (interrupt acknowledge) output, which is a signal that is generated by the 8085A to acknowledge that an interrupt signal has been received on the INTR pin. *The TRAP interrupt input is unusual because it cannot be disabled by the DI instruction.* This interrupt input is often used when a catastrophic problem is taking place, such as a power failure. If a power failure does occur, the TRAP interrupt can be used so that the contents of the registers are saved on disk or tape before power disappears entirely. The TRAP interrupt input does not have to be used to sense a power failure; it can be wired to anything you like. It just cannot be disabled.

If a TRAP or any other type of interrupt occurs, how does the 8085A know where the proper interrupt service subroutine is stored in memory? For the TRAP, RST 7.5, RST 6.5, and RST 5.5 interrupts, special vectors are generated internally by the 8085A so that the microprocessor executes the appropriate subroutines in memory. The addresses of these memory locations are summarized in Table 6-6. From this table, for

Table 6-6. The Memory Addresses That the 8085A Is Vectored to When an Interrupt Occurs

Interrupt	Memory Address		Hex
	Binary	Octal	
TRAP	00000000 00100100	000 044	0024
RST 7.5	00000000 00111100	000 074	003C
RST 6.5	00000000 00110100	000 064	0034
RST 5.5	00000000 00101100	000 054	002C

instance, if a TRAP interrupt is generated by a peripheral, the 8085A will execute the interrupt service subroutine stored in memory location 00000000 00100100.

The RST 7.5, RST 6.5, and RST 5.5 interrupts are different from TRAP. These three interrupts can all be enabled or disabled by EI and DI instructions, but they can also be masked (enabled or disabled) by a value contained in the A register *when the SIM instruction is executed.* To enable or disable any combination of these three interrupts, the three LSBs of the A register are used, as shown in Table 6-9. To enable an individual interrupt the corresponding bit is set to a logic zero, and to disable one of the interrupts the bit is set to a logic one. When a SIM instruction is executed to change the state of the SOD pin, bit D6 of the A register has to be a logic one. *To change the interrupt mask for these three interrupts, bit D3 in the A register must be a logic one when a SIM instruction is executed.* The possible interrupt masks and the interrupts that are enabled and disabled are shown in Table 6-7.

Table 6-7. The Interrupt Mask Bits That Must Be in the A Register When the 8085A Executes a SIM Instruction

D3	D2	D1	D0	Interrupts Enabled/Disabled
1	0	0	0	RST 7.5, 6.5, and 5.5 Enabled
1	0	0	1	RST 7.5 and 6.5 Enabled, 5.5 Disabled
1	0	1	0	RST 7.5 and 5.5 Enabled, 6.5 Disabled
1	0	1	1	RST 7.5 Enabled, 6.5 and 5.5 Disabled
1	1	0	0	RST 7.5 Disabled, 6.5 and 5.5 Enabled
1	1	0	1	RST 7.5 and 5.5 Disabled, 6.5 Enabled
1	1	1	0	RST 7.5 and 6.5 Disabled, 5.5 Enabled
1	1	1	1	RST 7.5, 6.5, and 5.5 Disabled
0	X	X	X	Interrupt Mask Not Changed

X = May be either a logic one or logic zero.

As you can see from this table, bit D3 in the A register must be a logic one for the interrupt mask to change when a SIM instruction is executed. *Of course, it does not matter which of these three interrupts is enabled by the SIM instruction if a DI instruction has been executed previously in a program.*

The assembly language program listed in Fig. 6-18 causes the interrupt mask to be changed twice. The first instruction in this program causes the A register to be loaded with the value 00001000. In the assembly language listing this value is listed as 08 hexadecimal. The hexadecimal numbering system is just another way of representing numbers. The SIM instruction then causes all three interrupts, RST 7.5, RST 6.5, and RST 5.5, to be enabled because bit D3 in the A register is a logic one when the SIM instruction is executed. At the same time, bits D0, D1, and D2 were logic zeroes, so the interrupt masks were enabled. The EI instruction then enables the interrupts of the 8085A. After the EI instruction is executed, the 8085A microprocessor performs a number of other tasks.

At some point later in the execution of the program the interrupt mask has to be changed. Therefore the A register is loaded with 00001010, which will cause the RST 7.5 and RST 5.5 interrupts to remain enabled. The RST 6.5 will be disabled. After the MVIA instruction

```
        •           ;ASSEMBLY LANGUAGE INSTRUCTIONS
        •           ;ARE STORED IN THESE MEMORY LOCATIONS
        •
        •
MVI     A,08H  ;LOAD THE A REGISTER WITH 00001000.
SIM            ;LOAD THE INTERRUPT MASK WITH THE CONTENT
EI             ;OF REG. A. ENABLE THE INTERRUPT.
        •
        •           ;ADDITIONAL ASSEMBLY LANGUAGE
        •           ;INSTRUCTIONS ARE STORED HERE
        •
MVI     A,0AH  ;LOAD REGISTER A WITH 00001010
SIM            ;LOAD THE INT. MASK WITH THIS VALUE
        •
        •           ;ADDITIONAL ASSEMBLY LANGUAGE INSTRUCTIONS
```

Fig. 6-18. Changing the 8085A interrupt mask with the SIM instruction.

is executed, the three least significant bits in the A register are transferred to the interrupt mask when the SIM instruction is executed. The interrupt is still enabled, so an EI instruction does not have to be executed. The remainder of the program is then executed.

The fifth interrupt input, INTR, is used in conjunction with the $\overline{\text{INTA}}$ output. In most microcomputer designs these signals are used with external hardware such as three-state buffers, priority encoders, and gates to generate the special interrupt instructions, or vectors, that were mentioned in a previous section of this chapter. This logic must cause the INTR pin to go to a logic one so that an interrupt is generated, and then, in response to the 8085A generating the $\overline{\text{INTA}}$ signal, this logic must place the vector on the data bus. As you can see, it is a little more difficult to use this interrupt (INTR) input. For additional information about the hardware required to generate interrupts refer to *Introductory Experiments in Digital Electronics and 8080A Microcomputer Programming and Interfacing, Book 2.*[4] If you are interested in exploring interrupt software in detail, refer to Reference 3.

Just as the set interrupt mask (SIM) instruction can be used to set or change the interrupt masks for the RST 7.5, RST 6.5, and RST 5.5 interrupt inputs, the read interrupt mask (RIM) instruction can be used to read the three masks, the state of the interrupt (enabled or disabled), the states of the three RST-type interrupt inputs (pending interrupts), and the SID pin. There are some unusual characteristics of both the RIM and SIM instructions that we will not discuss. For additional information about these instructions, refer to the *MCS-85 User's Manual, September 1978.*[5]

Although the five interrupt inputs of the 8085A can cause the microprocessor to be interrupted, different *types* of signals are required for the 8085A to be interrupted. The input characteristics of these five interrupt inputs are summarized in Table 6-8. As you can see from this table, three of the interrupt input signals must remain in the logic one

225

Table 6-8. The Input Characteristics of the Five Interrupt Inputs

Interrupt Input	Trigger Requirements
TRAP	Rising Edge *and* High Level Until Sampled
RST 7.5	Rising Edge (Internally Latched)
RST 6.5	High Level Until Sampled
RST 5.5	High Level Until Sampled
INTR	High Level Until Sampled

state until they are sampled by the microprocessor. The 8085A samples all interrupts on the trailing edge of CLK, one cycle before the end of the instruction being executed. Therefore, to interrupt the microprocessor the interrupt signal must be present at least 160 ns (assuming a 320-ns cycle time) before the trailing edge of the clock. This means that the microprocessor will finish executing an instruction before the three RST-type interrupt inputs will be sampled. Since the longest instruction requires 18 clock cycles to be executed, the interrupt signal must be present for at least 18 clock cycles less 160 ns. If the 8085A has a cycle time of 320 ns, this is 5.6 μs. If one of these three interrupt inputs is at a logic one for less time than this, there is no guarantee that the 8085A will be interrupted.

The RST 7.5 interrupt input is different because the positive edge of the interrupt signal will cause an internal flip-flop to be clocked. When the 8085A samples the interrupts, it is really sampling the other inputs and the output of the flip-flop. The minimum pulse width for this input is 160 ns (8085A). Since the RST 7.5 input is used to clock a flip-flop, the flip-flop is cleared by internal logic once the 8085A is interrupted. This flip-flop can also be cleared by clearing bit D4 of the A register to zero and then executing a SIM instruction.

PRELIMINARY INTERFACE DESIGN

Now that we have discussed the design of input ports, output ports, and the use of interrupts with the 8085A, you will have the opportunity to test your knowledge of these topics. As we saw in the previous sections of this chapter the microprocessor can communicate with peripheral devices using either accumulator I/O or memory-mapped I/O. Also, as was the case when memory systems were designed, both absolute and nonabsolute decoding can be used.

Preliminary Design No. 1

Using nonabsolute decoding, design an 8-bit input port with an SN74LS244, which has addresses 10000000 through 11111111. Also include in your design a 4-bit output port, using an SN74LS75, that latches bits D7, D5, D4, and D1 off the data bus. The output port should latch these bits of data off the data bus when any of the addresses be-

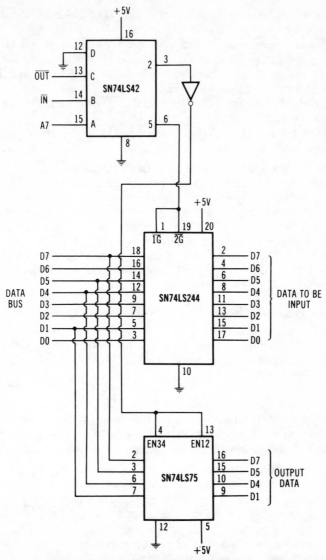

Fig. 6-19. An interface that contains an 8-bit input port and a 4-bit output port (accumulator I/O, nonabsolute addressing).

tween 00000000 and 01111111 are present on the address bus. You may use any additional integrated circuits that you need to complete this design.

Fig. 6-19 contains one possible design. Some of the design points you should check for in your design include:

1. Have the three-state outputs of the SN74LS244 been wired to the data bus?
2. Has A7 been used *exclusively* (the only address signal) in the decoder design for both the input and output port?
3. For the input port, has the combination of $A7 = 1$ and $IN = 0$ been used to enable the three-state outputs?
4. Has the combination of $A7 = 0$ and $\overline{OUT} = 0$ been used to enable the SN74LS75 latch?
5. Have the inputs of the latch been wired to the appropriate data lines in the data bus?

In this design a single SN74LS42 decoder was used to combine the $\overline{IN}$, $\overline{OUT}$, and A7 signals. Once these three signals are wired to the decoder, it is very easy to determine which outputs can be used to control the input and output port. In Fig. 6-19 $\overline{OUT}$ is wired to the C input, $\overline{IN}$ to the B input, and A7 to the A input. The two possible combinations of these signals that are of interest are $\overline{OUT} = 1$, $\overline{IN} = 0$, $A7 = 1$ and $\overline{OUT} = 0$, $\overline{IN} = 1$, $A7 = 0$. With these two possible input states (101 and 010), outputs 5 and 2 should be used to control the input and output ports, respectively.

Preliminary Design No. 2

Using absolute decoding, design an 8-bit *memory-mapped* output port using an SN74LS373 and an 8-bit input port using an 8212. The addresses for *both* devices should be 11111000 00111000. You may use any decoders, comparators, or gates required to complete this design.

Fig. 6-20 contains one design that solves this problem. Although your decoder is probably different from the one shown in Fig. 6-20, the input and output ports will probably be very similar. Some design points that you should look for in your design include:

1. Have all 16 address lines been used in the decoder design?
2. Has the output of the decoder been gated with $\overline{MEMR}$ and the resulting logic one pulse been used to control the 8212?
3. Has the output of the decoder been gated with $\overline{MEMW}$ and the resulting logic one pulse been used to control the SN74LS373?
4. Has pin 1 of the SN74LS373 been wired to ground so that the outputs are never in the third state?
5. There is only one way that the 8212 can be wired as an input port. Therefore, have the MD and $\overline{DS_1}$ inputs been wired to ground and the STB and $\overline{CLR}$ inputs been wired to +5 V?
6. Has a positive (logic one) control pulse been wired to the DS_2 input?

If you are not sure how the 8212 or SN74LS373 should be used in this design problem, refer to their descriptions in Chapter 2.

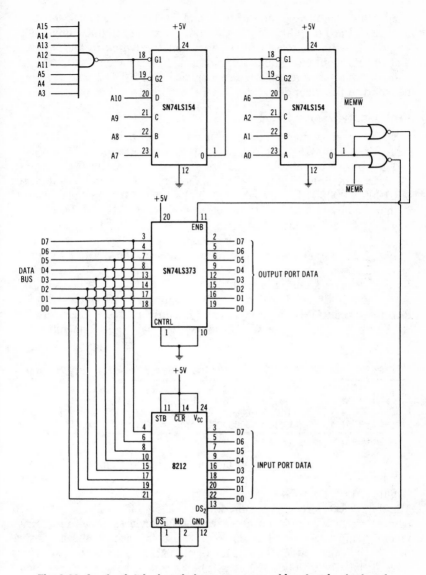

Fig. 6-20. An absolutely decoded memory-mapped input and output port.

One unusual feature of this design is the decoder. Both the input and output ports must have the address 11111000 00111000. In this particular address there are eight logic ones, so the corresponding address signals (A15, A14, A13, A12, A11, A5, A4, and A3) are all wired to the inputs of an 8-input NAND gate (SN74LS30). The eight logic zeroes were divided into two groups of four, and these are wired to SN74LS154 decoders. Since both SN74LS154 decoders decode the 0000 input state, any combination of these address lines could be wired to the decoders, and the zero outputs would still be used. For instance, A10, A1, A6, and A9 could be wired to one decoder, and A0, A8, A2, and A7 could be wired to the other decoder.

Preliminary Design No. 3

Using memory-mapped I/O design techniques, interface an 8255A PPI chip and an 8251A USART chip to the microcomputer. The 8255A should have the absolute addresses 00010000 00000000 through 00010000 00000011. The 8251A should have the absolute addresses 00010000 00000100 through 00010000 00000101. Include in your design the circuitry necessary to select four 1K ROMs and 3K of R/W memory, based on the 2114. Use absolute decoding throughout your design.

Fig. 6-21 contains a typical solution. To keep the drawing as simple as possible, only the decoder has been shown. Since 1K ROMs and 1K R/W memories are used in this design, A15, A14, A13, A12, A11, and A10 must be decoded. Address lines A9 through A0 would be wired directly to the ROMs and R/W memory. Those addresses that cause the ROMs to be selected are shown below, in Chart 6-3. Remember that

Chart 6-3. The ROM Addresses for the 8251A/8255A/Memory Interface

ROM 1	00000000	00000000	through 00000011	11111111
ROM 2	00000100	00000000	through 00000111	11111111
ROM 3	00001000	00000000	through 00001011	11111111
ROM 4	00001100	00000000	through 00001111	11111111

when the microprocessor is reset, the first instruction to be executed will be read from memory location zero. In most designs this is ROM.

Since 2114s are used in the R/W memory portion of the design, three 1K chip selects are also required. The 8255A and 8251A integrated circuits can also be thought of as "read/write devices," so a fourth R/W memory chip select signal is required. This chip select would be further decoded to select either the 8251A or the 8255A. Since the I/O chips start at 00010000 00000000, it will be easiest to have the R/W memory start at the beginning of the next 1K boundary of the microprocessor address space. Therefore R/W memory will have addresses 00010100 00000000 through 10011111 11111111. From these addresses you should notice that A15, A14, and A13 remain in the logic zero state, regardless of what is being addressed. Further, A12 is a logic zero when ROM is addressed and a logic one when R/W memory and the two I/O devices are addressed.

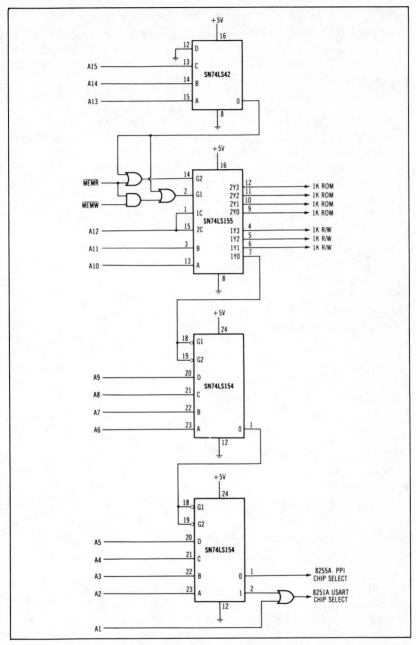

Fig. 6-21. An absolutely decoded memory-mapped interface for the 8255A PPI chip and the 8251A USART chip,

Some design points to look for in your design include:

1. Have A15, A14, and A13 been used to enable a decoder that decodes eight 1K blocks of the microprocessor address space?
2. Has $\overline{MEMR}$ been used to enable the decoder that generates the chip selects for the ROMs?
3. Have the $\overline{MEMR}$ and $\overline{MEMW}$ signals been used to enable the decoder that selects the R/W memories and I/O chips?
4. Has one of the "R/W memory chip selects" been used to enable additional decoders so that the memory addresses for the 8255A PPI chip and 8251A USART chip are absolutely decoded?
5. At a minimum, have A9 through A2 been decoded for the PPI and USART chip selects? Some designs may decode A9 through A0, and then gate four chip selects together for the PPI chip select, and gate two of the chip selects together for the 8251A USART chip select.

In Fig. 6-21 only A9 through A2 are decoded, since A1 and A0 are wired to the PPI chip. Only A0 is wired to the USART chip, however, so A1 is gated with one of the decoder outputs so that the USART is only selected when A1 is a logic zero and either a memory-read or memory-write operation is taking place.

To complete the interface in Fig. 6-21 the USART and PPI chips would both have to be wired to the microprocessor data bus. Both chips would also be wired to $\overline{MEMR}$ and $\overline{MEMW}$, A0, and RESET OUT. Since the PPI chip contains four I/O devices it would also be wired to A1. The USART requires a clock for proper operation, so CLK (OUT) of the 8085A would be wired to the CLK input of the USART.

CONCLUSION

In this chapter we have discussed accumulator and memory-mapped I/O and microprocessor interrupts. We have also discussed a number of different memory address and device address decoders, the use of three-state devices for input ports, the use of latches as output ports and two peripheral chips, the 8255A PPI chip, and the 8251A USART chip. We have also seen that simple integrated circuits can contain more than one input or output port. The 8255A PPI chip contains four I/O devices, three of which are general purpose and can be used to transfer data between peripheral devices and the microprocessor. The 8251A USART chip also contains four I/O devices, but only two can be used to transfer data between a peripheral, such as a crt or teletypewriter, and the microprocessor. In fact, other peripheral chips contain 16 or more I/O devices, although most of them are not general-purpose I/O ports.

We have discussed microprocessor interrupts and some of the terms that are often encountered in discussing interrupts. With the 8085A there is very little hardware design required if the TRAP, RST 7.5, RST 6.5, and RST 5.5 interrupt inputs are used. If the INTR input and $\overline{\text{INTA}}$ output are used in an interface, the hardware can be very complex. However, before one can use interrupts or even I/O ports to solve interfacing problems, assembly language programming must be learned.

In previous chapters we have seen that address decoders must not only decode an address on the address bus, but they also must (1) be enabled by a control signal or (2) the decoder outputs must be gated with a control signal before they can be used to select memory chips. The same is true when interfaces are designed for peripheral devices. However, the signals $\overline{\text{OUT}}$ and $\overline{\text{IN}}$ are used with accumulator I/O designs. If memory-mapped I/O is used, the memory control signals are used.

REFERENCES

1. Goldsbrough, P. *Microcomputer Interfacing with the 8255 PPI Chip,* Indianapolis: Howard W. Sams & Co., 1979.
2. Rony, P. R., Larsen, D. G., Titus, J. A., and Titus C. A. *Interfacing and Scientific Data Communications Experiments,* Indianapolis: Howard W. Sams & Co., Inc., 1979.
3. Titus, C. A. *8080/8085 Software Design, Book 2: Asynchronous Communications, Interrupt and Data Structure Software for 8080- and 8085-Based Microcomputers,* Indianapolis: Howard W. Sams & Co., Inc., 1979.
4. Larsen, D. G., Rony, P. R., and Titus J. A. *Introductory Experiments in Digital Electronics and 8080A Microcomputer Programming and Interfacing, Book 2,* Indianapolis: Howard W. Sams & Co., Inc., 1977.
5. Intel Corp. *The MCS-85 User's Manual, September 1978,* Santa Clara, CA 95051.

PROBLEMS

6-1. Design a memory-mapped input port that uses 1K of the microprocessor address space. In the same design include the decoding logic required for two 2708 EPROMs. The memory addresses for the EPROMs should be absolutely decoded and be contained in the 2K of the microprocessor address space that is immediately below the input port. The first "memory address" of the input port should be 00010100 00000000.

6-2. Design an 8-bit output port that can be accessed as either a memory mapped I/O port or as an accumulator I/O port. The memory address for the output port should be 00111000 11000000, and the accumulator I/O address should be 11000000.

6-3. Modify the design in Problem 6-2 so that the memory address for the output port is 00111000 11000000 and *the accumulator I/O address is 00111000*.

6-4. Design the circuitry required to generate a pulse when the microprocessor addresses memory locations 11111000 00000000 through 11111000 00000011. Each "memory location" should cause a different pulse to be generated. The duration of these pulses is unimportant, but they will typically be from 100 to 300 ns long, depending on the cycle time of the microprocessor. These pulses might be used to *control* a peripheral. No data. is transferred.

6-5. Once a particular accumulator I/O peripheral in a microcomputer system is accessed (for example, when the 8085A generates its 8-bit address and the IN signal), the peripheral requires 5 μs to respond to the device address and place data on the data bus. Design the accumulator I/O interface for this peripheral, using absolute addressing. Any device address may be used.

6-6. Determine the total sink and source current requirements of the design shown in Fig. 6-21. Include the sink, source, and leakage currents of the 8251A USART and 8255A PPI chip in your calculations.

6-7. Using two integrated circuits, design a nonabsolute accumulator I/O decoder that can be used with four input ports and four output ports.

6-8. Compare accumulator I/O and memory-mapped I/O techniques and list the advantages and disadvantages of each technique.

6-9. In a particular 8085A-based microcomputer system the duration of the $\overline{\text{IN}}$ signal during the execution of an IN instruction was measured as being 300 ns. Assume that the decoder design shown in Fig. 2-21 is used in the system. What is the cycle time of the microprocessor? Based on this cycle time, has an 8085A or a more expensive 8085A-2 been used in the system?

6-10. In a particular microcomputer system two 8-bit output ports and one 8-bit input port are required. Two possible solutions would be to use an 8255A PPI chip for all three ports, or to use two SN74LS373s for the output ports and one SN74LS244 for the input ports. List the advantages and disadvantages of each design.

6-11. Design a memory-mapped I/O port that information can be written to, and that (the same) information can be read from. This means that the I/O port looks like an R/W memory location to the microprocessor. In all of our previous designs the I/O ports have been either write-only (output ports) or read-only (input ports). Either absolute or nonabsolute decoding may be used. Any chips discussed in this book may be used, other than read/write memory integrated circuits.

6-12. Most ASCII keyboards generate an 8-bit ASCII code for the key that is pressed, and a strobe or flag signal that is a logic one for as long as *any* key is pressed. Design the complete interface required for this keyboard. The interface should be designed so that the microprocessor can monitor the state flag, and input the ASCII value for the key when the flag is in the proper state. Suggest an alternate design for this interface.

6-13. Using SN74LS193 synchronous 4-bit up/down counters, design an 8-bit output port using accumulator I/O. Use address 11111010.

6-14. A particular 8085A-based microprocessor system contains 49,152 (48K) of R/W memory and 16,384 (16K) of ROM. Therefore the entire 64K of the microprocessor address space has been used up. However, four 8-bit memory-mapped output ports must be added to the system. Can this be done? If it can be done, design the interface for the output ports using 8255A PPI chips.

6-15. Two 4-bit input ports must be designed for a microcomputer system. However, only one three-state integrated circuit can be used in the design. The accumulator I/O addresses for the input ports, which are both wired to D0, D1, D4, and D7 of the data bus, are 11101011 and 01011110. Design the decoder and input ports. Only integrated circuits discussed in this book may be used.

CHAPTER 7

8085A-Family
Compatible Chips

When the Intel engineers designed the 8085A they also designed five compatible ROM and R/W memory integrated circuits that can be used with the 8085A to create three- and four-chip microcomputers. All of these devices require just +5 V to operate and they use the multiplexed address/data bus directly. A demultiplexed address/data bus is not required by these integrated circuits. When these chips were designed Intel combined memory with I/O in the same package, a concept that Intel pioneered in the early 1970s with the 4004 microprocessor.

8085A-FAMILY-COMPATIBLE ROMS

There are two ROMs that were specifically designed for the 8085A. The 8355 is a 2K×8 mask ROM, and the 8755A is a 2K×8 EPROM. These two devices are pin-for-pin compatible, so the 8755A can be used during the development of a program and then the 8355 can be used once all of the "bugs" in the program have been eliminated. Since the devices are compatible we will use the 8355 device in our discussion although the 8755A would be just as applicable. When the two devices differ we will indicate which device we mean.

The pin configurations and block diagrams for these two integrated circuits are shown in Fig. 7-1. As you can see from the diagrams these two devices also contain two 8-bit I/O ports. However, unlike the three 8-bit I/O ports contained within the 8255A PPI chip, which we discussed in Chapter 6, *individual bits in the two I/O ports can be programmed as either input or output bits by executing software instruc-*

PIN CONFIGURATION

BLOCK DIAGRAM

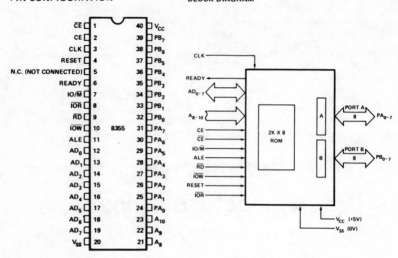

(A) The 8355 mask ROM.

PIN CONFIGURATION

BLOCK DIAGRAM

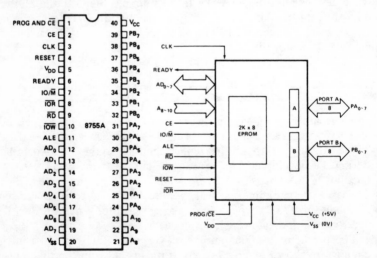

(B) The 8755 EPROM.

Courtesy Intel Corp.

Fig. 7-1. The pin configuration and block diagrams for the 8085A-family-compatible 2K × 8 ROMs.

tions. This means that 3 bits in a port can be input bits, such as D7, D3, and D1, and the remaining 5 bits, D6, D5, D4, D2, and D0, can be output bits. This gives the designer a tremendous amount of flexibility when designing interfaces that use these combination ROM-I/O chips.

To program the individual bits in these two ports as input or output bits, the 8355 contains two data direction registers (DDRs): one for port A and one for port B. A zero in a bit of a DDR will program the corresponding bit in the port as an input bit and a logic one will program the bit as an output bit. The addresses for the two I/O ports and these DDRs are summarized in Table 7-1.

Table 7-1. The I/O Device Addresses for the A and B Ports and the Data Direction Registers in the 8355/8755A

AD7	AD6	AD5	AD4	AD3	AD2	AD1	AD0	Port Selection
X	X	X	X	X	X	0	0	Port A
X	X	X	X	X	X	0	1	Port B
X	X	X	X	X	X	1	0	Port A Data Direction Register (DDR)
X	X	X	X	X	X	1	1	Port B Data Direction Register (DDR)

If we assume that these I/O devices have accumulator I/O addresses 00000000 through 00000011, two addresses for the I/O ports and two for the data direction register, we could program port A for 3 input bits and 5 output bits by writing 01110101 to DDR 00000010. This will program port A for the configuration that was mentioned above. Of course, to program all 8 bits of the port as input bits a 00000000 would be output to the appropriate DDR. To program a port as an output port a 11111111 would be output to the appropriate DDR.

Note that the RESET signal generated by the 8085A resets or clears the DDR latch contained within the 8355, so that the ports are configured as input ports when these devices are reset. Therefore the ports do not output any information until the appropriate software instructions are executed.

Accessing the ROM in the 8355 and 8755A

The ROM contained in both the 8355 and 8755A contains 2048 8-bit words. To address this much memory the 8355 and 8755A must be wired to A0 through A10. However, due to internal organization these two devices will latch address bits A0 through A7 from the multiplexed address/data bus when ALE is a logic one. The remaining address lines, A8, A9, and A10, are wired directly to these two chips.

These integrated circuits also have IO/$\overline{\text{M}}$, $\overline{\text{RD}}$, and $\overline{\text{IOW}}$ inputs, along with two chip select inputs, one of which is active high (CE_2) and one which is active low ($\overline{CE_1}$). When IO/$\overline{\text{M}}$ and $\overline{\text{RD}}$ are both logic zeroes and the chip has been selected, information will be read from the ROM.

There is no $\overline{WR}$ input to either of the two ROMs, since it is impossible to write information into the ROMs.

Accessing the I/O Ports

To access the I/O ports in the 8355 chip the IO/$\overline{M}$ signal applied to the chip must be a logic one, indicating that the 8085A is in an I/O transfer state. The I/O ports may be involved in either an input or an output operation, through the use of the 8085A read ($\overline{RD}$) and write ($\overline{WR}$) signals. In each case the address present on the AD0 and AD1 lines will be used by the 8355 chip to identify the I/O port or data direction register that will be involved in the data transfer. The data direction registers, however, may only be used in a write, or output operation, since reading their contents is not allowed by the internal operation of the 8355 chip. The 8355 chip read ($\overline{RD}$) input is used to designate the memory read as well as the I/O read operation. Since the ROM portion of the chip cannot be written into, a general write input is not provided. Instead, an I/O write ($\overline{IOW}$) input has been provided for the control of the I/O ports and their associated DDRs. Of course, when memory-read or I/O read/write operations are required the 8355 chip must be selected through the use of the chip select inputs.

The $\overline{IOW}$ signal is used only during I/O transfers, since the ROM is not able to accept data from the 8085A. Thus, when the $\overline{IOW}$ signal is asserted, the state of the IO/$\overline{M}$ is essentially ignored, since the only write operation that can involve the 8355 is one in which the I/O ports are having information transferred to them. The 8355 $\overline{IOW}$ signal may be directly wired to the 8085A $\overline{WR}$ output since it does not have to be "qualified" by the IO/$\overline{M}$ signal. This means that whenever the 8355 is selected by the chip select inputs and a write operation is taking place, the operation involves the I/O ports and not the memory portion of the chip.

When one of the ports in the 8355 is configured as an input port it does not make much sense to write data to this input port, although the circuitry for the ports allows this type of operation to take place without affecting the use of the port as an input port. The information written to the input port is stored in the output latch of the port, but this does not conflict with the information that is transferred to the 8085A during an I/O read or input operation.

An optional I/O read ($\overline{IOR}$) pin has been provided on the 8355 chip so that only the I/O ports may be accessed. This pin, when activated with a logic zero, performs the same function as IO/$\overline{M} = 1$ and $\overline{RD} = 0$. The $\overline{IOR}$ pin is normally unused and is connected to +5 volts, or logic one.

The 8355 and 8755A contain two general-purpose 8-bit I/O ports. They also contain two 8-bit DDRs, which are not general purpose and are not readily accessible to the user. When the 8085A accesses the 8355 or 8755A it can communicate with *one of four I/O devices,* yet the 8355 and 8755A contain only two general-purpose I/O ports. We will use the term "device" when we are discussing all of the I/O "registers" contained within a chip that can be accessed and the term "port" when we are discussing a register that can be used to output data to a peripheral or to input data from a peripheral.

Additional 8355/8755A Features

As mentioned previously each of these chips has two chip select inputs, one of which is active high and one one which is active low. The chips also have CLK and RESET inputs and a READY output. The CLK input is used to generate the READY output. The access time of the 8355 is 400 ns, and 450 ns for the 8755A. These devices are therefore fast enough for use, with no wait states, with a 6.25-MHz 8085A. However, if either of these devices is used with a 10-MHz 8085A-2, one wait state would have to be generated. One solution to this problem is to use faster parts, and Intel does have an 8355-2, which has an access time of 330 ns and which will operate with the 8085A-2 with no wait states. Unfortunately there is only one version of the 8755A (450 ns) available.

Since address signals AD0 through AD7 and A8 through A10 are wired *directly* to either of these two chips, A11 through A15 can be decoded to select one of 32 possible devices. Of course, this decoder logic must not only select the chip when the proper *memory address* is generated by the microprocessor but also when the proper *I/O device address* is generated. Let us assume that the 8085A is writing a value out to the DDR of port B. This DDR has an accumulator I/O device address 00000011, so we would expect 00000011 00000011 to be present on the 16-bit address bus. Since the 8355 only contains four I/O devices the address on A0 and A1 or on A8 and A9 will select the proper port. From this you might assume that A2 through A7 or A10 through A15 could be used to select the proper chip. However, A10 is already wired to the chip, so that all 2K of the ROM can be addressed. Therefore, when the 8355 is used, only A11 through A15 will be used to select the ROM or I/O devices. This means that A2 and A10 can be either a logic one or a logic zero when an I/O operation is being performed. *Each 8355 and 8755A will therefore appear to contain eight I/O devices, even though it only contains four.* One bit of the I/O address is wasted. If the 8085A writes out to port 00000100, it will really be writing to port A (00000000). To change the contents of the port B DDR a value could be output to device 00000011 or 00000111. Of course, it is possible to design a decoder that does not waste this I/O address space, which means that the decoder decodes A11 through A15 when a memory operation is taking place, and A10 through 15 when an I/O operation is taking place.

Additional Features of the 8755A EPROM

All of the features of the 8085A-family-compatible ROMs that were mentioned above apply to both the 8355 ROM and the 8755A EPROM. The only functional differences between the two chips, other than access times, deal with how the 8755A EPROM is programmed. Of course, since we cannot program the 8355 in the field as we can the 8755A or any other of the EPROMs that we have mentioned, the following discussion does not apply to the 8355.

As you can see from Fig. 7-1 the 8755A and the 8355 are pin-for-pin compatible. The only differences that can be seen are at pins 1 and 5. Pin 1 of the 8755A is used for a programming voltage during programming for the $\overline{CE}_1$ when it is being accessed. When it is being programmed this pin is pulsed with a logic zero for slightly more than 45 ms. Once the 8755A is programmed, this pin is used, along with pin 2, to select the ROM or I/O devices. Pin 5 of the 8355 is not used, but pin 5 on the 8755A is pulsed with +25 V when it is being programmed. Once the 8755A is programmed, pin 5 should be wired to +5 V. Since the 8355 does not use pin 5, this pin should be wired to +5 V in your designs so that either chip may be used. For additional programming information for the 8755A refer to Intel's *8085 User's Manual*.[1]

Electrical Characteristics of the 8355 and 8755A

Both of these devices are functionally the same, so you would expect them to have the same electrical characteristics. As you can see from Table 7-2, the dc characteristics are the same. The input voltages and currents (logic zero of 0.8 V maximum, 10 μA maximum; logic one of 2.0 V minimum, 10 μA maximum) are within the capabilities of the 8085A. Also, the 8355 and 8755A can source and sink more current at the appropriate voltage levels than the 8085A requires. For these reasons the 8355 (8355-2) and 8755A can be wired directly to the 8085A microprocessor in small systems. In large systems buffering probably would

Table 7-2. The DC Electrical Characteristics of the 8355 (8355-2) Mask ROM and the 8755A EPROM

SYMBOL	PARAMETER	MIN.	MAX.	UNITS	TEST CONDITIONS
V_{IL}	Input Low Voltage	-0.5	0.8	V	V_{CC} = 5.0V
V_{IH}	Input High Voltage	2.0	V_{CC}+0.5	V	V_{CC} = 5.0V
V_{OL}	Output Low Voltage		0.45	V	I_{OL} = 2mA
V_{OH}	Output High Voltage	2.4		V	I_{OH} = -400μA
I_{IL}	Input Leakage		10	μA	V_{IN} = V_{CC} to 0V
I_{LO}	Output Leakage Current		±10	μA	0.45V $\leq V_{OUT} \leq V_{CC}$
I_{CC}	V_{CC} Supply Current		180	mA	

Courtesy Intel Corp.

be used. Note that the 8355 and 8755A also have leakage currents of $\pm 10~\mu\text{A}$. The total amount of leakage current contributed by these and other integrated circuits must always be recognized in microcomputer designs.

INTERFACING THE 8355/8755A

Nonabsolute Address Decoding

By using either the 8355 or 8755A and the 8085A we can design a complete two-chip microcomputer that has 16 general-purpose I/O lines, two serial I/O lines, five interrupts, and 2K of ROM. However, the number of applications that this microcomputer has is very limited, because it does not have any R/W memory. One method of interconnecting the two integrated circuits is shown in Fig. 7-2.

Since we have only used one memory chip in this design, there is no reason to use absolute address decoding. When the microprocessor is reset it will generate memory address zero and place it on the address

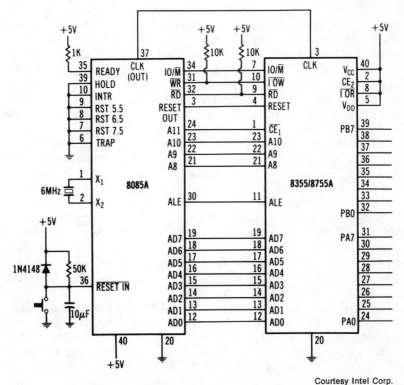

Courtesy Intel Corp.

Fig. 7-2. A two-chip microcomputer using the 8085A and 8355.

bus. This address must cause the 8355 to be selected. Address lines AD0 through AD7 and A8 through A10 are wired directly to the chip, so A11 is wired to CE_1 (active low). The other chip select input (CE_2) is wired directly to +5 V. The chip requires the IOW signal, so the WR output of the 8085A is used. This means that whenever a write operation takes place the 8085A will be writing information into the A or B ports or their DDRs.

What will the memory addresses of the ROM be? Since it contains 2K×8 words, the ROM will contain memory locations 00000000 00000000 through 00000111 11111111. What are the addresses of the I/O devices? The A and B ports have addresses 00000000 and 00000001 while the DDRs have addresses 00000010 and 00000011.

Note that in our design, pin 5 of the 8355 has been wired to +5 V. This means that we could pull the 8355 out of the microcomputer, replace it with an 8755A, and the microcomputer would still operate properly. Even though the 8355 does not use this pin we wired it to +5 V so that an 8755A could be used in its place.

One of the reasons that Intel designed the 8355 with two chip selects, one active high and one active low, was so that a number of ROMs could be used in a system without *any* decoding logic. If these devices had active low chip selects only, we would have to invert the unused address lines (A12 through A15) before they could be used to select the chips. Remember, A11 is wired to the active-low chip-select input of the first ROM. These inverters would simply add to the size and cost of a simple microcomputer. As a simple demonstration of the versatility of these two chip select inputs we can easily design a microcomputer that uses two of the 8355s (Fig. 7-3).

In this design we have assumed that all of the "usual" signals have already been wired between the two chips and the 8085A [AD0–AD7, ALE, A8–A10, RESET, CLK, IO/$\overline{M}$, $\overline{RD}$, and $\overline{WR}$ (to $\overline{IOW}$)]. The real point of interest is how the two chips are selected. As you can see, the simplest way is to wire A11 to the $\overline{CE}_1$ input of one ROM and to the CE_2 input of the other ROM. When A11 is a logic zero, which ROM is selected? Since A11 is wired to the $\overline{CE}_1$ input of ROM 1, it is selected. This means that ROM 1 contains memory location zero. What memory locations are contained in ROM 2? For this ROM to be selected, A11 must be a logic one, so ROM 2 contains memory locations 00001000 00000000 through 00001111 11111111.

What will the addresses of the I/O devices be for these two ROMs? Remember, during the execution of an I/O instruction the device address is placed on both A0–A7 and A8–15. For ROM 1 to be selected, A11 must be a logic zero in the device address. Therefore ROM 1 contains I/O devices XXXX0X00 through XXXX0X11, where X can be a logic one or logic zero. What I/O device will be selected, if any, when the I/O address 00000100 is generated? This will cause port A in ROM 1 to be

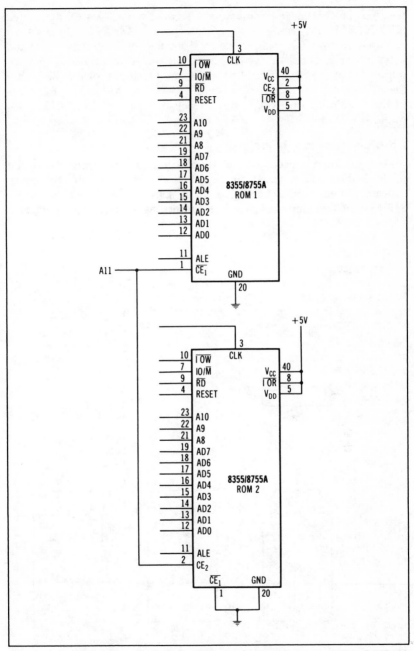

Fig. 7-3. Nonabsolutely decoding the chip select signals for two 8355 ROM-I/O integrated circuits.

selected. The I/O device addresses for ROM 2 are XXXX1X00 through XXXX1X11.

Based on Fig. 7-3, what is the total number of 8355s that we could have in a microcomputer system using this nonabsolute decoding technique? Six of the 8355s could be used. The $\overline{CE}_1$ input of one 8355 and the CE_2 input of another 8355 would be wired to A11. The CE_2 inputs of the remaining four ROMs would each be wired to A12, A13, A14, or A15.

Absolute Address Decoding

As you would expect, we can use absolute address decoding so that up to 64K of ROM, based on the 8355, can be used with the microprocessor. One typical starting point is shown in Fig. 7-4. Since the SN74LS154 decoder has active low outputs, as do most other decoders,

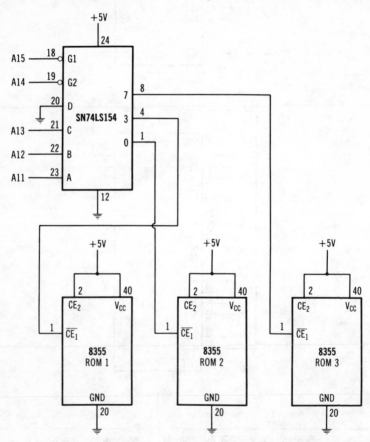

Fig. 7-4. Using absolute decoding with the 8355 ROM-I/O chip.

the CE_2 inputs of the ROMs are wired to +5 V and the $\overline{CE_1}$ inputs are wired to the outputs of the decoders. To select any one of the three ROMs shown in Fig. 7-4, A14 and A15 must be logic zero. To select ROM 1 output 3 of the decoder must be a logic zero, so ROM 1 is selected when the addresses 00011000 00000000 through 00011111 11111111 are generated by the microprocessor. For ROM 2 the addresses 00000000 00000000 through 00000111 11111111 must be generated, and for ROM 3, addresses 00111000 00000000 through 00111111 11111111. Based on these addresses, which ROM will be selected when the 8085A is reset? ROM 2 will be selected.

What are the addresses for the I/O devices contained within these three ROMs? Since the same decoder is used to enable the chips when memory or I/O devices are addressed, the I/O devices will have addresses that are very similar to the memory addresses. These I/O device addresses are summarized in Table 7-3.

Table 7-3. The I/O Device Addresses for the Three 8355/8755A ROMs Shown in Fig. 7-4

ROM	Port A	Port B	Port A DDR	Port B DDR
ROM 1	00011X00	00011X01	00011X10	00011X11
ROM 2	00000X00	00000X01	00000X10	00000X11
ROM 3	00111X00	00111X01	00111X10	00111X11

8085A-FAMILY-COMPATIBLE R/W MEMORIES

There are two 8085A-family-compatible R/W memories. The 8185/8185-2, which contains 1024 8-bit words, can be used with either the 8085A (8185) or the higher-speed 8085A-2 (8185-2). The 8155/8156 contains 256 8-bit words, two 8-bit I/O ports, one 6-bit I/O port, and a 14-bit timer. The 8155 and 8156 are basically the same chip, except one has an active low chip select (8155) and the other has an active high chip select (8156). Intel also manufacturers the 8155-2 and the 8156-2 for use with the 10-MHz 8085A-2. Of these two different types of R/W memories the 8185 is the simpler to use and understand.

THE 8185 1K×8 R/W MEMORY CHIP

The block diagram and pin configuration for the 8185 are shown in Fig. 7-5. As you can see, this integrated circuit contains an address latch so that the multiplexed address/data bus can be wired directly to this chip. This integrated circuit needs only +5 V, like all of the other R/W memory integrated circuits that we discussed in Chapter 5. Since this is a 1K R/W memory chip, AD0–AD7, A8, A9 along with $\overline{RD}$, $\overline{WR}$, IO/$\overline{M}$, and ALE have to wired to the chip. The 8185 also has two chip enable inputs and one chip select input. These two different types of inputs have completely different functions.

PIN CONFIGURATION

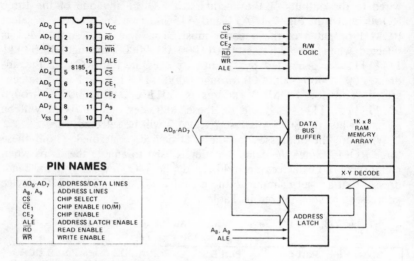

PIN NAMES

$AD_0 \cdot AD_7$	ADDRESS/DATA LINES
A_8, A_9	ADDRESS LINES
CS	CHIP SELECT
$\overline{CE_1}$	CHIP ENABLE (IO/$\overline{M}$)
CE_2	CHIP ENABLE
ALE	ADDRESS LATCH ENABLE
$\overline{RD}$	READ ENABLE
$\overline{WR}$	WRITE ENABLE

Fig. 7-5. The pin configuration and block diagram for the Intel 8185 1K × 8 static R/W memory.

The chip enable inputs, $\overline{CE_1}$ and CE_2, are latched into the 8185 by ALE and are used to reduce the power consumption of the integrated circuit. This may be important in battery-based systems, because power consumption can be reduced from 100 mA to 25 mA. If $\overline{CE_1}$ is a logic one or CE_2 is a logic zero when ALE is a logic one, power consumption will be reduced to 25 mA. During this time, however, the memory cannot be accessed. For it to be accessed the chip must be "powered up" and selected.

To select the chip the $\overline{CS}$ input must go to a logic zero. The CS signal is not latched into the 8185 by ALE, so the address decoder has hundreds of nanoseconds to decode the memory address and select the appropriate memory chip.

As an example, the ALE signal will be a logic one for a minimum of 140 ns (6.25-MHz 8085A). The *chip enable* ($\overline{CE_1}$ and CE_2) must be present 30 ns before the falling edge of ALE in order to be latched into the 8185 and power-down the chip. This means that the decoder logic must have a total propagation delay of 110 ns or less to power-down the 8185. For the 8085A-2 this decoder propagation delay must be 50 ns or less. Because of these very short times most designers do not try to power-down the 8185s. In one of Intel's designs IO/M is wired to the $\overline{CE_1}$ input so that power is saved during I/O and interrupt operations. Not much power will be saved if this design is used. The simplest solution is to wire CE_2 to +5 V and $\overline{CE_1}$ to ground and to wire $\overline{CS}$ to the address decoder logic. Since both $\overline{\text{RD}}$ and $\overline{\text{WR}}$ are wired to the 8185 this address decoder logic should only be enabled when $\text{IO}/\overline{\text{M}}$ is a logic zero.

Address bits A10 through A15 could be absolutely decoded, so that one of 64 possible 8185s is selected. However, this number of 8185s would probably not be used. Instead we would probably have a few thousand words of ROM so that a program could be loaded into R/W memory from disk, cassette, paper tape, or from a crt.

8185 Electrical Characteristics

The 8185 has electrical characteristics that are very similar to those of the 8355 and 8755A (see Table 7-4). The only difference is the power

Table 7-4. The DC Electrical Characteristics of the 8185 1K × 8 R/W Memory

Symbol	Parameter	Min.	Max.	Units	Test Conditions
V_{IL}	Input Low Voltage	-0.5	0.8	V	
V_{IH}	Input High Voltage	2.0	V_{CC}+0.5	V	
V_{OL}	Output Low Voltage		0.45	V	I_{OL} = 2mA
V_{OH}	Output High Voltage	2.4			I_{OH} = 400μA
I_{IL}	Input Leakage		±10	μA	V_{IN} = V_{CC} to 0V
I_{LO}	Output Leakage Current		±10	μA	0.45V ≤ V_{OUT} ≤ V_{CC}
I_{CC}	V_{CC} Supply Current				
	Powered Up		100	mA	
	Powered Down		25	mA	

Courtesy Intel Corp.

dissipation of the device. The inputs to this memory integrated circuit source -10 μA at 0.8 V maximum, and sink 10 μA at 2.0 V minimum. The 8085A can source -400 μA at 2.4 V minimum and sink 2 mA at 0.45 V maximum, so it has no trouble driving this integrated circuit. The 8185 outputs will source -400 μA at 2.4 V minimum and sink 2 mA at 0.45 V maximum. The inputs of the 8085A require 10 μA at 2.0 V minimum and -10 μA at 0.8 V maximum, so the 8185 has no trouble driving the inputs of the 8085A.

Of course, to determine whether or not the microcomputer will function as designed, we would have to determine the electrical requirements of *all* of the integrated circuits in the system and determine the electrical capabilities of the components in the system. As long as the system requirements are less than the system capabilities, the system will work. Therefore, as we saw in previous chapters, we have to determine the leakage currents of all of the unselected memories, the current required to drive the inputs of the memory address decoders, output ports, and so on.

Interfacing the 8185

Like all of the other memory integrated circuits that we have discussed, this device can be wired to the microcomputer using both nonabsolute (Fig. 7-6) and absolute (Fig. 7-7) decoding techniques. In

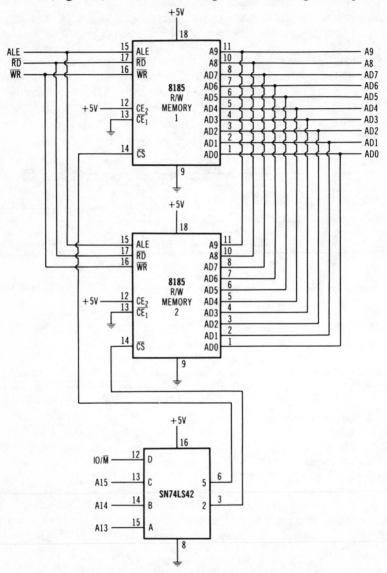

Fig. 7-6. A nonabsolute decoding design for use with the 8185 1K × 8 R/W memory.

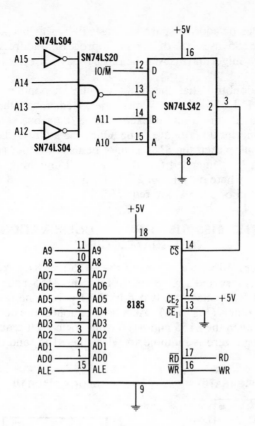

Fig. 7-7. Absolutely decoding a memory address for the 8185 1K × 8 R/W memory.

Fig. 7-6 the 8185 R/W memory integrated circuits have been wired to the appropriate address bus, address/data bus, and control signals. Since these chips internally demultiplex the address/data bus, no external latch is required.

To keep the design simple the power-down feature of the 8185 has not been used, so $\overline{CE}_1$ is wired to ground and CE_2 is wired to +5 V. Even though nonabsolute address decoding has been used, the $IO/\overline{M}$ signal must be used to "qualify" the address on the buses as a memory address. Therefore $IO/\overline{M}$ is wired to the D input of the SN74LS42 decoder. Only when this signal is a logic zero can any of the outputs between 0 and 7 go to a logic zero. The A, B, and C inputs are wired to A13, A14, and A15 respectively. As you would expect, R/W memory 1 is selected when the microprocessor generates the addresses between 101XXX00 00000000 and 101XXX11 11111111, where X is a logic one or a logic zero. Read/write memory 2 is selected when the addresses 010XXX00 00000000 through 010XXX11 11111111 are generated. How much of the microprocessor address space is "wasted" by this decoding method? Each 1K×8 8185 uses 8K of the microprocessor address space. This means that we might have seven of the 8185s in a system, along with a 1K ROM.

It is very doubtful that the 8185 will be as popular as the 2102 (1K×1) or 2114 (1K×4) R/W memories. Remember, the 8185 memory must be used with a multiplexed address/data bus, while the 2102 and 2114 memories do not have to be. Once the address/data bus of the 8085A is demultiplexed the 8185 cannot be used without additional circuitry. The 8185 is intended for use in a small, minimum-configuration 8085A system, where only 1K or 2K of R/W memory and a few ROMs, such as the 8355 or 8755A, are required.

THE 8155/8156 R/W-I/O COMBINATION INTEGRATED CIRCUIT

The 8155 and 8156 are similar to the 8355 and 8755A because they all contain memory and I/O ports. In fact, the 8155 and 8156 contain 256 words of R/W memory, two 8-bit I/O ports, one 6-bit I/O port, and a 14-bit timer (Fig. 7-8). As was mentioned previously the only difference between the 8155 and 8156 is the logic level required to select the chip. A logic zero is required to select the 8155, and a logic one is

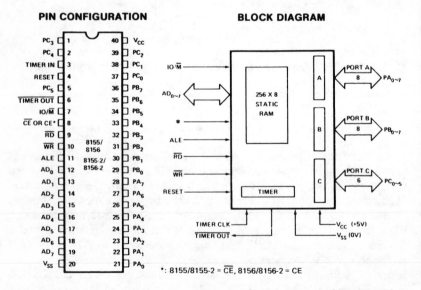

Courtesy Intel Corp.

Fig. 7-8. The pin configuration and block diagram for the 8155/8156 R/W memory-I/O integrated circuit.

required to select the 8156. Other than the logic level required for the chip select input, these devices are identical. Therefore in our discussion we will only use the term 8155, although the 8156 could be just as easily used. If there are cases when only one or the other can be used, we will specify which one. The high-speed versions of these devices (8155-2, 8156-2) are also available for use with the 10-MHz 8085A-2. By using these devices no wait states are required. Of all of the family-compatible chips these two devices are probably the most complex to use and understand. The pin configuration and block diagrams for these integrated circuits are shown in Fig. 7-8.

Both of these devices, like all of the other family-compatible integrated circuits, demultiplex the address/data bus. Therefore AD0–AD7 and ALE are wired directly to the chip. Both the memory and I/O devices in the chip are read/write, so IO/$\overline{M}$, $\overline{RD}$, and $\overline{WR}$ are also wired to each chip. Internal logic generates the appropriate memory and I/O control signals from these signals.

The 14-bit timer has a single input and a single output. The timer input (TIMER IN) can be wired to the CLK (OUT) signal of the 8085A so that the microcomputer can perform a sequence of timed events that are accurate to within ±320 ns (200 ns if the 8155-2 or 8156-2 is used with the 8085A-2 at 10 MHz). The TIMER IN input can also be driven by other suitable TTL-compatible clocks, as we shall see. The timer output ($\overline{\text{TIMER OUT}}$) can be wired to one of the interrupt inputs of the 8085A (other than INTR) that we discussed in the previous chapter. It can also be wired to one of the bits in an input port of the 8155. Of course, if this is done, the particular port in the 8155 would have to be programmed as an input port.

8155/8156 I/O

The 8155 and 8156 contain two 8-bit I/O ports, one 6-bit I/O port, and a 14-bit timer. The three I/O ports can be programmed as either input or output ports, so they are very similar to the I/O ports contained in the 8255 PPI chip, but the *entire port* must be programmed as either an input or as an output port. Bits of the I/O ports cannot be configured individually, as was the case with the 8355 and 8755A. In addition, the 6-bit port can be configured as a control port that generates handshaking signals between the microprocessor and a peripheral.

Because of all its I/O capabilities the 8155 contains six I/O devices, three of which are general-purpose I/O ports. The addresses of these devices are summarized in Table 7-5. Like the previous I/O chips, such as the 8255 PPI, 8251 USART, and 8355/8755A ROM-I/O chip, there is a command/status register (address XXXXX000) that is used to program the operation of the other devices. As you would expect, each of the three general-purpose ports (A, B, and C, where C is the 6-bit port) has its own address. The 14-bit timer can be loaded with any 14-bit

Table 7-5. The I/O Device Addresses for the Six I/O Devices Contained Within the 8155/8156 R/W Memory-I/O Integrated Circuit

AD7	AD6	AD5	AD4	AD3	AD2	AD1	AD0	Device
X	X	X	X	X	0	0	0	Command/Status Register
X	X	X	X	X	0	0	1	Port A
X	X	X	X	X	0	1	0	Port B
X	X	X	X	X	0	1	1	Port C
X	X	X	X	X	1	0	0	8 LSBs of Timer
X	X	X	X	X	1	0	1	6 MSBs of Timer

value, so the 8 least significant bits (LSBs) have been assigned one device address (XXXXX100) and the 6 most significant bits (MSBs) another device address (XXXXX101).

The 8 bits in the command/status register control the operation of the three I/O ports and the timer, as can be seen in Fig. 7-9. From Fig. 7-9, you can see that ports A and B can be programmed as either input or output ports; individual bits cannot be programmed as either input or output. Port C can be programmed with one of four possible I/O functions. These will be discussed in detail in another section of this chapter. Depending on how port C is programmed, ports A and B can use port C as a handshaking/interrupt port. The 2 most significant bits in the command/status register are used to do the following: (1) stop the counter regardless of what it is doing, (2) stop the counter once it has counted down to zero, and (3) load and restart the counter once it has counted down to zero.

The A, B, and C I/O Ports

The A and B ports are used in a straightforward manner. They can be used as either input or output ports, depending on the state of bits D0 and D1 in the command/status register. On the other hand, port C can be programmed to operate in one of four possible configurations, as shown in Table 7-6. If port C is configured as ALT 1 or ALT 2 in the command/status register, it will simply be a 6-bit input or output port. If the ALT 3 configuration is used, 3 bits of port C are used as an output port and 3 bits are used for handshaking with port A. If the ALT 4 configuration is used, port C is used for handshaking with both port A and port B. This handshaking logic can be used regardless of whether the A and B ports are input or output ports.

PORT C HANDSHAKING

Output Port Handshaking

As an example, suppose that port A is to be used as an output port with handshaking and port B is to be used as an input port with handshaking. For port A there are three control signals in port C: A INTR,

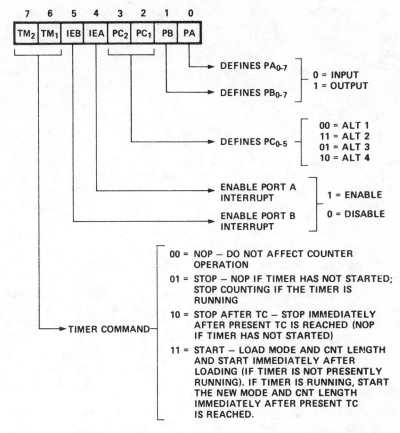

Fig. 7-9. Defining the command/status register bits.

A BF, and A STB. Since port A is to be used as an output port, these signals will be used to transfer or aid in the transfer of data from the

Table 7-6. The Four Possible Configurations for Port C in the 8155/8156 R/W Memory-I/O Chip

Pin	ALT 1	ALT 2	ALT 3	ALT 4
PC0	Input Port	Output Port	A INTR (Port A Interrupt)	A INTR (Port A Interrupt)
PC1	Input Port	Output Port	A BF (Port A Buffer Full)	A BF (Port A Buffer Full)
PC2	Input Port	Output Port	A STB (Port A Strobe)	A STB (Port A Strobe)
PC3	Input Port	Output Port	Output Port	B INTR (Port B Interrupt)
PC4	Input Port	Output Port	Output Port	B BF (Port B Buffer Full)
PC5	Input Port	Output Port	Output Port	B STB (Port B Strobe)

output port to the peripheral. To output data to the peripheral the 8085A would first output a value to port A. This will cause the A BF (buffer full) signal to go to a logic one, indicating to the peripheral that a data value has been output and that it is available for the peripheral. The peripheral reads this value from port A and acknowledges receipt of the data by pulsing the $\overline{\text{A STB}}$ (port A strobe) pin at port C with a logic zero. If the port A enable interrupt bit in the command/status register is set to a logic zero, this pulse will cause the A INTR output at port C to go to a logic one. This signal may be wired to one of the 8085 interrupt inputs so that another data value could be output to the peripheral when the interrupt is recognized. The port A interrupt request signal may not be wired to an interrupt in many cases, since the state of the "interrupt request" line may be monitored by reading the command/status register information. The interrupt request flag is cleared within the 8155 when the next output transfer to port A takes place.

The timing relationships of these operations are shown in Fig. 7-10. As you can see, the 8085A first outputs the data to port A. This not only causes port A to latch the data but it also clears the interrupt (INTR) output to a logic zero.

There is only one possible problem with this method of transferring data between the 8085A and the peripheral device. Does the microprocessor have to output the first data value and then wait for the peripheral to interrupt, or is an interrupt generated first, so that the first data value is output to the peripheral? When port C is programmed in either the ALT 3 or ALT 4 configuration, the BF, INTR, and $\overline{\text{STB}}$ signals are set to the states shown in Table 7-7. From Table 7-7 we can see that

Table 7-7. The Initial States of the BF, INTR, and $\overline{\text{STB}}$ Pins When Port C of the 8155/8156 Is Programmed for ALT3 and ALT4 Operation

CONTROL	INPUT MODE	OUTPUT MODE
BF	Low	Low
INTR	Low	High
$\overline{\text{STB}}$	Input Control	Input Control

Courtesy Intel Corp.

the INTR signal is set to a logic one, so the microprocessor will be interrupted, which will cause the first data value to be output to the peripheral device.

Of course, before any data can be transferred using this technique, a number of initialization or enabling steps must be performed. If the INTR output is wired to one of the RST inputs of the 8085A, an interrupt mask would have to be loaded into the A register and transferred to the interrupt mask register by means of an SIM instruction. The 8155 command/status register would also have to be loaded with an 8-bit value. Within this value the mode of operation of the ports would have to be programmed and the A and/or B interrupts enabled. Finally, the 8085A would have to execute an EI instruction so that the interrupt is enabled. The microprocessor would then be interrupted and the first data value would be output to the peripheral when the 8085A executes the appropriate interrupt service subroutine. Of course, due to the flexibility designed into the 8155, the B port can also be used as a handshaking output port.

Input Port Handshaking

In our original example, port A is an output port and port B is an input port. If handshaking is used with an input port, the peripheral device first writes data into port B with the B $\overline{\text{STB}}$ signal. In response to this pulse the $\overline{\text{B BF}}$ (port B buffer full) signal goes to a logic one. This signal is used to indicate to the peripheral that the 8155 input buffer is now filled. This signal is essentially a "busy" flag from the 8155 to the peripheral input device. The INTR signal also goes to a logic one, so that the 8085A is interrupted. In the interrupt service subroutine for this peripheral device the 8085A inputs the data value from the 8155. The $\overline{\text{RD}}$ signal that the 8085A generates during this operation causes the INTR signal and the $\overline{\text{B BF}}$ signal to go back to logic zeroes. The peripheral device senses that $\overline{\text{B BF}}$ is a logic zero (not busy or buffer empty), so it writes another data value into the 8155 (Fig. 7-11).

From Table 7-7 we can see the states of $\overline{\text{BF}}$, INTR, and $\overline{\text{STB}}$ once port C is programmed in the ALT 3 or ALT 4 configurations. As you would expect, $\overline{\text{STB}}$ and INTR are logic zeroes, so the peripheral has to provide data to the 8155 before the 8085A is interrupted and inputs the data value.

Handshaking Without Interrupts

When Intel designed the 8155 and 8156 it decided that the handshaking features of port C should still be available even if interrupts are not used. We saw in a previous section of this chapter that the command/status register must be programmed by writing a value out to device address XXXX000. *If a read operation is performed using this same device address, the command/status word written out to the 8155 will not be read.* Instead, the *status* of the A and B ports will be read, along with the state of the timer interrupt (Fig. 7-12). In general, the software would simply have to monitor the states of the buffer full/buffer empty bits. The use of port C as a handshaking port is summarized in Fig. 7-13.

Timer Characteristics and Use

We have already seen that two I/O ports (XXXXX100 and XXXXX101) are used by the timer (Table 7-5). The organization of these two ports is shown in Fig. 7-14. As you can see, 14 bits of these

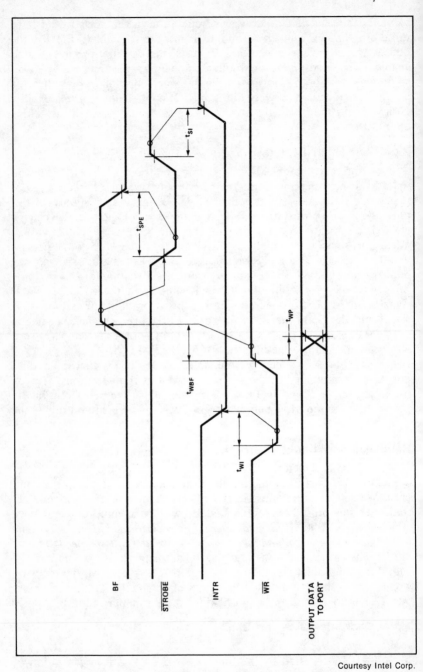

Courtesy Intel Corp.

Fig. 7-10. Strobed output timing for the 8155/8156 R/W memory-I/O chip.

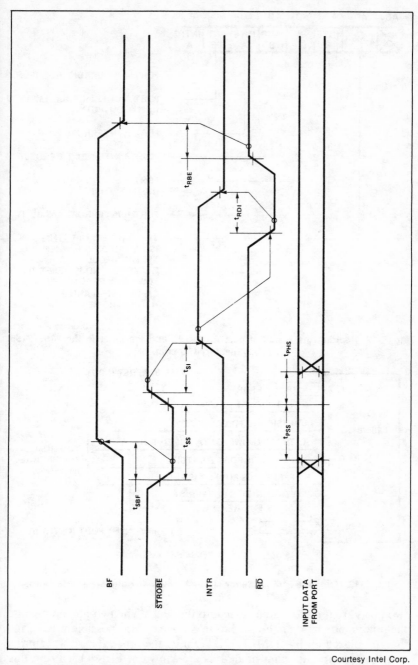

Courtesy Intel Corp.

Fig. 7-11. Strobed input timing for the 8155/8156 R/W memory-I/O chip.

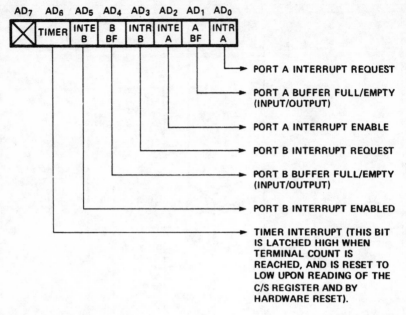

Courtesy Intel Corp.

Fig. 7-12. Reading the status of port A, port B, and the timer in the 8155/8156 R/W memory-I/O chip.

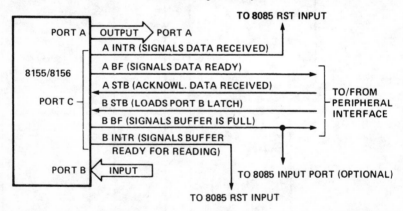

Courtesy Intel Corp.

Fig. 7-13. Using the 8155/8156 for strobed input and output (handshaking).

two ports are used to load a value into the timer. The two remaining bits, the timer mode bits, can be used to select one of four possible waveforms that are placed on the $\overline{\text{TIMER OUT}}$ pin by the timer. These waveforms and the appropriate timer mode bits are shown in Fig. 7-15. From this figure we see that the timer will generate either a square wave or a single

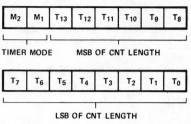

TIMER MODE   MSB OF CNT LENGTH

LSB OF CNT LENGTH

Courtesy Intel Corp.

Fig. 7-14. The organization of the two timer ports (XXXXX100 and XXXXX101) in the 8155/8156.

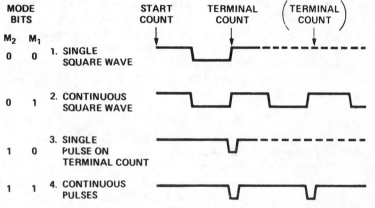

Courtesy Intel Corp.

Fig. 7-15. The four possible modes of operation for the timer in the 8155/8156 and the waveforms present in the TIMER OUT output.

pulse. Also, it is possible for the timer to generate these signals once or continuously.

If a square wave output is generated, the $\overline{\text{TIMER OUT}}$ output will be a logic one for half of the count and a logic zero for the remaining half of the count. As an example, if the timer is loaded with decimal 20, the output will be a logic one for 10 counts and a logic zero for the remaining 10 counts. *If an odd count is loaded into the timer, the output will be in the logic one state for one more count than in the logic zero state.* Fig. 7-16 shows the square wave output that is generated if a count of 9 is used.

Regardless of whether a square wave or pulse is generated, the timer should never be loaded with a count less than 2. It would be difficult to determine the type of waveform generated if a one or zero is loaded into the timer.

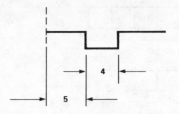

Fig. 7-16. The square wave output of the timer when an odd count is used.

Note: 5 and 4 refer to the number of clock cycles in that time period.

Courtesy Intel Corp.

You will recall that two bits in the command/status register are also used to control the timer (Fig. 7-9). To start the timer initially, bits D7 and D6 of the command/status register must be logic ones. However, is the timer first loaded, followed by the command/status register, or is the command/status register loaded first, followed by the timer? *The command/status register is first loaded with 11XXXXXX and then the LSBs of the timer are loaded, followed by the MSBs.* Once the 6 MSBs and the timer mode bits are loaded into the 8155, the timer will begin to count down.

As mentioned previously, the TIMER IN input of the 8155 can be wired to the CLK (OUT) output of the 8085A. It can also be wired to a number of other clock sources. In fact, it can be wired to any clock as long as its frequency is not greater than 3.125 MHz (8155 or 8156) or 5 MHz (8155-2 or 8156-2). For instance, if the TIMER IN input is wired to a line-frequency–derived 60-Hz TTL signal, the timer can be used to generate delays of 1 minute, 30 seconds, or 173 seconds, to name a few.

In some applications you might like to count events, possibly the number of cans that pass a certain point on a conveyor belt. The timer in the 8155 can be used to do this, but it takes a short assembly language program to convert the value in the timer to a count. The TIMER IN input of the 8155 would be wired to some type of can sensor near the conveyor belt and the $\overline{\text{TIMER OUT}}$ output would not be wired to anything. At some point your software could read the contents of the timer, using I/O device addresses XXXXX100 and XXXXX101. Then, by using a short program that Intel has provided (Fig. 7-17),[2] the contents of the timer can be converted to a count.

Using the $\overline{\text{TIMER OUT}}$ Output of the 8155

Although the timer can generate two types of waveforms it is not ordinarily used to do this. Instead, the output of the timer is often wired to one of the interrupt inputs of the 8085A. This means that the timer could be programmed in one of the "continuous" modes of operation so that

Following is an actual sequence of program steps that adjusts the 8155/56 count register contents to obtain the count, extracted from Intel® Application Note AP38. "Application Techniques for the Intel 8085A Bus." First store the value of the full original count in register HL of the 8085A. Then stop the count to avoid getting an incorrect count value. Then sample the timer-counter, storing the lower-order byte of the current count register in register C and the higher-order count byte in register B. Then, call the following 8080A/8085A subroutine:

ADJUST, 78	MOV A,B	;Load accumulator with upper half ; of count.
E63F	ANI 3F	;Reset upper 2 bits and clear carry.
1F	RAR	;Rotate right through carry.
47	MOV B,A	;Store shifted value back in B.
79	MOV A,C	;Load accumulator with lower half.
1F	RAR	;Rotate right through carry.
4F	MOV C,A	;Store lower byte in C.
DØ	RNC	;If in 2nd half of count, return. ;If in 1st half, go on.
3F	CMC	;Clear carry.
7C	MOV A,H	;Divide full count by 2. (If HL ;is odd, disregard remainder.)
1F	RAR	
67	MOV H,A	
7D	MOV A,L	
1F	RAR	
6F	MOV L,A	
09	DAD B	;Double-precision add HL and BC.
44	MOV B,H	;Store results back in BC.
4D	MOV C,L	
C9	RET	;Return.

After executing the subroutine, BC will contain the remaining count in the current count cycle.

Courtesy Intel Corp.

Fig. 7-17. The assembly language subroutine that converts the content of the timer in the 8155/8156 to a count.

the microprocessor is interrupted every 1 or 5 ms. When the interrupt occurs the microprocessor could check some peripheral device, update a multiplexed LED display, or the like.

If you do not have any interrupt inputs left or if you do not want to use interrupts, the state of the timer (busy/done) can be monitored with software. By re-examining Fig. 7-12 you will see that we can read the state of the timer into bit D6 of the A register by reading the contents of the status register contained within the 8155. If this bit is a logic zero, the timer is still counting down. If it is a logic one, the timer has counted down to zero.

Electrical Characteristics of the 8155/8156

The 8155 and 8156 have the same electrical characteristics (Table 7-8) as all of the other chips that were designed for the 8085A (8185,

Table 7-8. The DC Electrical Characteristics of the 8155 (8155-2) and 8156 (8156-2) R/W-I/O Chips

SYMBOL	PARAMETER	MIN.	MAX.	UNITS	TEST CONDITIONS
V_{IL}	Input Low Voltage	-0.5	0.8	V	
V_{IH}	Input High Voltage	2.0	V_{CC}+0.5	V	
V_{OL}	Output Low Voltage		0.45	V	I_{OL} = 2mA
V_{OH}	Output High Voltage	2.4		V	I_{OH} = -400μA
I_{IL}	Input Leakage		±10	μA	V_{IN} = V_{CC} to 0V
I_{LO}	Output Leakage Current		±10	μA	0.45V $\leqslant$ V_{OUT} $\leqslant$ V_{CC}
I_{CC}	V_{CC} Supply Current		180	mA	
I_{IL} (CE)	Chip Enable Leakage 8155 8156		+100 -100	μA μA	V_{IN} = V_{CC} to 0V

Courtesy Intel Corp.

8355, and 8755A). This means that the input and output voltages and current levels are the same. The only differences are the power consumption of the devices (180 mA for the 8155 and 8156) and the leakage currents of the chip enable inputs. For the 8155, which has an active-low chip-enable input, the leakage current is specified at 100 μA. For the 8156, with an active-high chip enable, the leakage current is specified at -100 μA. These leakage currents could be significant, particularly in small, unbuffered microcomputer designs. These types of designs will be discussed in the next section.

Interfacing the 8155/8156

When we discussed the 8355/8755A ROM-I/O combination chip we say that there was only one chip select for both the ROM and I/O sections of the chip. The 8355 and 8755A contain a 2K×8 ROM, so AD0 through AD7, along with A8, A9, and A10 must be wired to the integrated circuit. Since these chips only contain four I/O devices the device addresses used by the chip will be placed on A0 and A1, and on A8 and A9, when an I/O instruction is executed. This means that A10 is used only by the ROM. It is not used to select an I/O port. As we saw, because of the feature, I/O addresses XXXXX100 through XXXXX111 will cause the same ports to be addressed as XXXXX000 through XXXXX011. Thus each ROM appears to contain eight I/O devices, even though it contains only four.

We have the same type of anomaly with the 8155 and 8156, but in this case there are "more" I/O ports than R/W memory. We know that the 256×8-word R/W memory can be addressed with only AD0 through AD7. The I/O devices have to use 3 bits of the address bus because there are six I/O devices. This means that XXXXX110 and XXXXX111 are unused device addresses (Table 7-5). Therefore only address bits A11, A12, A13, A14, and A15 can be decoded to select an 8155 or 8156. These address bits are the only ones that can be used to select the chip, because the 3-bit device address will be placed on A0, A1, A2 and A8, A9, and A10 when one of the devices in the chip is addressed. This means that A8, A9, and A10 cannot be used in our decoder.

With only A11 through A15 available for use with the decoder we have 2^5 or 32 possible chip selects. This means that only 32 8155s or 8K of R/W memory can be used in the system. Also, since each 8155 is not absolutely decoded, the 8155s will use 2K of the microprocessor address space. It is possible to absolutely decode the 256 words of R/W memory and the I/O device addresses, but this is *not* a simple task.

One of the problems that you will have to live with if 8355/8755As and/or 8155/8156s are used in a microcomputer system is that memory address space and I/O address space will be wasted. In small systems, however, this will not be a problem. If you need to design a small microcomputer system that may have to be expanded up to 64K of memory and many I/O devices, it would be better to start the design with 2114 R/W memories, 2708/2716 EPROMs, and 8255A I/O integrated circuits.

MEMORY-MAPPED I/O WITH COMBINATION CHIPS

One of the features of the combination (memory and I/O) chips that has not been mentioned is the fact that we can use memory-mapped I/O with them. In Fig. 7-18 an 8355 has been wired as a memory-mapped I/O device. As you can see from this figure A15 has been used as the IO/M signal. This means that if A15 is a logic zero, the memory section of the chip will be selected. If A15 is a logic one, one of the I/O devices within the 8355 will be selected.

Since A11 is wired to the $\overline{CE}_1$ input of the 8355, what are the addresses of the ROM and I/O devices? The ROM occupies the first 2K of the 8085A address space from 00000000 00000000 through 00000111 11111111. Note that both A11 and A15 are zeroes in these addresses. To select the I/O devices A15 must be a logic one and A11 must be a logic zero. Therefore the memory-mapped I/O devices have addresses

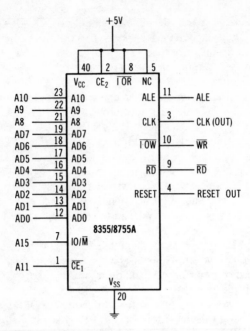

Fig. 7-18. Configuring the 8355/8755A ROM-I/O combination chip for memory-mapped I/O.

10000000 00000000 through 10000000 00000011. Note that even though nonabsolute address decoding was used in Fig. 7-18 absolute address decoding could have been used.

One subtle point of this design is the fact that the I/O devices can now be addressed as either memory-mapped or accumulator I/O devices. The only restriction that is placed on the addresses used for these devices is that A15 must be a logic one to select the I/O devices and that A11 must be a logic zero to select the chip. Suppose that we want to address accumulator I/O device 10000000. What information will the 8085A place on the address bus when the I/O instruction is executed that contains this device address? The address bus will contain 10000000 10000000. As you can see, A11 is a logic zero, so the chip is selected, and A15 is a logic one, so the I/O devices within the chip are selected. Since A0 and A1 are logic zeroes, the microprocessor is communicating with the port A. Therefore we can communicate with the I/O devices contained within the 8355 if either memory addresses 10000000 00000000 through 10000000 00000011 or accumulator I/O addresses 10000000 through 10000011 are used. Of course, since nonabsolute memory address decoding has been used, there are many other addresses that can cause the chip to be selected and the I/O devices to be communicated with. Note that the only reason that we can use either memory addresses (memory-mapped I/O) or device addresses (accumulator I/O) is the fact that the 8085A places the device addresses from accumulator I/O instructions on both the low (A0 through A7) and high (A8 through A15) address buses.

Multiple Memory-Mapped I/O Combination Chips

In Fig. 7-19 two 8155s and one 8355 have been interfaced to the microprocessor using memory-mapped I/O techniques. The figure does not show the "standard" connections (signals) between these three chips and the 8085A. We are really just interested in how the different chips are selected. As before, A15 has been used as the IO/M signal. In addition, A11, A12, A13, and A14 have been decoded with an SN74LS42.

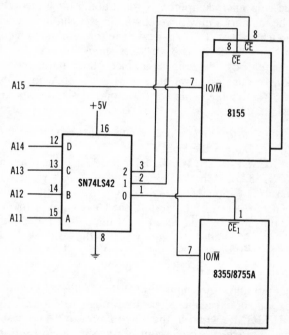

Fig. 7-19. Using memory-mapped I/O with memory-I/O combination chips.

Why have A11, A12, A13, and A14 been wired to the decoder, rather than A8, A9, A10, and A11? Since the 8355 contains a 2K×8 ROM, AD0 through AD7, and A8, A9, and A10 must be wired directly to the chip. Also, the 8155 contains six I/O devices, which means that their device addresses will be contained in A0, A1, and A2 along with A8, A9, and A10. Therefore A11, A12, A13, and A14 are wired to the decoder and A15 is used as the IO/$\overline{\text{M}}$ signal going to the chips.

PRELIMINARY DESIGN USING THE
8085A-FAMILY-COMPATIBLE CHIPS

As you can see, Intel has done a good job of designing "combination" chips for the 8085A. With these chips it is very easy for us to design three- and four-chip microcomputer systems. As we saw in Fig. 7-2 it is even possible for us to design a two-chip system, as long as we do not need any R/W memory. On the other hand, even though the 8355 and 8155 do waste some of the microprocessor address space, powerful microcomputer systems can be designed around them.

Preliminary Design No. 1

Using an 8085A, an 8355/8755A, and either an 8155 or 8156, design a three-chip microcomputer. No additional integrated circuits may be used. The memories may have any addresses that are consistent with good design techniques. The I/O devices in the combination chips should be accumulator I/O devices. All devices should be addressable.

One of the few possible designs that meets these requirements is shown in Fig. 7-20. In this design we have used the 8085A, the 8355/8755A, and an 8156 (active high chip select). Some design points to check for in your design include:

1. Has the *multiplexed* address/data bus been wired to both the 8355/8755A and the 8156?
2. Have RESET, ALE, IO/$\overline{M}$, $\overline{RD}$, and $\overline{WR}$ been wired to both the 8355/8755A and the 8156? Remember, $\overline{WR}$ is wired to the $\overline{IO/W}$ input of the 8355 since we can only write to output devices.
3. Has CLK (OUT) been wired to the CLK input of the 8355?
4. Have pins 5 (NC) and 2 (CE$_2$) of the 8355 been wired to +5 V?
5. Have A8, A9, and A10 been wired to the 8355?
6. Has $\overline{CE}_1$ of the 8355 been wired to A11 and CE of the 8156 been wired to A11, A12, A13, A14, or A15?

Although not all of the connections between the 8355 and the 8085A are shown, you should realize that D0 through AD7, ALE, IO/$\overline{M}$, $\overline{RD}$, $\overline{WR}$, and RESET are wired to the microprocessor. The reason that only "short wires" are shown coming out of the 8355 is to keep the drawing simple. This is a common drawing technique found in other books and publications.

What sections of the microprocessor address space are occupied by the 8355 and 8156? The active-low chip-enable input of the 8355 is wired to A11, so if A11 is a logic zero, it will be selected. This was done because the microprocessor will fetch the first instruction to be executed from memory location zero. This input, of course, could have been wired to any of the other more significant address lines, since they will all be logic zero when the microprocessor is reset. Since the 8156 has an active

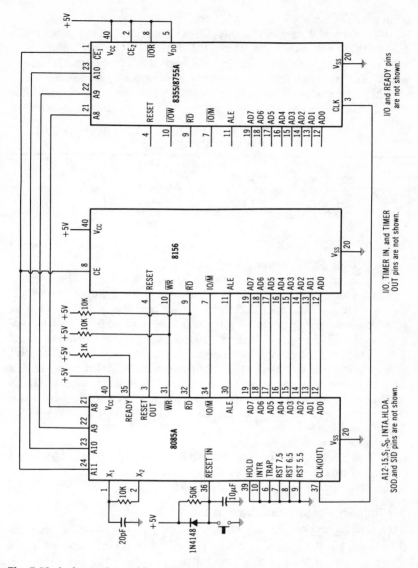

Fig. 7-20. A simple three-chip microcomputer system with 2K of ROM, 256 words of R/W memory, and 38 I/O lines.

high chip select, it will not be selected when the microprocessor is reset. In fact, since one chip select (8355) is active low and the other is active high (8156), it is impossible to select both chips in Fig. 7-20 at the same time. Therefore the 8355 occupies memory address space from 00000000 00000000 through 00000111 11111111. What are the memory addresses for the R/W memory in the 8156, based on the design in Fig. 7-20? The R/W memory will be selected when the microprocessor generates the addresses 00001000 00000000 through 00001000 11111111. Since non-absolute memory address decoding has been used, any memory address where A11 is a logic one will cause the R/W memory to be selected.

Which integrated circuit will be selected when the memory addresses shown in Table 7-9 are generated by the 8085A? The first two addresses

Table 7-9. Addresses That Select Either the 8355 ROM-I/O Chip or the 8156 R/W-I/O Chip

Address		8355	8156
00001011	01011100		R/W
00111110	00000000		R/W
00100000	11111111	ROM	
00000111	00001111	ROM	
00000000	10111101	ROM	
11111110	11000111		R/W

will select the R/W memory in the 8156, because A11 is a logic one. The next three addresses will cause the ROM in the 8355 to be selected. The last address will cause the R/W memory in the 8156 to be selected.

What are the addresses for the I/O devices? Since A11 is used to select one or the other chip, it must be a logic zero when one of the devices in the 8355 needs to be accessed, and a logic one when one of the devices in the 8156 must be accessed. This means that the four devices in the 8355 have addresses 00000000 through 00000011 and that the devices in the 8156 have addresses 00001000 through 00001101. Of course, since nonabsolute address decoding has been used, there are a number of other I/O addresses that can be used to communicate with the I/O devices in these two chips.

Because these two chips are "combination" chips we must be *very* careful in deciding which address bit or combination of address bits should be used to select one or the other chip. *In particular, A8, A9, and A10 must not be used to select the 8156.*

Preliminary Family Chip Design No. 2

Using two 8355s and two 8185s, design a nonabsolute memory address decoder. To keep this design simple, show the interconnection of the decoder and these four chips, but do not show the 8085A microprocessor. Accumulator I/O should be used.

One design that can be used is shown in Fig. 7-21. In this design we have used an SN74LS42 decoder, two SN74LS32 OR gates, two 8355s, and two 8185s. Some design points that you should check for in your design include:

1. Have at least A11 and A12 been used in the decoder portion of the design?

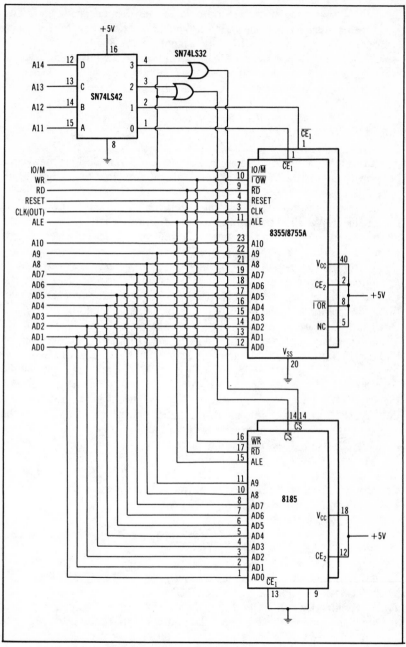

Fig. 7-21. A microcomputer design that has 2K of R/W memory (8185) and 4K of ROM (8355/8755A).

2. Is IO/$\overline{\text{M}}$ gated with two outputs of the decoder with OR gates, rather than having been used to enable the decoder?
3. Has $\overline{\text{WR}}$ been used as the $\overline{\text{IOW}}$ signal for the 8355s?
4. Have the control signals CLK (OUT) and RESET been wired to the 8355s?
5. Have the control signals $\overline{\text{RD}}$, $\overline{\text{WR}}$, and ALE been wired to all of the 8355s and 8185s?
6. Have A8, A9, and A10 been wired to the 8355s?
7. Have AD0–AD7 been wired to all four "family" chips?

As you might expect, there are hundreds of different designs that could be used to enable the "family" chips at the appropriate times. Some will probably be simpler, and some more complex, than others.

Perhaps the most important point to remember about this design is the use of the IO/$\overline{\text{M}}$ signal. We must be careful how it is used because the design includes chips that contain I/O devices (8355s) and chips that do not (8185). *The 8185s must be selected only when the proper address is on the address bus and either a memory-read or memory-write operation is taking place.* Since the address bus is also used to send device addresses to peripheral devices during the execution of I/O instructions, the contents of the address bus must be "qualified" by IO/M before the 8185s are selected.

Suppose that instead of wiring A14 to the D input of the decoder we had used IO/$\overline{\text{M}}$. Would the microprocessor be able to use all of the features of the 8355s and 8185s? By wiring IO/$\overline{\text{M}}$ to the D input of the decoder, outputs 0 to 7 of the decoder would only go to a logic zero if memory is being accessed. Therefore the I/O devices in the 8355s could not be used. As we already know, the 8355s must be selected when the proper address is on the address bus and either memory *or* an I/O device is being accessed. This means that the decoder must not be enabled by IO/$\overline{\text{M}}$. Since the 8185s only contain R/W memory, however, they must only be selected when memory is being addressed, so the outputs of the decoder are gated with IO/$\overline{\text{M}}$. The outputs of the OR gates are then wired to the $\overline{\text{CS}}$ inputs of the 8185s.

CONCLUSION

In this chapter we have discussed, and based designs on, the five powerful integrated circuits that Intel designed for the 8085A—the 8355 mask ROM-I/O chip, the 8755A EPROM-I/O chip, the 8155 and 8156 R/W memory-I/O chips, and the 8185 R/W memory chip. Because of the sophistication of these devices the address/data bus does not have to be demultiplexed. In fact, using three of these chips a three-chip microcomputer system can be designed that contains 2K of ROM, 256 or 1K words of R/W memory, and numerous I/O and interrupt signals.

One disadvantage of the 8355/8755A and the 8155/8156 chips is that they cause either I/O address space or memory address space to be "wasted." The 8355/8755A contains only four I/O devices, but when wired to the microcomputer it will appear to contain eight devices. On the other hand, the 8155/8156 contains six I/O devices, so the 256 words of R/W memory contained within it will appear as if they are a 2K memory; 2K of the microprocessor address space will be used.

As a result of these disadvantages these two types of chips will probably not be found in a "full-blown" 8085A microcomputer system that has 32K or more of R/W memory, 10K to 15K of ROM, and many I/O devices. However, if you need a small, low-cost microcomputer or controller, these chips are ideal. Since the 8185 1K×8 R/W memory chip contains no I/O devices, we could actually use many of them in an 8085A-based microcomputer.

REFERENCES

1. Intel Corp. *The MCS-85 User's Manual, September 1978*, Santa Clara, CA 95051.
2. *ibid.*, pages 5–23, 5–24.

PROBLEMS

7-1. A 450-ns 8755A must be used with a 10-MHz 8085A-2 (200-ns cycle time). Design the wait state circuitry required so that the 8755A can be properly accessed by the 8085A-2.

7-2. Interface five 8155/8156 R/W-I/O chips to an 8085A microprocessor using nonabsolute decoding. No other integrated circuits may be used in this design. Why were five and not six of these chips interfaced to the 8085A microprocessor?

7-3. Design the "power-down" circuitry for the 8185 1K×8 R/W memory so that when the 8085A is not accessing the 8185 the power consumed by the 8185 is reduced from 100 mA to 25 mA. The internal power-down capabilities of the chip should be used in this design.

7-4. In a particular 8085A-based microcomputer the address/data bus has been demultiplexed. Therefore the signals A0 through A15 and D0 through D7 are the only address and data signals available for use by memories and peripheral devices. The "usual" memory and I/O control signals are available (MEMR, MEMW, IN, OUT). Design the circuitry so that an 8185 R/W memory can be used with these signals. Absolute or nonabsolute address decoding may be used. Any 1K of the 8085A address space may be used.

7-5. Design a decoder for an 8155 that decodes A8 through A15 when the R/W memory in the chip is accessed, and decodes A11 through A15 when an I/O device in the chip is accessed. Accumulator I/O should be used.

7-6. Design the circuitry required so that the 8085A is interrupted every 1 ms and is vectored to memory location 00000000 00110100 so that the interrupt is serviced. Only 8085A-family-compatible chips may be used in this design. Do not be concerned with any assembly language programming that may be required by this design.

7-7 Design an absolute memory address decoder for an 8355/8755A ROM. The starting address of the ROM should be 11000000 00000000. Design the decoder so that the I/O device in the chip cannot be accessed and do not use any of the microcomputer accumulator I/O address space or memory address space.

7-8. Interface an 8155/8156 to the microcomputer so that only the I/O devices in the chip can be accessed. The first I/O device should have address 01010000. The R/W memory should not be accessible to the user and should not use any of the microprocessor address space.

7-9. Add an 8185 to an 8085A-based microcomputer so that only 256 words of R/W memory within the chip can be accessed. Use either absolute or non-absolute address decoding.

7-10. Wire six 8355/8755As to an 8085A, using nonabsolute address decoding. No additional integrated circuits may be used in this design.

7-11. In Fig. 7-6 the IO/$\overline{M}$ signal is wired to the D input of the SN74LS42 decoder. Change this design, using no additional integrated circuits, so that IO/$\overline{M}$ is no longer wired to the decoder. However, the R/W memory chips must still only be selected when the 8085A is accessing memory.

7-12. Determine the amount of power consumed by the microcomputer shown in Fig. 7-20. Also determine the total input current requirements and current capabilities of the integrated circuits. Are the current capabilities of the chips used in this design sufficient so that the computer will work?

7-13. Add an 8755A EPROM to the design solution for Problem 7-2. Nonabsolute decoding must still be used, and no additional integrated circuits may be used. What is the first memory address used by the EPROM?

7-14. Design a decoder for either an 8355 ROM or an 8755A EPROM so that A11 through A15 are decoded when the ROM in the chip is accessed, and A10 through A15 are decoded when an I/O device in the chip is accessed. The chip is selected only when one of the four I/O devices or when one of the 2048 memory locations within the chip is addressed. Accumulator I/O should be used in this design.

7-15. Using two SN74LS04 inverters, how many 8355s can be selected if nonabsolute addressing is used?

CHAPTER 8

A Simple 8085A Microcomputer Design

In this chapter we will discuss a number of topics and how they relate to a specific microcomputer design. In previous chapters the discussions were limited to the relationships between three or four components. By designing the entire microcomputer system in this chapter a number of these topics can be discussed and a number of conclusions can be reached. However, before these topics can be discussed we must know exactly what the capabilities and limitations of the microcomputer are.

DEFINING THE MICROCOMPUTER SYSTEM

There are thousands of microcomputers today that contain 32K or more of R/W memory, dual floppy disks, EPROM programmers, high-speed paper-tape readers and punches, and a number of crt's or teletype-writers. Unfortunately, these systems are far too complex to study in detail in this book. Instead, we will study a microcomputer that may contain 10 or 15 chips and have a limited amount of memory and a few peripheral devices.

The specifications for the system that we want to study are compiled in Chart 8-1. Although this system has a small amount of memory and only a few peripheral devices, it can be used as a small industrial controller, a sophisticated darkroom timer, an automotive mileage/economy computer, an EPROM programmer, an intelligent controller for a printer, a weather station, a solar collector controller, a telephone dialer, or even a low-cost microcomputer trainer for use at home, work, or in a college or university environment.

Chart 8-1. The Specifications for a Small, Low-Cost, 8085A-Based Microcomputer

CPU Chip	8085A
Memory	2K–4K EPROM, 1K R/W memory
I/O Required	Serial I/O for a Teletypewriter or CRT
	Parallel I/O for a Keyboard and Display
	or for Control Applications
Additional Features	System Should Be Expandable for Additional
	Memory or I/O Devices

The specifications were arbitrarily chosen, but, even so, most of the applications that were just mentioned could be satisfied with this simple microcomputer. Of course, for some applications analog-to-digital or digital-to-analog converters, solid-state relays, stepper motors, light-emitting diodes, or keyboards may be required. But all of these devices are peripherals, so once a number of input and output ports are designed and built into the microcomputer system the microcomputer can communicate with a stepper motor, solid-state relay, or digital-to-analog converter. Therefore the microcomputer design can be the same for a number of applications. The only difference between one application and another is the software and peripheral devices used. Once the initial specifications for the microcomputer have been determined, the topics discussed in the previous chapters can be applied to the design of this microcomputer.

THE CPU CHIP AND ITS CONTROL

Since the 8085A chip will be used as the heart of this system, there are a number of questions that must be answered concerning the methods used to wire this chip into the system. Should a quartz crystal or an *RC* network be used to clock the chip? The best way would be to use a quartz crystal, since the microcomputer may be used for serial communications. Should a USART be used or should software-controlled communications be used? To keep the cost of the microcomputer as low as possible, a USART will not be used. Instead, a "software-based" UART will be employed, using the SID and SOD pins of the 8085A. This means that the microcomputer must be able to time events very precisely, thus the need for a quartz crystal (Fig. 8-1).

For asynchronous communications the SID and SOD pins will be used, along with some assembly language software. Most teletypewriter and crt's do not work with TTL-level signals, so the TTL voltage levels used by the 8085A have to be converted to either 20 mA of current or to ±12 V for peripherals that use the RS-232C communications standard. This "level-shifting" hardware is shown in Fig. 8-2. The circuitry shown in this figure is used to convert the TTL levels of the 8085A to 20 mA of current. Two integrated circuits (MC1488 and MC1489) can be used to convert to/from TTL to/from the RS-232C (Fig. 8-3).

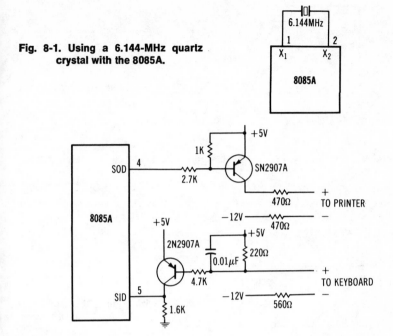

Fig. 8-1. Using a 6.144-MHz quartz crystal with the 8085A.

Fig. 8-2. Converting the TTL--compatible SID and SOD pins to a 20-mA current input and output.

None of the applications that were mentioned previously are particularly high speed (very few photographic exposures are less than 1 second, the economy of a car won't change very much every 1 or 2 seconds, an EPROM may require 100 or 200 seconds for all 1K or 2K memory locations to be programmed, etc.), so interrupts *probably* will not be required. At some point in the future, however, interrupts may be required. The simplest solution here is to "pull up" all of the interrupt inputs to +5 V and then jumper the appropriate interrupt inputs to ground. By designing the interrupt hardware properly you should be able to use the interrupt inputs *very easily,* if required. Again, since none of our peripherals are high-speed devices (such as a floppy or fixed-head disk), no direct-memory-access (dma) operations will be required. Therefore the HOLD input to the cpu can be wired directly to ground (Fig. 8-4).

When power is first applied to the microcomputer, you want the microcomputer to begin executing the program stored in memory location zero. Also, if the microprocessor completes a particular task, you might like to reset it so that the task is performed again. Therefore a push-button reset circuit *and* a power-on reset circuit is required. This circuitry is shown in Fig. 8-5.

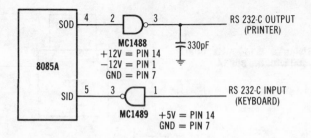

Fig. 8-3. Converting the TTL-compatible SID and SOD pins to the RS-232C voltage convention.

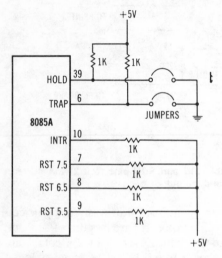

Fig. 8-4. Wiring the HOLD and interrupt inputs of the 8085A to ground or +5 V.

Based on the discussions in Chapters 4 and 5 the READY input of the 8085A will probably not be used. Fast memories (access times of 450 ns or less) are relatively inexpensive, so little will be gained by using wait states and slow memories. In fact, much of the memory available today can be used with a 6.25-MHz 8085A with no wait states. Less expensive memories can be used if wait states are inserted, but the wait state circuitry adds to the complexity and cost of the microcomputer. Therefore you should assume that no wait states are required (Fig. 8-6).

Since there will be ROM, R/W memory, and peripherals in this microcomputer system, the $\overline{RD}$, $\overline{WR}$, IO/$\overline{M}$, and ALE signals will probably be used in the microcomputer design. The discussion of these signals will be deferred to other sections of this chapter.

By now you should know why the microprocessor integrated circuit is wired as shown in Figs. 8-1 through 8-6. We have made some assumptions, and, based on these assumptions, the use of the microprocessor has

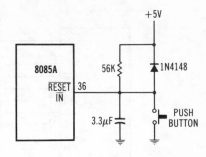

Fig. 8-5. Resetting
the microprocessor.

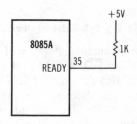

Fig. 8-6. Wiring the READY input of
the 8085A to +5 V so that no wait
states are inserted into the microprocessor timing.

been determined. You may find that some of these assumptions are in-
valid (wait states may be required, there may be a dma-oriented disk
wired to the system, interrupts may be required, etc.). Therefore this
microcomputer design may have to be changed as more of the microcomputer *system* functions are defined.

BUFFERING THE DATA BUS

The 8085A has a limited amount of current sourcing and sinking
capability (2 mA at 0.45 V, −400 μA at 2.4 V). By the time peripherals
and memory chips are wired to the bidirectional data bus, the 8085A
may not be able to drive all of these chips. Therefore the bidirectional
data bus should be buffered. Two SN74LS373s could be used to do this,
but they require a lot of space in the microcomputer. The data bus could
also be buffered with two 8216s, but these devices require an inverter
so that the RD control signal can be used to control the flow of information on the data bus. Therefore a chip such as the SN74LS245 will be
used to buffer the data bus (Fig. 8-7). This chip should be wired between the 8085A and the address demultiplexer. This means that only
the SN74LS245 is driven by the 8085A, rather than both the SN74LS-
245 and the address demultiplexing circuitry. Of course, once the entire
microcomputer is designed, we may find that the SN74LS245 is not required. If this is the case, the design can be easily changed.

281

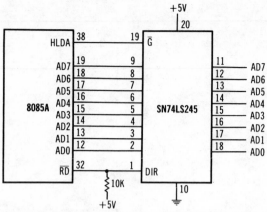

Fig. 8-7. Buffering the data bus with an SN74LS245.

We have assumed that the INTR interrupt input is not going to be used. Therefore $\overline{RD}$ is *not* gated with $\overline{INTA}$ to control the flow of information (DIR) through the SN74LS245 (see Chapter 5, "The 8216").

As you can see, there are many questions that must be answered before one chip should be used instead of another in a design. Some of these questions include physical size, power consumption, current capabilities and requirements, availability, the number of manufacturers making the part, and the speed at which the part operates. The number of chips used in the complete design will also affect the size of the printed-circuit boards, the number of sockets required for each chip, and the number of power supply decoupling capacitors used. Unfortunately there is no simple relationship among all of these factors.

DEMULTIPLEXING THE ADDRESS/DATA BUS

One of the best chips that can be used to demultiplex the address/data bus is the 8212. This chip has low input current requirements and has high output current capabilities. A chip such as the SN74LS373 is slightly less expensive than the 8212, but the 8212 is available from a number of manufacturers, so it is somewhat easier to obtain. A number of low-cost latches, such as the SN74LS75, could be used (less than $1.00 each), but they require buffer circuitry on the enable inputs. The amount of space used by the two latches and buffer circuitry is more than that used by the 8212. The use of an 8212 to demultiplex the address/data bus can be seen in Fig. 8-8.

Another advantage in using the 8212 is the fact that if additional memory or peripheral integrated circuits are added to the system, the 8212 will be able to drive more additional integrated circuits than either the SN74LS75 or the SN74LS373. Eight-bit latches with higher current capabilities than the 8212 are available, but are expensive and scarce.

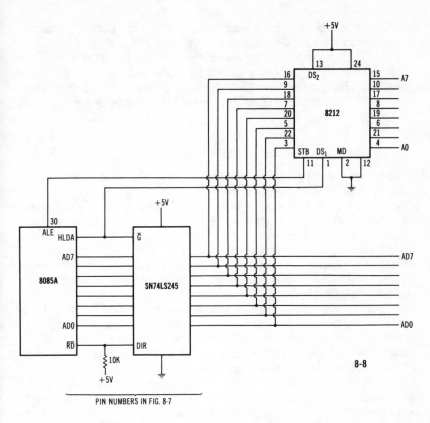

Fig. 8-8. Demultiplexing the address/data bus with an 8212.

READ-ONLY MEMORY

If the microcomputer has to have 2K of EPROM, then two 2708s, one TMS 2716, or a TMS 2516 could be used. However, in general, the 2K EPROM chips are about four times more expensive than the 1K×8 2708 EPROMs. On the other hand, the TMS 2516 and 2716 require only +5 V, whereas the 2708 requires +5 V, +12 V, and −5 V. The *tradeoff* here is three power supplies *vs.* one, and one EPROM that costs four times as much as another EPROM. The 2708 is probably the best choice, because even though it requires three power supply voltages a number of peripheral chips require the same or similar voltages. Therefore, if analog-to-digital converters, operational amplifiers, sample-and-holds, or analog multiplexers are used in a system, they will require either ±12 or ±15 V. The 2708 is also readily available. Fortunately, because the pin configurations of all of these EPROMs are very similar, few if any modifications will be required to the printed-circuit board

283

used in the microcomputer system, so that 2716s or "denser" memories can be used *in the sockets that were originally designed for 2708s.*

There is also the possibility that a chip such as the 8755A might be used, since it contains both a 2K×8 EPROM and also two 8-bit I/O ports. This chip requires just +5 V. However, these chips are very expensive (more than $50 each), so they would not ordinarily be used in a low-cost microcomputer.

READ/WRITE MEMORY

There are three possible R/W memory chips that you might consider using in your microcomputer: the 2102, the 2114, and the 8185. The 2102 is very inexpensive (less than $1 each), but eight of them would be required, along with output buffer circuitry and some control logic. The 2114, on the other hand, can be wired directly to the microcomputer buses and requires even less control circuitry. The 2114s, however, cost about $5.00 each. The 8185 is not low-cost (more than $35 each), but the address bus does not have to be demultiplexed. Which chip should be used? The 2114.

The 2102-type memories are inexpensive, but they take up a lot of space in the microcomputer system (eight chips are required), and peripheral circuitry is required (at least two additional integrated circuits). This, combined with the number of sockets and decoupling capacitors required and the added cost of the printed-circuit board, means that 2102 are rarely used in new designs today. There are, however, a tremendous number of systems that do use 2102s. The 2114 *chip* is more expensive than a 2102 chip, but fewer sockets (two *vs.* eight) are required and buffer circuitry is not required. Therefore the total cost of using 2114s is less than the cost of using 2102s.

The 8185 does not require a multiplexed address/data bus, but the EPROMs that have been chosen for the system (2708s) do require a demultiplexed address/data bus. Therefore the fact that the 8185 does not require this circuitry does not save you anything; the address demultiplexing circuitry must be in the design for use by the EPROMs anyway. The only reason that 8185s would be used in a system is if *size* and not cost is a determining factor. Also, the power consumed by R/W memory might be less if 8185s are used with careful design. The interconnection of read-only and R/W memory can be seen in Fig. 8-9.

MEMORY DECODING

As you know from our previous discussions, R/W memory and ROM must gate data off of, or gate data on to, the data bus only at specific times. In all of our designs memory control signals, such as $\overline{MEMR}$ and $\overline{MEMW}$, have been generated by some type of decoder, and these signals

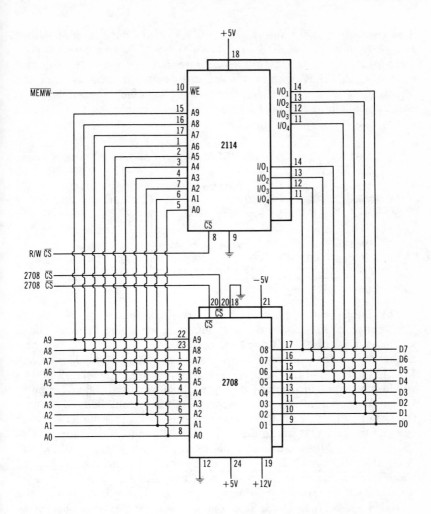

Fig. 8-9. Adding ROM and R/W memory to the microcomputer.

have been used to control the flow of information on the data bus. Therefore, not only must these control signals be generated, but we must also determine the addresses for R/W memory and the EPROMs.

Since the microprocessor executes the instruction stored in memory location zero when it is reset, you must have EPROM at memory location zero in your design. Where will R/W memory start? If two 2708s are used in the system, they would probably use the microprocessor address space from 00000000 00000000 through 00000111 11111111. From this you might guess that R/W memory should start at 00001000 00000000 and go to 00001011 11111111. What will happen, however,

285

if at some time in the future, 2716 2K×8 EPROMs, or even denser EPROMs, are used instead of 2708s? These EPROMs contain more memory locations, so they will need to use more of the microprocessor address space. If R/W memory addresses start immediately after the addresses of the 2708 EPROM, there will be a conflict between the R/W memory and the EPROM locations contained within the two "larger" 2716s (Chart 8-2).

Chart 8-2. Possible R/W-EPROM Memory Address Conflicts

2708 No. 1	2708 No. 2	R/W
00000000 00000000 00000011 11111111	00000100 00000000 00000111 11111111	00001000 00000000 00001011 11111111
2716 No. 1	**2716 No. 2**	**R/W**
00000000 00000000 00000111 11111111	00001000 00000000* 00001111 11111111*	00001000 00000000* 00001011 11111111*

*Same addresses used by two or more chips.

The simplest solution to this problem would be to place R/W memory in a portion of the microprocessor address space where there is little if any possibility of a "collision" between ROM and itself. At first you might be inclined to use addresses 11111100 00000000 through 11111111 11111111. There is very little chance, however, that you would have this much memory in your small, low-cost microcomputer system. One alternative is to use addresses 00111100 00000000 through 00111111 11111111 for R/W memory. This means that the R/W memory and the EPROM are in the first 16K of the microprocessor address space. If two 2708s are used and R/W memory starts at 00111100 00000000, there is 13K of address space between these two sections of memory. This means that two 2K×8 or two 4K×8 EPROMs could be used instead of 2708s, and there would be no conflict between the EPROM and R/W memory. Since two 4K×8 EPROMs would use memory address 00000000 00000000 through 00011111 11111111, R/W memory might even start at 00100000 00000.

If you assume that the addresses for the two 2708 EPROMs start at zero and that R/W memory starts at 00111100 00000000, a simple *absolute* memory address decoder can be designed (Fig. 8-10). Remember, there is the possibility that this microcomputer system will be expanded (more memory and peripherals may be added to the system). So absolute addressing should be used. Based on the design shown in Fig. 8-10 you probably can see that nonabsolute addressing would save one or possibly two integrated circuits. But as we shall see, *all* of the absolute memory and peripheral addressing can be done with a *single* integrated circuit.

286

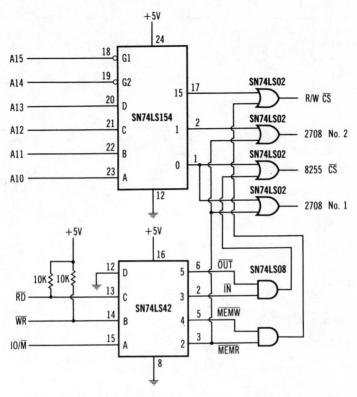

Fig. 8-10. Generating the memory and I/O chip select signals.

MEMORY AND PERIPHERAL DECODING

In Chapter 4 a number of different types of ROMs (mask, programmable, and erasable and programmable) were described. Suppose that we have a 256×4 PROM, such as the 93427PC (Fairchild) or SN74S-287 (Texas Instruments). Since these PROMs contain 256 words, there are eight address inputs. There are also two active-low chip-select inputs and four outputs. The pin configuration and block diagram for the 93427PC are shown in Fig. 8-11. Fortunately, the pin configurations for many 256×4 PROMs are the same. In fact, the SN74S287 is pin-for-pin compatible with the 93427PC.

If we forget for a moment that the 93427PC is a PROM and instead consider it to be a programmable logic device, we can see that this "logic device" has ten inputs (two of which must be logic zeroes) and four outputs. Remember also that the computer has three 1K blocks of memory, composed of two 2708s and two 2114s (arranged as 1K×8 of R/W memory). By wiring the 93427PC to the 8085A as you would nor-

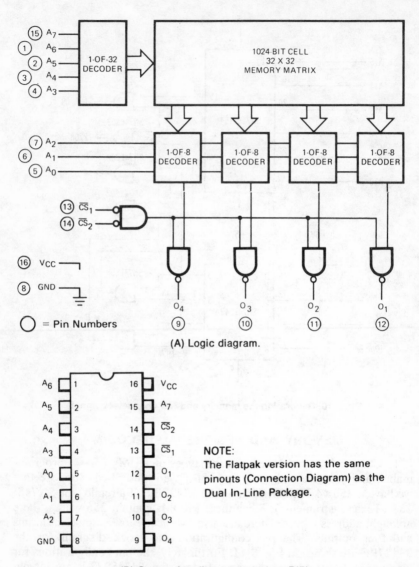

(A) Logic diagram.

A6 □ 1   16 □ Vcc

A5 □ 2   15 □ A7

A4 □ 3   14 □ $\overline{CS}_2$

A3 □ 4   13 □ $\overline{CS}_1$

A0 □ 5   12 □ O1

A1 □ 6   11 □ O2

A2 □ 7   10 □ O3

GND □ 8   9 □ O4

NOTE:
The Flatpak version has the same
pinouts (Connection Diagram) as the
Dual In-Line Package.

(B) Connection diagram (top view, DIP).

Courtesy Fairchild Camera and Instrument Corp.

Fig. 8-11. The logic diagram and pin configuration of the Fairchild 93427PC 256 × 4 PROM.

mally wire address decoders and control signal decoders, and wiring the outputs of the PROM to the $\overline{CS}$ inputs of the memories, a custom "decoder" integrated circuit can be created. The set of conditions required to select one of the three blocks of memory (or none of them) would then have to be determined.

These conditions really represent an "address" in the PROM, since A10 through A15, $\overline{RD}$, $\overline{WR}$, and IO/$\overline{M}$ are wired to the "decoder" PROM (Fig. 8-12), instead of eight address lines (A0 through A7). Thus these control signals are used to select a location in the "decoder" PROM, and the content of that location is used to specify which memory

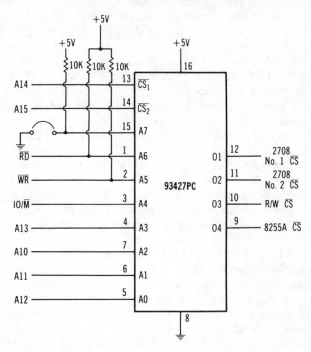

Fig. 8-12. Using a PROM to generate memory and I/O chip select signals.

chip(s) are selected and which are not. Depending on which memory device should be selected based on the condition of the PROM inputs, a single bit of the 4-bit word that is output by the PROM would be programmed in the logic zero state. Only 1 bit in the appropriate word is programmed in the logic zero state, so that only one block of memory is selected at any time.

Suppose that the signals generated by the 8085A are wired to the 256×4 PROM as shown in Chart 8-3. What PROM address would be

Chart 8-3. Using a PROM as a Programmable Decoder

8085A Signals	A15	A14	+5 V	$\overline{RD}$	$\overline{WR}$	IO/$\overline{M}$	A13	A10	A11	A12
93427PC Inputs	CS2	CS1	A7	A6	A5	A4	A3	A2	A1	A0

generated when the 8085A reads the content of memory location zero? If we assume that the A7 input of the PROM is wired to +5 V, reading from memory location zero will cause memory location 10100000 to be addressed in the PROM. Remember, A14 and A15 are logic zeroes, so the PROM is selected. The remaining address lines, A10 through A13, are also logic zeroes, and since the 8085A is *reading,* $\overline{RD}$ is a logic zero, $\overline{WR}$ is a logic one, and IO/$\overline{M}$ is a logic zero. One characteristic of the 93427PC PROM is the fact that all memory locations contain logic ones before this PROM is programmed. Therefore, when location 10100000 is addressed, 1111 will be output by the PROM. Depending on which PROM output is wired to which $\overline{CS}$ input, a 0111 might be programmed into this PROM location. This would mean that the most significant bit output by the PROM would be wired to 2708 No. 1, which contains memory location zero. Since the 8085A can only read from this 2708 EPROM, *PROM location 10100000 is the only PROM location that contains a logic zero in its most significant bit.*

Suppose that 2708 No. 2 is addressed. Which PROM location will be addressed? In this PROM address A10 will be a logic one and, since information can only be read from a ROM, *PROM location 10100100 will be addressed whenever the 8085A addresses 2708 No. 2.* As you can see, the only difference in the two PROM addresses is that A10 is a logic zero in one address and a logic one in the other address. Therefore this PROM location might be programmed with 1011.

What happens if R/W memory, from address 00111100 00000000 through 0011111111 11111111, is addressed? If R/W memory is addressed, PROM locations 10101111 and 11001111 will be addressed. One location will be addressed when information is read from R/W memory, and the other will be addressed when information is written into R/W memory. Therefore *both* of these PROM locations would be programmed with 1101, so that R/W memory is selected when the proper address is generated by the 8085A and either a memory-read or memory-write operation is taking place.

As you can see, by using a PROM the decoder circuitry required for absolute addressing can be greatly simplified. Instead of three or four integrated circuits, only one has to be used. *Only a PROM, and not a mask ROM or EPROM, can be used in this design, since most PROMs have access times of 30 to 50 ns.* This means that the chip select signals will be generated very soon after the address and control outputs of the 8085A change. A 300- or 450-ns mask ROM or EPROM would just barely select the R/W or read-only memory in the microcomputer before the microcomputer performed the next operation.

Unfortunately, PROMs in general sink and source more current on their address inputs, and leak more current to/from their outputs, than typical mask ROMs or EPROMs. For the Fairchild 93427PC the address bus must be able to source 40 μA at 2.4 V for a logic one, and sink

−160 μA at 0.45 V for a logic zero. The leakage current for this same device is ±50 μA, depending on the logic level that *would be* output if the device were selected. However, the 93427PC can also sink −16 mA of current at 0.45 V maximum, and source −2 mA at 2.4 V minimum. Therefore the outputs of this PROM can "chip select" just about any peripheral integrated circuit.

INPUT/OUTPUT CAPABILITIES

We have already discussed the fact that the microcomputer may have to be used with an asynchronous communications-type peripheral (crt, teletypewriter, printer, etc.). Because of this requirement the SID and SOD pins of the 8085A are wired to some *level-conversion electronics* (Figs. 8-2 and 8-3). These electronics convert the TTL-compatible input and output of the 8085A so that it can be used with a peripheral that uses either a 20-mA current loop or the RS-232C standard.

One of the *system* requirements is the fact that the microcomputer must have parallel I/O capabilities for use with a keyboard and display or for use in control applications where solid-state relays and lamps might be controlled. One of the simplest chips to use in this application is the 8255A PPI chip. This chip typically sells for slightly over $5.00, so you might think that it is possible to build three input or output ports with individual I/O chips for less money. Since, however, you may have a number of applications that have to be solved by this microcomputer, the slightly higher cost of the 8255A gives the microcomputer a great deal of flexibility. By simply changing a *single* assembly language instruction the 8255A can be configured as either three input ports, three output ports, or any combination of input and output ports. Remember, also, that three individual input or output ports will require a number of IC sockets, decoupling capacitors, a decoder that decodes A0 and A1 to select one of the three ports and more printed-circuit board "real estate."

The 8255A and how it is wired to the microcomputer buses is shown in Fig. 8-13. No peripheral devices are shown wired to this integrated circuit since it may be used in a variety of applications.

MOUNTING THE MICROCOMPUTER COMPONENTS

There are a number of different methods that can be used to interconnect the various microcomputer components, including (1) solderless breadboarding (Fig. 8-14), wire-wrapping (Fig. 8-15), and a printed-circuit board (Fig. 8-16). Each method has its advantages and disadvantages. The solderless breadboard might be used when the microcomputer is initially designed. With this technique the initial design can be easily and quickly changed so that different decoding techniques or

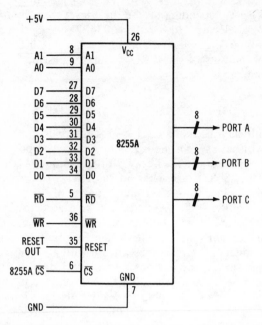

Fig. 8-13. Adding an 8255A PPI chip to the microcomputer.

Courtesy Tychon, Inc.
Fig. 8-14. Using solderless breadboarding for a microcomputer design.

Fig. 8-15. Wirewrapping a microcomputer.

Fig. 8-16. Using a printed-circuit board for the microcomputer.

memory circuits can be tried in the system. The microcomputer that is created this way is not very sturdy, since wires can be easily removed and it would not be easy to transport from application to application. Therefore solderless breadboarding is only intended for the *initial* hardware design. Once all of the bugs have been eliminated from the microcomputer, either a wire-wrap board or a printed-circuit board can be used for a "permanent" version of the microcomputer.

If wire-wrapping techniques are used, a sturdy microcomputer can be built in only a few hours. A large amount of very fine wire and patience is required. If a second or third microcomputer has to be built, then the same amount of time, wire and patience will be required. If only one or two microcomputers are required, however, this is an acceptable construction technique.

For large quantities of microcomputers a printed-circuit board is the lowest-cost alternative. With a printed-circuit board a small microcomputer can be assembled in less than one hour. Since the "wires" are already contained on the printed-circuit board, the components simply have to be soldered in place. However, a long time is initially required in order to obtain printed-circuit board versions of the microcomputer. Large tape-ups must be prepared, where each line of tape on a clear sheet of plastic represents each wire required by the microcomputer. Component outlines and tape must be placed on the plastic very carefully. Quite often double-sided printed-circuit boards must be used, where there are wires on both sides of the fiberglass or phenolic printed-circuit board material. If a double-sided board must be designed, two sheets of clear plastic must be used, and the optical registration between the components on each sheet of plastic must be excellent. As you might guess, making tape-ups for printed-circuit boards requires a large amount of time. This utilization of time is justifiable only if 10, 20, or more microcomputers are to be built.

SYSTEM EXPANSION

Since one of the original system requirements was that the microcomputer should be expandable, an edge connector should be used on either the wire-wrap or printed-circuit board version of the microcomputer. The use of an edge connector means that the 8085A address bus, data bus, and control signals can be connected to other memory or peripheral boards in the microcomputer system. Each of the cards is plugged into an edge connector, and all edge connectors are connected together using either individual wires or a *motherboard*. A motherboard is simply a printed-circuit board that contains a number of parallel connections between a number of edge connectors. The parallel connections between the edge connectors (either wires or printed-circuit board traces) are called a *bus*. By using a bus, individual cards can be plugged into the bus *anywhere,* and the microcomputer will still operate properly. By using a bus and individual printed-circuit boards the size of the microcomputer system can be increased or decreased at any time.

If a card with an edge connector is used for the microcomputer, what size should be used? Since the microcomputer itself only requires six or seven integrated circuits, the card can be very small. Cards 4.5 by 6.5 inches (11.4 by 16.5 cm) are available and they contain a 44-finger or contact edge connector, on one of the 4.5-inch sides. This number of contacts in the edge connector is more than enough for use in an 8085A-based microcomputer system.

POWER SUPPLY REQUIREMENTS

Since EPROMs are used in the microcomputer system, +5-, +12-, and −12-volt supplies will be required. EPROMs such as the 2708 require voltages of +5, +12, and −5 V, so a small inexpensive voltage regulator will be required on the microcomputer board so that the −12 V is regulated down to −5 V. Remember, analog-to-digital and digital-to-analog converters may have to be used in the microcomputer system. These devices may require either ±12 or ±15 V. Therefore the main power supply should *not* generate +5, +12, and −5 V.

If analog-to-digital converters or any other types of analog functions *will not* be used in the microcomputer, and a *large* number of microcomputers are to be produced, considerable money can be saved by using mask ROMs. These devices generally require only +5 V, so the entire microcomputer system could be powered with only +5 V! If CMOS versions of the 8085A become available, the entire microprocessor could be powered by a 6-V lantern battery or even solar cells.

A SMALL, LOW-COST, 8085A-BASED MICROCOMPUTER

A complete two-board 8085A-based microcomputer is shown in Fig. 8-17. The cpu card contains the 8085A cpu chip, the 2708 EPROMs, 2114 R/W memories, and the memory-I/O address decoder. The cpu card also includes the reset, interrupt, clock, and 20-mA loop circuitry. The cpu card does not contain the 8255A PPI chip. This chip is contained on the keyboard/display card. In this particular application the PPI chip is dedicated to a keyboard and up to nine seven-segment displays. In another application a card might be constructed that contains the PPI chip and solid-state relays, analog-to-digital converters, or a number of other peripheral devices.

All of the signals required by the PPI chip go through the 16-conductor ribbon cable that connects the two boards. By interconnecting the two boards in this manner a number of other boards, each containing a PPI chip or equivalent circuitry, can be connected to the cpu card. Both

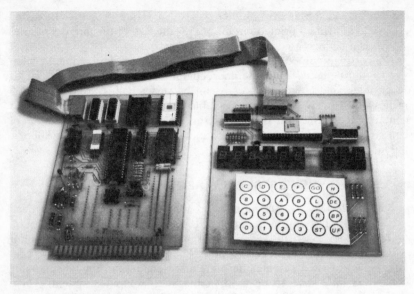

Fig. 8-17. A small, low-cost, 8085A-based microcomputer.

the cpu card and the keyboard/display board could have been interconnected using the 44-pin bus. However, doing this would increase the cost of the microcomputer by $20 or $30. The two 16-pin sockets and the flexible ribbon cable required to interconnect the two boards in the present design cost less than $4.00. Also, by using flexible cable the cpu card can be plugged into a motherboard contained in an enclosure along with power supplies, and the board containing the PPI chip, keyboard, and displays can still be used to program the microcomputer from outside of the box.

The schematic diagram for the cpu card is shown in Fig. 8-18 and the schematic diagram for the keyboard/display card is shown in Fig. 8-19. A set of double-sided, plated-though-hole, printed-circuit boards, for both the cpu card and the keyboard/display card, along with a number of hard-to-find parts, are available from:

PACCOM
14905 N.E. 40th St.
Redmond, WA 98052
(206) 883-9200

CONCLUSION

Unfortunately every book is a compromise, and this book is no exception. We have not discussed the capacitive loads that the microprocessor or other chips can drive, the possibility of reflections on the bus signals, pull-up/pull-down resistor networks for decreasing the noise of signals, the proper layout techniques to be used with printed-circuit boards, or even how PROMs and EPROMs are programmed. Some of these topics are extremely complex and require long and detailed mathematical studies. If the principles discussed in this book are used, you should have no trouble designing 20- or 30-chip microcomputer systems that work.

Again, because of limited space, we have not discussed microcomputer programming or microcomputer interfacing in great detail. However, the authors have already written a number of books that can be used to pursue these and a number of other topics.

If you are interested in programming 8080- or 8085A-based microcomputers using assembly language, the books *8080/8085 Software Design, Books 1 and 2,*[1,2] contain hundreds of software examples along with detailed discussions of the instructions and why they are used. In fact, if you actually build the microcomputer and keyboard/display board shown in Fig. 8-17, these books can be used with the microcomputer to start you off on assembly language programming. The TEA[3] and DBUG[4] books contain long and complex assembly language programs that can actually be executed on your microcomputer. To do this, however, additional memory and peripherals (a teletypewriter or crt) will be required.

If you are interested in interfacing peripheral devices to an 8080- or 8085A-based microcomputer, *Introductory Experiments in Digital Electronics and 8080A Microcomputer Programming and Interfacing, Books 1 and 2,*[5,6] contain many examples and experiments that can actually be performed in digital electronics and with an 8080- or 8085A-based microcomputer. Once the interfacing techniques used in these books have been mastered, two other books can be used to interface specific chips to the microcomputer.

The *Microcomputer-Analog Converter Software and Hardware Interfacing* book[7] contains many interfaces and software examples required for use with analog-to-digital and digital-to-analog converters. These converters are extremely important in data acquisition applications where an analog voltage must be converted to a digital value so that the microcomputer can make decisions about events or conditions. This book would help you if you are interested in solar collector controllers, automotive mileage/economy "meters," temperature controllers, industrial controllers, data loggers, or small data acquisition systems for laboratory work.

A book has also been written about the 8255A PPI chip,[8] since it has great flexibility in solving a number of interfacing applications. As was mentioned this chip can be used simply as input and output ports, but it can also be used to generate strobe pulses or be used in multiprocessor communications systems.

Finally, if you are interested in interfacing a peripheral to a micro-computer and then using a higher-level language than assembly language for data acquisition and reduction, the *TRS-80 Interfacing* book[9] can be used. Although this book uses the Radio-Shack TRS-80 microcomputer in all of its examples, many of the interfacing techniques that you already know can be applied to this microcomputer. The advantage of using this

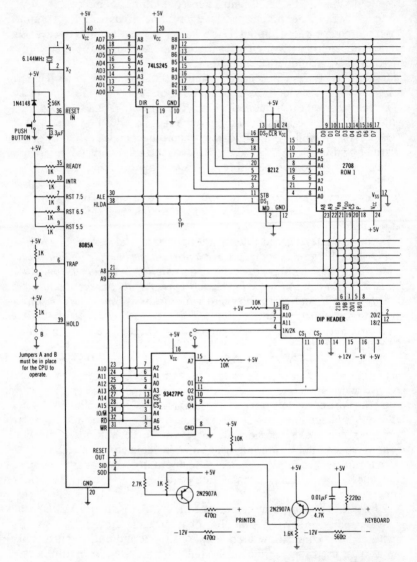

Fig. 8-18. The schematic diagram

microcomputer over the type of microcomputers that have been designed in this book is the fact that the TRS-80 can be programmed in the BASIC language. This language is easier to learn and use than assembly language, so many users favor it. A flowchart containing these books is shown in Fig. 8-20. Based on your knowledge of microcomputer-related subjects, you should be able to find books that meet your interests.

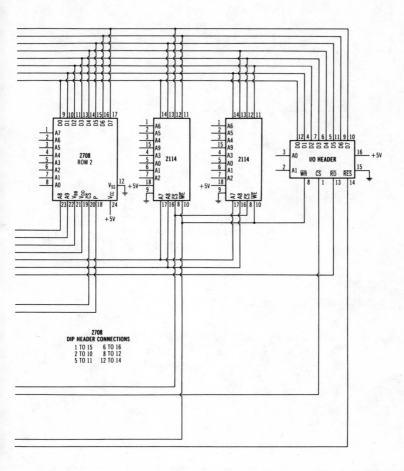

for the 8085A-based cpu card.

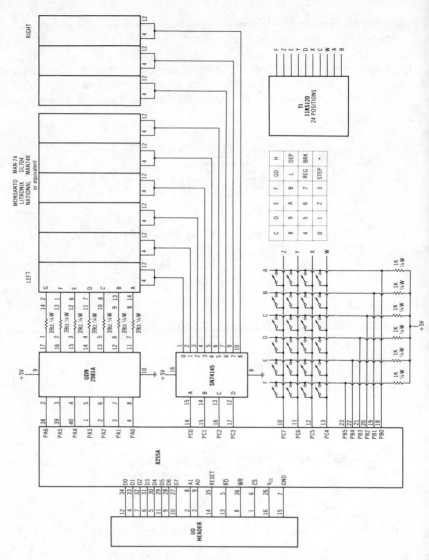

Fig. 8-19. The schematic diagram for the keyboard/display card.

BIBLIOGRAPHY

1. Titus, C. A., Rony, P. R., Larsen, D. G., and J. A. Titus, *8080/8085 Software Design, Book 1,* Indianapolis: Howard W. Sams & Co., Inc., 1978.
2. Titus, C. A., Larsen, D. G., and J. A. Titus, *8080/8085 Software Design, Book 2,* Indianapolis: Howard W. Sams & Co., Inc., 1979.
3. Titus, C. A. *TEA: an 8080/8085 Co-Resident Editor/Assembler,* Indianapolis: Howard W. Sams & Co., Inc., 1979.

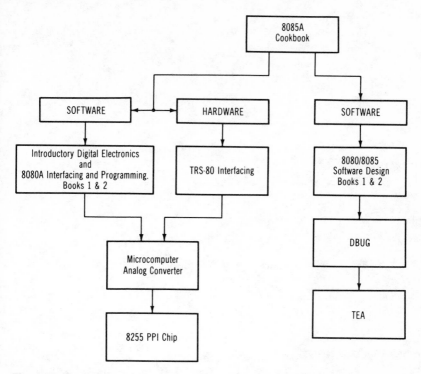

Fig. 8-20. Exploring new areas in electronics with the Blacksburg Continuing Education Series.

4. Titus, C. A. and J. A. Titus, *DBUG: an 8080 Interpretive Debugger,* Indianapolis: Howard W. Sams & Co., Inc., 1978.
5. Rony, P. R., Larsen, D. G., and J. A Titus, *Introductory Experiments in Digital Electronics and 8080A Microcomputer Programming and Interfacing, Book 1,* Indianapolis: Howard W Sams & Co., Inc., 1979.
6. Larsen, D. G., Rony, P. R., and J. A. Titus, *Introductory Experiments in Digital Electronics and 8080A Microcomputer Programming and Interfacing, Book 2,* Indianapolis: Howard W. Sams & Co., Inc., 1979.
7. Titus, J. A., Titus, C. A., Rony, P. R., and D. G. Larsen, *Microcomputer-Analog Converter Software & Hardware Interfacing,* Indianapolis: Howard W. Sams & Co., 1978.
8. Goldsbrough, P. F. *Microcomputer Interfacing with the 8255 PPI Chip,* Indianapolis: Howard W. Sams & Co., Inc., 1979.
9. Titus, J. A. *TRS-80 Interfacing,* Indianapolis: Howard W. Sams & Co., Inc., 1979.

8085A Instruction Set Summary

Mnemonic	Description	D7	D6	D5	D4	D3	D2	D1	D0	Clock(2) Cycles
MOVE. LOAD. AND STORE										
MOV r1 r2	Move register to register	0	1	D	D	D	S	S	S	4
MOV M r	Move register to memory	0	1	1	1	0	S	S	S	7
MOV r M	Move memory to register	0	1	D	D	D	1	1	0	7
MVI r	Move immediate register	0	0	D	D	D	1	1	0	7
MVI M	Move immediate memory	0	0	1	1	0	1	1	0	10
LXI B	Load immediate register Pair B & C	0	0	0	0	0	0	0	1	10
LXI D	Load immediate register Pair D & E	0	0	0	1	0	0	0	1	10
LXI H	Load immediate register Pair H & L	0	0	1	0	0	0	0	1	10
LXI SP	Load immediate stack pointer	0	0	1	1	0	0	0	1	10
STAX B	Store A indirect	0	0	0	0	0	0	1	0	7
STAX D	Store A indirect	0	0	0	1	0	0	1	0	7
LDAX B	Load A indirect	0	0	0	0	1	0	1	0	7
LDAX D	Load A indirect	0	0	0	1	1	0	1	0	7
STA	Store A direct	0	0	1	1	0	0	1	0	13
LDA	Load A direct	0	0	1	1	1	0	1	0	13
SHLD	Store H & L direct	0	0	1	0	0	0	1	0	16
LHLD	Load H & L direct	0	0	1	0	1	0	1	0	16
XCHG	Exchange D & E H & L Registers	1	1	1	0	1	0	1	1	4
STACK OPS										
PUSH B	Push register Pair B & C on stack	1	1	0	0	0	1	0	1	12
PUSH D	Push register Pair D & E on stack	1	1	0	1	0	1	0	1	12
PUSH H	Push register Pair H & L on stack	1	1	1	0	0	1	0	1	12
PUSH PSW	Push A and Flags on stack	1	1	1	1	0	1	0	1	12
POP B	Pop register Pair B & C off stack	1	1	0	0	0	0	0	1	10
POP D	Pop register Pair D & E off stack	1	1	0	1	0	0	0	1	10
POP H	Pop register Pair H & L off stack	1	1	1	0	0	0	0	1	10
POP PSW	Pop A and Flags off stack	1	1	1	1	0	0	0	1	10
XTHL	Exchange top of stack H & L	1	1	1	0	0	0	1	1	16
SPHL	H & L to stack pointer	1	1	1	1	1	0	0	1	6
JUMP										
JMP	Jump unconditional	1	1	0	0	0	0	1	1	10
JC	Jump on carry	1	1	0	1	1	0	1	0	7/10
JNC	Jump on no carry	1	1	0	1	0	0	1	0	7/10
JZ	Jump on zero	1	1	0	0	1	0	1	0	7/10
JNZ	Jump on no zero	1	1	0	0	0	0	1	0	7/10
JP	Jump on positive	1	1	1	1	0	0	1	0	7/10
JM	Jump on minus	1	1	1	1	1	0	1	0	7/10
JPE	Jump on parity even	1	1	1	0	1	0	1	0	7/10
JPO	Jump on parity odd	1	1	1	0	0	0	1	0	7/10
PCHL	H & L to program counter	1	1	1	0	1	0	0	1	6
CALL										
CALL	Call unconditional	1	1	0	0	1	1	0	1	18
CC	Call on carry	1	1	0	1	1	1	0	0	9/18
CNC	Call on no carry	1	1	0	1	0	1	0	0	9/18
CZ	Call on zero	1	1	0	0	1	1	0	0	9/18
CNZ	Call on no zero	1	1	0	0	0	1	0	0	9/18
CP	Call on positive	1	1	1	1	0	1	0	0	9/18
CM	Call on minus	1	1	1	1	1	1	0	0	9/18

Mnemonic	Description	D7	D6	D5	D4	D3	D2	D1	D0	Clock(2) Cycles
CPE	Call on parity even	1	1	1	0	1	1	0	0	9/18
CPO	Call on parity odd	1	1	1	0	0	1	0	0	9/18
RETURN										
RET	Return	1	1	0	0	1	0	0	1	10
RC	Return on carry	1	1	0	1	1	0	0	0	6/12
RNC	Return on no carry	1	1	0	1	0	0	0	0	6/12
RZ	Return on zero	1	1	0	0	1	0	0	0	6/12
RNZ	Return on no zero	1	1	0	0	0	0	0	0	6/12
RP	Return on positive	1	1	1	1	0	0	0	0	6/12
RM	Return on minus	1	1	1	1	1	0	0	0	6/12
RPE	Return on parity even	1	1	1	0	1	0	0	0	6/12
RPO	Return on parity odd	1	1	1	0	0	0	0	0	6/12
RESTART										
RST	Restart	1	1	A	A	A	1	1	1	12
INPUT/OUTPUT										
IN	Input	1	1	0	1	1	0	1	1	10
OUT	Output	1	1	0	1	0	0	1	1	10
INCREMENT AND DECREMENT										
INR r	Increment register	0	0	D	D	D	1	0	0	4
DCR r	Decrement register	0	0	D	D	D	1	0	1	4
INR M	Increment memory	0	0	1	1	0	1	0	0	10
DCR M	Decrement memory	0	0	1	1	0	1	0	1	10
INX B	Increment B & C registers	0	0	0	0	0	0	1	1	6
INX D	Increment D & E registers	0	0	0	1	0	0	1	1	6
INX H	Increment H & L registers	0	0	1	0	0	0	1	1	6
INX SP	Increment stack pointer	0	0	1	1	0	0	1	1	6
DCX B	Decrement B & C	0	0	0	0	1	0	1	1	6
DCX D	Decrement D & E	0	0	0	1	1	0	1	1	6
DCX H	Decrement H & L	0	0	1	0	1	0	1	1	6
DCX SP	Decrement stack pointer	0	0	1	1	1	0	1	1	6
ADD										
ADD r	Add register to A	1	0	0	0	0	S	S	S	4
ADC r	Add register to A with carry	1	0	0	0	1	S	S	S	4
ADD M	Add memory to A	1	0	0	0	0	1	1	0	7
ADC M	Add memory to A with carry	1	0	0	0	1	1	1	0	7
ADI	Add immediate to A	1	1	0	0	0	1	1	0	7
ACI	Add immediate to A with carry	1	1	0	0	1	1	1	0	7
DAD B	Add B & C to H & L	0	0	0	0	1	0	0	1	10
DAD D	Add D & E to H & L	0	0	0	1	1	0	0	1	10
DAD H	Add H & L to H & L	0	0	1	0	1	0	0	1	10
DAD SP	Add stack pointer to H & L	0	0	1	1	1	0	0	1	10
SUBTRACT										
SUB r	Subtract register from A	1	0	0	1	0	S	S	S	4
SBB r	Subtract register from A with borrow	1	0	0	1	1	S	S	S	4
SUB M	Subtract memory from A	1	0	0	1	0	1	1	0	7
SBB M	Subtract memory from A with borrow	1	0	0	1	1	1	1	0	7
SUI	Subtract immediate from A	1	1	0	1	0	1	1	0	7
SBI	Subtract immediate from A with borrow	1	1	0	1	1	1	1	0	7
LOGICAL										
ANA r	And register with A	1	0	1	0	0	S	S	S	4

Courtesy Intel Corp.

Mnemonic	Description	D7	D6	D5	D4	D3	D2	D1	D0	Clock Cycles
XRA r	Exclusive Or register with A	1	0	1	0	1	S	S	S	4
ORA r	Or register with A	1	0	1	1	0	S	S	S	4
CMP r	Compare register with A	1	0	1	1	1	S	S	S	4
ANA M	And memory with A	1	0	1	0	0	1	1	0	7
XRA M	Exclusive Or memory with A	1	0	1	0	1	1	1	0	7
ORA M	Or memory with A	1	0	1	1	0	1	1	0	7
CMP M	Compare memory with A	1	0	1	1	1	1	1	0	7
ANI	And immediate with A	1	1	1	0	0	1	1	0	7
XRI	Exclusive Or immediate with A	1	1	1	0	1	1	1	0	7
ORI	Or immediate with A	1	1	1	1	0	1	1	0	7
CPI	Compare immediate with A	1	1	1	1	1	1	1	0	7

ROTATE

Mnemonic	Description	D7	D6	D5	D4	D3	D2	D1	D0	Clock Cycles
RLC	Rotate A left	0	0	0	0	0	1	1	1	4
RRC	Rotate A right	0	0	0	0	1	1	1	1	4

Mnemonic	Description	D7	D6	D5	D4	D3	D2	D1	D0	Clock Cycles
RAL	Rotate A left through carry	0	0	0	1	0	1	1	1	4
RAR	Rotate A right through carry	0	0	0	1	1	1	1	1	4

SPECIALS

Mnemonic	Description	D7	D6	D5	D4	D3	D2	D1	D0	Clock Cycles
CMA	Complement A	0	0	1	0	1	1	1	1	4
STC	Set carry	0	0	1	1	0	1	1	1	4
CMC	Complement carry	0	0	1	1	1	1	1	1	4
DAA	Decimal adjust A	0	0	1	0	0	1	1	1	4

CONTROL

Mnemonic	Description	D7	D6	D5	D4	D3	D2	D1	D0	Clock Cycles
EI	Enable Interrupts	1	1	1	1	1	0	1	1	4
DI	Disable Interrupt	1	1	1	1	0	0	1	1	4
NOP	No-operation	0	0	0	0	0	0	0	0	4
HLT	Halt	0	1	1	1	0	1	1	0	5

NEW 8085A INSTRUCTIONS

Mnemonic	Description	D7	D6	D5	D4	D3	D2	D1	D0	Clock Cycles
RIM	Read Interrupt Mask	0	0	1	0	0	0	0	0	4
SIM	Set Interrupt Mask	0	0	1	1	0	0	0	0	4

NOTES 1 DDD or SSS B 000 C 001 D 010 E 011 H 100 L 101 Memory 110 A 111
    2 Two possible cycle times (6/12) indicate instruction cycles dependent on condition flags

Courtesy Intel Corp.

APPENDIX B

Data Sheets

TTL
MSI

TYPES SN54LS373, SN54LS374, SN54S373, SN54S374, SN74LS373, SN74LS374, SN74S373, SN74S374 OCTAL D-TYPE TRANSPARENT LATCHES AND EDGE-TRIGGERED FLIP-FLOPS

- Choice of 8 Latches or 8 D-Type Flip-Flops In a Single Package
- 3-State Bus-Driving Outputs
- Full Parallel-Access for Loading
- Buffered Control Inputs
- Clock/Enable Input Has Hysteresis to Improve Noise Rejection
- P-N-P Inputs Reduce D-C Loading on Data Lines ('S373 and 'S374)
- SN54LS363 and SN74LS364 Are Similar But Have Higher V_{OH} For MOS Interface

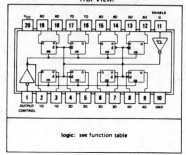

SN54LS373, SN54S373 . . . J PACKAGE
SN74LS373, SN74S373 . . . J OR N PACKAGE
(TOP VIEW)

logic: see function table

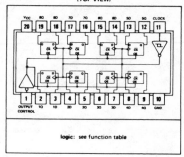

SN54LS374, SN54S374 . . . J PACKAGE
SN74LS374, SN74S374 . . . J OR N PACKAGE
(TOP VIEW)

logic: see function table

'LS373, 'S373
FUNCTION TABLE

OUTPUT CONTROL	ENABLE G	D	OUTPUT
L	H	H	H
L	H	L	L
L	L	X	Q_0
H	X	X	Z

'LS374, 'S374
FUNCTION TABLE

OUTPUT CONTROL	CLOCK	D	OUTPUT
L	↑	H	H
L	↑	L	L
L	L	X	Q_0
H	X	X	Z

See explanation of function tables on page 3-8.

description

These 8-bit registers feature totem-pole three-state outputs designed specifically for driving highly-capacitive or relatively low-impedance loads. The high-impedance third state and increased high-logic-level drive provide these registers with the capability of being connected directly to and driving the bus lines in a bus-organized system without need for interface or pull-up components. They are particularly attractive for implementing buffer registers, I/O ports, bidirectional bus drivers, and working registers.

The eight latches of the 'LS373 and 'S373 are transparent D-type latches meaning that while the enable (G) is high the Q outputs will follow the data (D) inputs. When the enable is taken low the output will be latched at the level of the data that was setup.

Courtesy Texas Instruments, Inc.

TYPES SN54LS373, SN54LS374, SN54S373, SN54S374, SN74LS373, SN74LS374, SN74S373, SN74S374
OCTAL D-TYPE TRANSPARENT LATCHES AND EDGE-TRIGGERED FLIP-FLOPS

description (continued)

The eight flip-flops of the 'LS374 and 'S374 are edge-triggered D-type flip-flops. On the positive transition of the clock, the Q outputs will be set to the logic states that were setup at the D inputs.

Schmitt-trigger buffered inputs at the enable/clock lines simplify system design as ac and dc noise rejection is improved by typically 400 mV due to the input hysteresis. A buffered output control input can be used to place the eight outputs in either a normal logic state (high or low logic levels) or a high-impedance state. In the high-impedance state the outputs neither load nor drive the bus lines significantly.

The output control does not affect the internal operation of the latches or flip-flops. That is, the old data can be retained or new data can be entered even while the outputs are off.

'LS373, 'S373
TRANSPARENT LATCHES

'LS374, 'S374
POSITIVE-EDGE-TRIGGERED FLIP-FLOPS

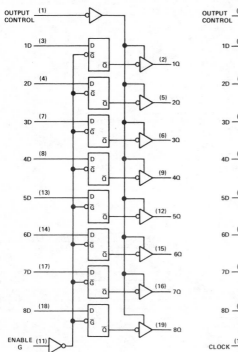
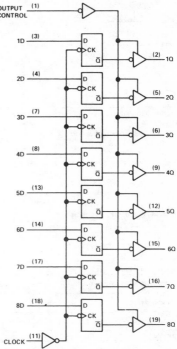

Courtesy Texas Instruments, Inc.

schematic of inputs and outputs 'LS373

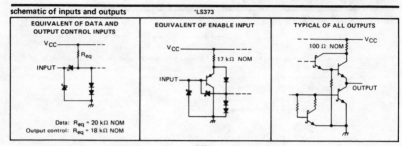

'LS374

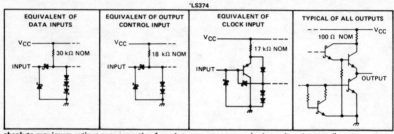

absolute maximum ratings over operating free-air temperature range (unless otherwise noted)

Supply voltage, V_{CC} (see Note 1) . . . . 7 V
Input voltage . . . . 7 V
Off-state output voltage . . . . 7 V
Operating free-air temperature range: SN54LS' . . . . −55°C to 125°C
SN74LS' . . . . 0°C to 70°C
Storage temperature range . . . . −65°C to 150°C

NOTE 1: Voltage values are with respect to network ground terminal.

recommended operating conditions

		SN54LS'			SN74LS'			UNIT
		MIN	NOM	MAX	MIN	NOM	MAX	
Supply voltage, V_{CC}		4.5	5	5.5	4.75	5	5.25	V
High-level output voltage, V_{OH}				5.5			5.5	V
High-level output current, I_{OH}				−1			−2.6	mA
Width of clock/enable pulse, t_w	High	15			15			ns
	Low	15			15			
Data setup time, t_{su}	'LS373	0↓			0↓			ns
	'LS374	20↑			20↑			
Data hold time, t_h	'LS373	10↓			10↓			ns
	'LS374	0↑			0↑			
Operating free-air temperature, T_A		−55		125	0		70	°C

↑↓ The arrow indicates the transition of the clock/enable input used for reference: ↑ for the low-to-high transition, ↓ for the high-to-low transition.

Courtesy Texas Instruments, Inc.

TYPES SN54LS373, SN54LS374, SN74LS373, SN74LS374
OCTAL D-TYPE TRANSPARENT LATCHES AND
EDGE-TRIGGERED FLIP-FLOPS

electrical characteristics over recommended operating free-air temperature range (unless otherwise noted)

PARAMETER		TEST CONDITIONS†		SN54LS' MIN	TYP‡	MAX	SN74LS' MIN	TYP‡	MAX	UNIT
V_{IH}	High-level input voltage			2			2			V
V_{IL}	Low-level input voltage					0.7			0.8	V
V_{IK}	Input clamp voltage	V_{CC} = MIN, I_I = −18 mA				−1.5			−1.5	V
V_{OH}	High-level output voltage	V_{CC} = MIN, V_{IH} = 2 V, V_{IL} = V_{IL}max, I_{OH} = MAX		2.4	3.4		2.4	3.1		V
V_{OL}	Low-level output voltage	V_{CC} = MIN, V_{IH} = 2 V, V_{IL} = V_{IL}max	I_{OL} = 12 mA		0.25	0.4		0.25	0.4	V
			I_{OL} = 24 mA					0.35	0.5	
I_{OZH}	Off-state output current, high-level voltage applied	V_{CC} = MAX, V_{IH} = 2 V, V_O = 2.7 V				20			20	μA
I_{OZL}	Off-state output current, low-level voltage applied	V_{CC} = MAX, V_{IH} = 2 V, V_O = 0.4 V				−20			−20	μA
I_I	Input current at maximum input voltage	V_{CC} = MAX, V_I = 7 V				0.1			0.1	mA
I_{IH}	High-level input current	V_{CC} = MAX, V_I = 2.7 V				20			20	μA
I_{IL}	Low-level input current	V_{CC} = MAX, V_I = 0.4 V				−0.4			−0.4	mA
I_{OS}	Short-circuit output current§	V_{CC} = MAX		−30		−130	−30		−130	mA
I_{CC}	Supply current	V_{CC} = MAX, Output control at 4.5 V	'LS373		24	40		24	40	mA
			'LS374		27	40		27	40	

† For conditions shown as MIN or MAX, use the appropriate value specified under recommended operating conditions.
‡ All typical values are at V_{CC} = 5 V, T_A = 25°C.
§ Not more than one output should be shorted at a time and duration of the short circuit should not exceed one second.

switching characteristics, V_{CC} = 5 V, T_A = 25°C

PARAMETER	FROM (INPUT)	TO (OUTPUT)	TEST CONDITIONS	'LS373 MIN	TYP	MAX	'LS374 MIN	TYP	MAX	UNIT
f_{max}							35	50		MHz
t_{PLH}	Data	Any Q			12	18				ns
t_{PHL}					12	18				
t_{PLH}	Clock or enable	Any Q	C_L = 45 pF, R_L = 667 Ω, See Notes 2 and 3		20	30		15	28	ns
t_{PHL}					18	30		19	28	
t_{PZH}	Output Control	Any Q			15	28		20	28	ns
t_{PZL}					25	36		21	28	
t_{PHZ}	Output Control	Any Q	C_L = 5 pF, R_L = 667 Ω, See Note 3		12	20		12	20	ns
t_{PLZ}					15	25		14	25	

NOTES: 2. Maximum clock frequency is tested with all outputs loaded.
3. See load circuits and waveforms on page 3-11.

f_{max} ≡ maximum clock frequency
t_{PLH} ≡ propagation delay time, low-to-high-level output
t_{PHL} ≡ propagation delay time, high-to-low-level output
t_{PZH} ≡ output enable time to high level
t_{PZL} ≡ output enable time to low level
t_{PHZ} ≡ output disable time from high level
t_{PLZ} ≡ output disable time from low level

Courtesy Texas Instruments, Inc.

TYPES SN5475, SN5477, SN54L75, SN54L77, SN54LS75, SN54LS77, SN7475, SN74L75, SN74L77, SN74LS75
4-BIT BISTABLE LATCHES

logic

FUNCTION TABLE
(Each Latch)

INPUTS		OUTPUTS	
D	G	Q	$\overline{Q}$
L	H	L	H
H	H	H	L
X	L	Q_0	$\overline{Q}_0$

H = high level, L = low level, X = irrelevant
Q_0 = the level of Q before the high-to-low transition of G

description

These latches are ideally suited for use as temporary storage for binary information between processing units and input/output or indicator units. Information present at a data (D) input is transferred to the Q output when the enable (G) is high and the Q output will follow the data input as long as the enable remains high. When the enable goes low, the information (that was present at the data input at the time the transition occurred) is retained at the Q output until the enable is permitted to go high.

The '75, 'L75, and 'LS75 feature complementary Q and $\overline{Q}$ outputs from a 4-bit latch, and are available in various 16-pin packages. For higher component density applications, the '77, 'L77, and 'LS77 4-bit latches are available in 14-pin flat packages.

These circuits are completely compatible with all popular TTL or DTL families. All inputs are diode-clamped to minimize transmission-line effects and simplify system design. Series 54, 54L, and 54LS devices are characterized for operation over the full military temperature range of $-55°C$ to $125°C$; Series 74, 74L, and 74LS devices are characterized for operation from $0°C$ to $70°C$.

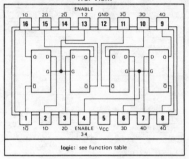

SN5475, SN54LS75 . . . J OR W PACKAGE
SN54L75 . . . J PACKAGE
SN7475, SN74L75, SN74LS75 . . . J OR N PACKAGE
(TOP VIEW)

logic: see function table

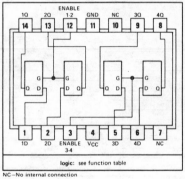

SN5477, SN54L77 . . . W PACKAGE
SN54L77, SN74L77 . . . T PACKAGE

logic: see function table

NC—No internal connection

absolute maximum ratings over operating free-air temperature range (unless otherwise noted)

Supply voltage, V_{CC} (see Note 1) . . . . 7 V
Input voltage: '75, 'L75, '77, 'L77 . . . . 5.5 V
            'LS75, 'LS77 . . . . 7 V
Interemitter voltage (see Note 2) . . . . 5.5 V
Operating free-air temperature range: SN54', SN54L', SN54LS' Circuits . . . . $-55°C$ to $125°C$
                    SN74', SN74L', SN74LS' Circuits . . . . $0°C$ to $70°C$
Storage temperature range . . . . $-65°C$ to $150°C$

NOTES: 1. Voltage values, except interemitter voltage, are with respect to network ground terminal.
       2. This is the voltage between two emitters of a multiple-emitter input transistor and is not applicable to the 'LS75 and 'LS77.

Courtesy Texas Instruments, Inc.

functional block diagrams (each latch)

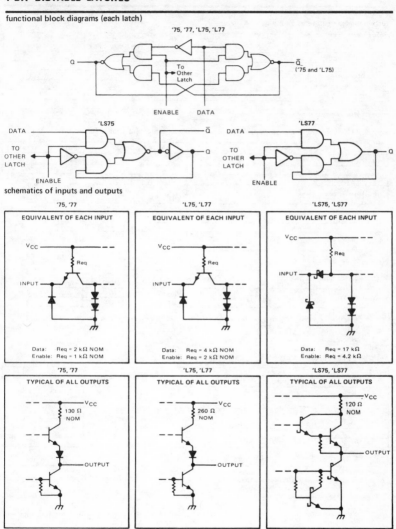

schematics of inputs and outputs

Courtesy Texas Instruments, Inc.

recommended operating conditions

	SN5475, SN5477			SN7475			UNIT
	MIN	NOM	MAX	MIN	NOM	MAX	
Supply voltage, V_{CC}	4.5	5	5.5	4.75	5	5.25	V
High-level output current, I_{OH}			−400			−400	μA
Low-level output current, I_{OL}			16			16	mA
Width of enabling pulse, t_w	20			20			ns
Setup time, t_{su}	20			20			ns
Hold time, t_h	5			5			ns
Operating free-air temperature, T_A	−55		125	0		70	°C

electrical characteristics over recommended operating free-air temperature range (unless otherwise noted)

PARAMETER		TEST CONDITIONS[†]		MIN	TYP[‡]	MAX	UNIT
V_{IH} High-level input voltage				2			V
V_{IL} Low-level input voltage						0.8	V
V_{IK} Input clamp voltage		V_{CC} = MIN,	I_I = −12 mA			−1.5	V
V_{OH} High-level output voltage		V_{CC} = MIN, V_{IH} = 2 V, V_{IL} = 0.8 V, I_{OH} = −400 μA		2.4	3.4		V
V_{OL} Low-level output voltage		V_{CC} = MIN, V_{IH} = 2 V, V_{IL} = 0.8 V, I_{OL} = 16 mA			0.2	0.4	V
I_I Input current at maximum input voltage		V_{CC} = MAX,	V_I = 5.5 V			1	mA
I_{IH} High-level input current	D input	V_{CC} = MAX,	V_I = 2.4 V			80	μA
	G input					160	
I_{IL} Low-level input current	D input	V_{CC} = MAX,	V_I = 0.4 V			−3.2	mA
	G input					−6.4	
I_{OS} Short-circuit output current[§]		V_{CC} = MAX	SN54'	−20		−57	mA
			SN74'	−18		−57	
I_{CC} Supply current		V_{CC} = MAX, See Note 3	SN54'		32	46	mA
			SN74'		32	53	

[†] For conditions shown as MIN or MAX, use the appropriate value specified under recommended operating conditions.
[‡] All typical values are at V_{CC} = 5 V, T_A = 25°C.
[§] Not more than one output should be shorted at a time.
NOTE 3: I_{CC} is tested with all inputs grounded and all outputs open.

switching characteristics, V_{CC} = 5 V, T_A = 25°C

PARAMETER	FROM (INPUT)	TO (OUTPUT)	TEST CONDITIONS	MIN	TYP	MAX	UNIT
t_{PLH}	D	Q			16	30	ns
t_{PHL}					14	25	
t_{PLH}[¶]	D	$\bar{Q}$			24	40	ns
t_{PHL}[¶]			C_L = 15 pF, R_L = 400 Ω, See Figure 1		7	15	
t_{PLH}	G	Q			16	30	ns
t_{PHL}					7	15	
t_{PLH}[¶]	G	$\bar{Q}$			16	30	ns
t_{PHL}[¶]					7	15	

t_{PLH} propagation delay time, low-to-high-level output
t_{PHL} propagation delay time, high-to-low-level output
[¶] These parameters are not applicable for the SN5477.

Courtesy Texas Instruments, Inc.

TYPES SN54L75, SN54L77, SN74L75, SN74L77
4-BIT BISTABLE LATCHES

recommended operating conditions

	SN54L75, SN54L77			SN74L75, SN74L77			UNIT
	MIN	NOM	MAX	MIN	NOM	MAX	
Supply voltage, V_{CC}	4.5	5	5.5	4.75	5	5.25	V
High-level output current, I_{OH}			−200			−200	μA
Low-level output current, I_{OL}			8			8	mA
Width of enabling pulse, t_w	100			100			ns
Setup time, t_{su}	40			40			ns
Hold time, t_h	10			10			ns
Operating free-air temperature, T_A	−55		125	0		70	°C

electrical characteristics over recommended operating free-air temperature range (unless otherwise noted)

PARAMETER		TEST CONDITIONS[†]		MIN	TYP[‡]	MAX	UNIT
V_{IH}	High-level input voltage			2			V
V_{IL}	Low-level input voltage					0.8	V
V_{IK}	Input clamp voltage	V_{CC} = MIN,	I_I = −12 mA			−1.5	V
V_{OH}	High-level output voltage	V_{CC} = MIN,	V_{IH} = 2 V,	2.4	3.4		V
		V_{IL} = 0.8 V,	I_{OH} = −200 μA				
V_{OL}	Low-level output voltage	V_{CC} = MIN,	V_{IH} = 2 V,		0.2	0.4	V
		V_{IL} = 0.8 V,	I_{OL} = 8 mA				
I_I	Input current at maximum input voltage	V_{CC} = MAX,	V_I = 5.5 V			1	mA
I_{IH}	High-level input current	D input	V_{CC} = MAX, V_I = 2.4 V			40	μA
		G input				80	
I_{IL}	Low-level input current	D input	V_{CC} = MAX, V_I = 0.4 V			−1.6	mA
		G input				−3.2	
I_{OS}	Short-circuit output current[§]	SN54L'	V_{CC} = MAX	−10		−29	mA
		SN74L'		−9		−29	
I_{CC}	Supply current	SN54L'	V_{CC} = MAX, See Note 3		16	23	mA
		SN74L'			16	27	

[†]For conditions shown as MIN or MAX, use the appropriate value specified under recommended operating conditions.
[‡]All typical values are at V_{CC} = 5 V, T_A = 25°C.
[§]Nor more than one output should be shorted at a time.
NOTE 3: I_{CC} is tested with all inputs grounded and all outputs open.

switching characteristics, V_{CC} = 5 V, T_A = 25°C

PARAMETER[◊]	FROM (INPUT)	TO (OUTPUT)	TEST CONDITIONS	MIN	TYP	MAX	UNIT
t_{PLH}	D	Q			32	60	ns
t_{PHL}					28	50	
t_{PLH}[¶]	D	$\overline{Q}$	C_L = 15 pF,		48	80	ns
t_{PHL}[¶]			R_L = 800 Ω,		14	30	
t_{PLH}	G	Q	See Figure 1		32	60	ns
t_{PHL}					14	30	
t_{PLH}[¶]	G	$\overline{Q}$			32	60	ns
t_{PHL}[¶]					14	30	

[◊]t_{PLH} ≡ propagation delay time, low-to-high-level output
t_{PHL} ≡ propagation delay time, high-to-low-level output
[¶] These parameters are not applicable for the SN54L77 and SN74L77.

Courtesy Texas Instruments, Inc.

recommended operating conditions

	SN54LS75 SN54LS77			SN74LS75			UNIT
	MIN	NOM	MAX	MIN	NOM	MAX	
Supply voltage, V_{CC}	4.5	5	5.5	4.75	5	5.25	V
High-level output current, I_{OH}			−400			−400	μA
Low-level output current, I_{OL}			4			8	mA
Width of enabling pulse, t_w	20			20			ns
Setup time, t_{su}	20			20			ns
Hold time, t_h	0			0			ns
Operating free-air temperature, T_A	−55		125	0		70	°C

electrical characteristics over recommended operating free-air temperature range (unless otherwise noted)

PARAMETER		TEST CONDITIONS[†]		SN54LS75 SN54LS77			SN74LS75			UNIT
				MIN	TYP[‡]	MAX	MIN	TYP[‡]	MAX	
V_{IH}	High-level input voltage			2			2			V
V_{IL}	Low-level input voltage					0.7			0.8	V
V_{IK}	Input clamp voltage	V_{CC} = MIN, I_I = −18 mA				−1.5			−1.5	V
V_{OH}	High-level output voltage	V_{CC} = MIN, V_{IH} = 2 V, $V_{IL} = V_{IL}$ max, I_{OH} = −400 μA		2.5	3.5		2.7	3.5		V
V_{OL}	Low-level output voltage	V_{CC} = MIN, V_{IH} = 2 V, $V_{IL} = V_{IL}$ max	I_{OL} = 4 mA		0.25	0.4		0.25	0.4	V
			I_{OL} = 8 mA					0.35	0.5	
I_I	Input current at maximum input voltage	V_{CC} = MAX, V_I = 7 V	D input			0.1			0.1	mA
			G input			0.4			0.4	
I_{IH}	High-level input current	V_{CC} = MAX, V_I = 2.7 V	D input			20			20	μA
			G input			80			80	
I_{IL}	Low-level input current	V_{CC} = MAX, V_I = 0.4 V	D input			−0.4			−0.4	mA
			G input			−1.6			−1.6	
I_{OS}	Short-circuit output current[§]	V_{CC} = MAX		−20		−100	−20		−100	mA
I_{CC}	Supply current	V_{CC} = MAX, See Note 2	'LS75		6.3	12		6.3	12	mA
			'LS77		6.9	13				

[†] For conditions shown as MIN or MAX, use the appropriate value specified under recommended operating conditions.
[‡] All typical values are at V_{CC} = 5 V, T_A = 25°C.
[§] Not more than one output should be shorted at a time, and duration of the short-circuit should not exceed one second
NOTE 2: I_{CC} is tested with all inputs grounded and all outputs open.

switching characteristics, V_{CC} = 5 V, T_A = 25°C

PARAMETER[◊]	FROM (INPUT)	TO (OUTPUT)	TEST CONDITIONS	'LS75			'LS77			UNIT
				MIN	TYP	MAX	MIN	TYP	MAX	
t_{PLH}	D	Q			15	27		11	19	ns
t_{PHL}					9	17		9	17	
t_{PLH}	D	$\bar{Q}$	C_L = 15 pF, R_L = 2 kΩ, See Figure 1		12	20				ns
t_{PHL}					7	15				
t_{PLH}	G	Q			15	27		10	18	ns
t_{PHL}					14	25		10	18	
t_{PLH}	G	$\bar{Q}$			16	30				ns
t_{PHL}					7	15				

[◊] t_{PLH} ≡ propagation delay time, low-to-high-level output
t_{PHL} ≡ propagation delay time, high-to-low-level output

Courtesy Texas Instruments, Inc.

PARAMETER MEASUREMENT INFORMATION

switching characteristics

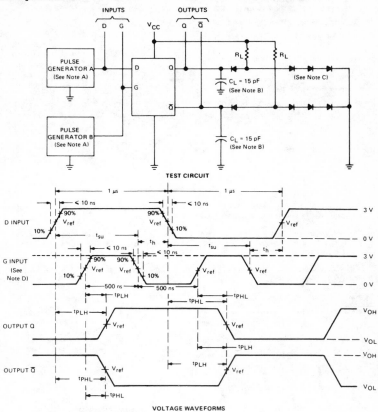

TEST CIRCUIT

VOLTAGE WAVEFORMS

NOTES: A. The pulse generators have the following characteristics: $Z_{out} \approx 50\ \Omega$; for pulse generator A, PRR ≤ 500 kHz; for pulse generator B, PRR ≤ 1 MHz. Positions of D and G input pulses are varied with respect to each other to verify setup times.
   B. C_L includes probe and jig capacitance.
   C. All diodes are 1N3064.
   D. When measuring propagation delay times from the D input, the corresponding G input must be held high.
   E. For '75, '77, 'L75, and 'L77, V_{ref} = 1.5 V; for 'LS75 and 'LS77, V_{ref} = 1.3 V.
†Complementary Q outputs are on the '75, 'L75, and 'LS75 only.

Courtesy Texas Instruments, Inc.

- Bi-directional Bus Transceiver in a High-Density 20-Pin Package
- 3-State Outputs Drive Bus Lines Directly
- P-N-P Inputs Reduce D-C Loading on Bus Lines
- Hysteresis at Bus Inputs Improve Noise Margins
- Typical Propagation Delay Times, Port-to-Port . . . 8 ns
- Typical Enable/Disable Times . . . 17 ns

TYPE	I_{OL} (SINK CURRENT)	I_{OH} (SOURCE CURRENT)
SN54LS245	12 mA	−12 mA
SN74LS245	24 mA	−15 mA

SN54LS245 . . . J PACKAGE
SN74LS245 . . . J OR N PACKAGE
(TOP VIEW)

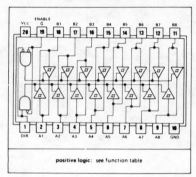

positive logic: see function table

description

These octal bus transceivers are designed for asynchronous two-way communication between data buses. The control function implementation minimizes external timing requirements.

The device allows data transmission from the A bus to the B bus or from the B bus to the A bus depending upon the logic level at the direction control (DIR) input. The enable input ($\overline{G}$) can be used to disable the device so that the buses are effectively isolated.

The SN54LS245 is characterized for operation over the full military temperature range of −55°C to 125°C. The SN74LS245 is characterized for operation from 0°C to 70°C.

schematics of inputs and outputs

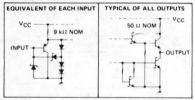

FUNCTION TABLE

ENABLE $\overline{G}$	DIRECTION CONTROL DIR	OPERATION
L	L	B data to A bus
L	H	A data to B bus
H	X	Isolation

H = high level, L = low level, X = irrelevant

absolute maximum ratings over operating free-air temperature range (unless otherwise noted)

Supply voltage, V_{CC} (see Note 1) . . . . 7 V
Input voltage . . . . 7 V
Operating free-air temperature range: SN54LS245 . . . . −55°C to 125°C
                                        SN74LS245 . . . . 0°C to 70°C
Storage temperature range . . . . −65°C to 150°C

NOTE 1: Voltage values are with respect to network ground terminal.

Courtesy Texas Instruments, Inc.

recommended operating conditions

PARAMETER	SN54LS245			SN74LS245			UNIT
	MIN	NOM	MAX	MIN	NOM	MAX	
Supply voltage, V_{CC}	4.5	5	5.5	4.75	5	5.25	V
High-level output current, I_{OH}			−12			−15	mA
Low-level output current, I_{OL}			12			24	mA
Operating free-air temperature, T_A	−55		125	0		70	°C

electrical characteristics over recommended operating free-air temperature range (unless otherwise noted)

PARAMETER		TEST CONDITIONS†		SN54LS245			SN74LS245			UNIT
				MIN	TYP‡	MAX	MIN	TYP‡	MAX	
V_{IH}	High-level input voltage			2			2			V
V_{IL}	Low-level input voltage					0.7			0.8	V
V_{IK}	Input clamp voltage	V_{CC} = MIN,	I_I = −18 mA			−1.5			−1.5	V
	Hysteresis $(V_{T+} - V_{T-})$A or B input	V_{CC} = MIN		0.2	0.4		0.2	0.4		V
V_{OH}	High-level output voltage	V_{CC} = MIN, V_{IH} = 2 V, $V_{IL} = V_{IL}$ max	I_{OH} = −3 mA	2.4	3.4		2.4	3.4		V
			I_{OH} = MAX	2			2			
V_{OL}	Low-level output voltage	V_{CC} = MIN, V_{IH} = 2 V, $V_{IL} = V_{IL}$ max	I_{OL} = 12 mA			0.4			0.4	V
			I_{OL} = 24 mA						0.5	
I_{OZH}	Off-state output current, high-level voltage applied	V_{CC} = MAX, $\overline{G}$ at 2 V	V_O = 2.7 V			10			10	μA
I_{OZL}	Off-state output current, low-level voltage applied		V_O = 0.4 V			−200			−200	
I_I	Input current at maximum input voltage	A or B	V_{CC} = MAX,	V_I = 5.5 V			0.1			0.1	mA
		DIR or $\overline{G}$		V_I = 7 V			0.1			0.1	
I_{IH}	High-level input current	V_{CC} = MAX,	V_{IH} = 2.7 V			20			20	μA
I_{IL}	Low-level input current	V_{CC} = MAX,	V_{IL} = 0.4 V			−0.2			−0.2	mA
I_{OS}	Short-circuit output current¶	V_{CC} = MAX		−40		−225	−40		−225	mA
I_{CC}	Supply current	Total, outputs high	V_{CC} = MAX, Outputs open		48	70		48	70	mA
		Total, outputs low			62	90		62	90	
		Outputs at Hi-Z			64	95		64	95	

†For conditions shown as MIN or MAX, use the appropriate value specified under recommended operating conditions.
‡All typical values are at V_{CC} = 5 V, T_A = 25°C.
¶Not more than one output should be shorted at a time, and duration of the short-circuit should not exceed one second.

switching characteristics, V_{CC} = 5 V, T_A = 25°C

PARAMETER		TEST CONDITIONS		MIN	TYP	MAX	UNIT
t_{PLH}	Propagation delay time, low-to-high-level output	C_L = 45 pF,	R_L = 667 Ω, See Note 2		8	12	ns
t_{PHL}	Propagation delay time, high-to-low-level output				8	12	ns
t_{PZL}	Output enable time to low level				27	40	ns
t_{PZH}	Output enable time to high level				25	40	ns
t_{PLZ}	Output disable time from low level	C_L = 5 pF,	R_L = 667 Ω, See Note 2		15	25	ns
t_{PHZ}	Output disable time from high level				15	25	ns

NOTE 2: Load circuit and waveforms are shown on page 3-11.

Courtesy Texas Instruments, Inc.

APPENDIX C

Electrical Characteristics of Typical ROMs

FEATURES

- High performance replacement for Intel 2308/8308, and TI 4700
- 350ns max access time
- Single +5V ±10% power supply
- Contact programmed for fast turn-around
- Two programmable chip selects
- Inputs and three-state outputs TTL compatible
- Eight bit output for use with microprocessor systems
- Pin compatible with MK 2708 EPROM

DESCRIPTION

The MK 30000 is a 8,192 bit Read Only Memory designed as a high performance replacement for the Intel 2308/8308 and the TI 4700. The MK 30000 is organized as a 1K x 8 array which makes the device very attractive for use with 8-bit microprocessors such as the F8, 8080, 6800, Z-80 or any memory application requiring a high performance, high bit density ROM.

The device uses a single +5V (± 10% tolerance) power supply. The two chip select inputs can be programmed for any desired combination of active high's or low's. These programmable chip select inputs coupled with the three-state TTL compatible outputs provide a high performance memory circuit with extremely simple interface requirements.

An outstanding feature of the MK 30000 is the use of contact programming instead of gate mask programming. Since the contact mask is applied at a later processing stage, wafers can be partially processed and stored. When an order is received, a contact mask, which represents the desired bit pattern, is generated and applied to the wafers. Only a few processing steps are left to complete the part. Therefore, the use of contact programming reduces the turnaround time for a custom ROM.

The MK 30000 is fabricated with N-channel silicon gate MOS technology for optimum size and circuit performance. Ion-implantation is utilized to allow full TTL compatibility at the inputs and outputs. All inputs are protected against static charge.

FUNCTIONAL DIAGRAM

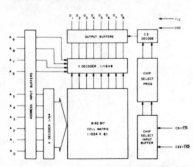

PIN CONNECTIONS

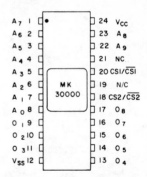

Courtesy Mostek

322

ABSOLUTE MAXIMUM RATINGS*

Voltage on Any Terminal Relative to Ground . . . . −0.5V to + 7V

Operating Temperature T$_A$ (Ambient) . . . . 0°C to + 70°C

Storage Temperature — Ceramic (Ambient) . . . . −65°C to + 150°C

Storage Temperature — Plastic (Ambient) . . . . −55°C to +125°C

Power Dissipation . . . . 1 Watt

*Stresses greater than those listed under "Absolute Maximum Ratings" may cause permanent damage to the device. This is a stress rating only and functional operation of the device at these or any other conditions above those indicated in the operating sections of this specification is not implied. Exposure to absolute maximum rating conditions for extended periods may affect device reliability.

RECOMMENDED DC OPERATING CONDITIONS
(V$_{CC}$ = 5V ± 10%; 0°C ≤ T$_A$ ≤ + 70°C)

	PARAMETER	MIN	TYP	MAX	UNITS	NOTES
V$_{CC}$	Power Supply Voltage	4.5	5.0	5.5	Volts	6
V$_{IL}$	Input Logic 0 Voltage	−0.5		0.8	Volts	
V$_{IH}$	Input Logic 1 Voltage	2.0		V$_{CC}$	Volts	

D C ELECTRICAL CHARACTERISTICS
(V$_{CC}$ = 5V ± 10%; 0°C ≤ T$_A$ ≤ + 70°C)[6]

	PARAMETER	MIN	MAX	UNITS	NOTES
I$_{CC}$	V$_{CC}$ Power Supply Current		60	mA	1
I$_{I(L)}$	Input Leakage Current		10	μ A	2
I$_{O(L)}$	Output Leakage Current		10	μ A	3
V$_{OL}$	Output Logic 0 Voltage @ I$_{OUT}$ = 3.3mA		0.4	volts	
V$_{OH}$	Output Logic 1 Voltage @ I$_{OUT}$ = −220 μA	2.4	V$_{CC}$	volts	

A C ELECTRICAL CHARACTERISTICS
(V$_{CC}$ = 5V ± 10%; 0°C ≤ T$_A$ ≤ + 70°C)[6]

	PARAMETER	MIN	MAX	UNITS	NOTES
t$_{ACC}$	Address to output delay time		350	ns	4
t$_{CS}$	Chip select to output delay time		175	ns	4
t$_{CD}$	Chip deselect to output delay time		150	ns	4

CAPACITANCE

	PARAMETER	TYP	MAX	UNITS	NOTES
C$_{IN}$	Input Capacitance	6	8	pF	5
C$_{OUT}$	Output Capacitance	10	15	pF	5

NOTES:

1. All inputs 5.5V; Data Outputs open.
2. V$_{IN}$ = 0V to 5.5V
3. Device unselected; V$_{OUT}$ = 0V to 5.5V.
4. Measured with 2 TTL loads and 100pF, transition times = 20ns

5. Capacitance measured with Boonton Meter or effective capacitance calculated from the equation :
   $$C = \frac{I \Delta t}{\Delta V}$$ with current equal to a constant 20mA.
6. A minimum 100 μs time delay is required after the application of V$_{CC}$ (+5) before proper device operation is achieved.

Courtesy Mostek

 **MOTOROLA**

MCM68764
MCM68A764

Advance Information

MOS
(N-CHANNEL, SILICON-GATE)
8192 X 8-BIT
UV ERASABLE PROM

8192 X 8-BIT UV ERASABLE PROM

The MCM68764/68A764 is a 65,536-bit Erasable and Electrically Reprogrammable PROM designed for system debug usage and similar applications requiring nonvolatile memory that could be reprogrammed periodically or for replacing 64K ROMs for fast turnaround time. The transparent window on the package allows the memory content to be erased with ultraviolet light.

For ease of use, the device operates from a single power supply and has a static power-down mode. Pin-for-pin mask programmable ROMs are available for large volume production runs of systems initially using the MCM68764/68A764.

- Single +5 V Power Supply
- Automatic Power-down Mode (Standby) with Chip Enable
- Organized as 8192 Bytes of 8 Bits
- Low Power Dissipation
- Fully TTL Compatible
- Maximum Access Time = 450 ns MCM68764
                         350 ns MCM68A764
- Standard 24-Pin DIP for EPROM Upgradability
- Pin Compatible to MCM68A364 Mask Programmable ROM

C SUFFIX
FRIT-SEAL PACKAGE
CASE 623A

L SUFFIX
CERAMIC PACKAGE
CASE 716

PIN ASSIGNMENT

1 A7	VCC 24
2 A6	A8 23
3 A5	A9 22
4 A4	A12 21
5 A3	E/Vpp 20
6 A2	A10 19
7 A1	A11 18
8 A0	DQ7 17
9 DQ0	DQ6 16
10 DQ1	DQ5 15
11 DQ2	DQ4 14
12 VSS	DQ3 13

MODE SELECTION

Mode	PIN NUMBER			
	9-11, 13-17, DQ	12 V_{SS}	20 $\overline{E}/V_{PP}$	24 V_{CC}
Read	Data out	V_{SS}	V_{IL}	V_{CC}
Output Disable	Hi-Z	V_{SS}	V_{IH}	V_{CC}
Standby	Hi-Z	V_{SS}	V_{IH}	V_{CC}
Program	Data in	V_{SS}	Pulsed V_{ILP} to V_{IHP}	V_{CC}

PIN NAMES

A	Address
DQ	Data Input/Output
E/Vpp	Chip Enable/Program
G	Output Enable

*New industry standard nomenclature

ABSOLUTE MAXIMUM RATINGS (1)

Rating	Value	Unit
Temperature Under Bias	–10 to +80	°C
Storage Temperature	–65 to +125	°C
All Input or Output Voltages with Respect to V_{SS} during Read	+ 6 to –0.3	Vdc
Vpp Supply Voltage with Respect to V_{SS}	+28 to –0.3	Vdc

NOTE 1. Permanent device damage may occur if ABSOLUTE MAXIMUM RATINGS are exceeded. Functional operation should be restricted to RECOMMENDED OPERATING CONDITIONS. Exposure to higher than recommended voltages for extended periods of time could affect device reliability.

This is advance information and specifications are subject to change without notice.

Courtesy Motorola Semiconductor Products, Inc.

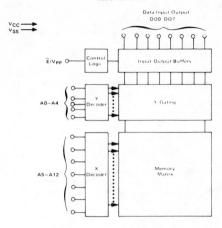

BLOCK DIAGRAM

DC OPERATING CONDITIONS AND CHARACTERISTICS
(Full operating voltage and temperature range unless otherwise noted)

RECOMMENDED DC READ OPERATING CONDITIONS (T_A = 0° to +70°C)

Parameter		Symbol	Min	Nom	Max	Unit
Supply Voltage*	MCM68764	V_{CC}	4.75	5.0	5.25	Vdc
	MCM68A764		4.5	5.0	5.5	
Input High Voltage		V_{IH}	2.0	–	V_{CC} +1.0	Vdc
Input Low Voltage		V_{IL}	–0.1	–	0.8	Vdc

READ OPERATING DC CHARACTERISTICS

Characteristic	Condition	Symbol	Min	Typ	Max	Unit
Address Input Sink Current	V_{in} = 5.25 V	I_{in}	–	–	10	μA
Output Leakage Current	V_{out} = 5.25 V	I_{LO}	–	–	10	μA
E/Vpp Input Sink Current	$\overline{E}$/Vpp = V_{IL}	I_{EL}	–	–	10	μA
	$\overline{E}$/Vpp = V_{IH}	I_{EH} = I_{PL}	–	–	200	μA
	$\overline{E}$/Vpp = V_{IHP}	I_{PH}	–	–	30	mA
V_{CC} Supply Current (Active)	$\overline{E}$/Vpp = V_{IL}	I_{CC1}	–	–	160	mA
V_{CC} Supply Current (Standby)	$\overline{E}$/Vpp = V_{IH}	I_{CC2}	–	–	25	mA
Output Low Voltage	I_{OL} = 2.1 mA	V_{OL}	–	0.1	0.45	V
Output High Voltage	I_{OH} = –400 μA	V_{OH}	2.4	4.0	–	V

CAPACITANCE
(f = 1.0 MHz, T_A = 25°C, periodically sampled rather than 100% tested.)

Characteristic	Symbol	Typ	Max	Unit
Input Capacitance (V_{in} = 0 V)	C_{in}	4.0	6.0	pF
Output Capacitance (V_{out} = 0 V)	C_{out}	8.0	12	pF

Capacitance measured with a Boonton Meter or effective capacitance calculated from the equation $C = \dfrac{I \Delta t}{\Delta V}$.

This device contains circuitry to protect the inputs against damage due to high static voltages or electric fields; however, it is advised that normal precautions be taken to avoid application of any voltage higher than maximum rated voltages to this high-impedance circuit.

Courtesy Motorola Semiconductor Products, Inc.

FULLY DECODED 16,384 BIT MASK PROGRAMMABLE READ ONLY MEMORY

DESCRIPTION   The NEC μPD2316E is a high speed 16,384 bit mask programmable Read Only Memory organized as 2048 words by 8 bits. The μPD2316E is fabricated with N-channel MOS technology.

The inputs and outputs are fully TTL compatible. The device operates with a single +5V power supply. The three chip select inputs are programmable. Any combination of active high or low level chip select inputs can be defined and desired chip select code is fixed during the masking process.

FEATURES
- Access Time 450 ns Max
- 2048 Words x 8 Bits Organization
- Single +5V ±10% Power Supply Voltage
- Directly TTL Compatible — All Inputs and Outputs
- Three Programmable Chip Select Inputs for Easy Memory Expansion
- Three-State Output — OR-Tie Capability
- On-Chip Address Fully Decoded
- All Inputs Protected Against Static Charge
- Direct Replacement for 2316E
- Available in 24-pin plastic or ceramic packages

PIN CONFIGURATION

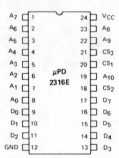

PIN NAMES	
$A_0 - A_{10}$	Address Inputs
$D_1 - D_8$	Data Outputs
$CS_1 - CS_3$	Programmable Chip Select Inputs

Courtesy NEC Microcomputers, Inc.

μPD2316E

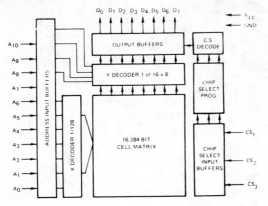

BLOCK DIAGRAM

Operating Temperature . . . . −10°C to +70°C
Storage Temperature . . . . −65°C to +125°C
Voltage on Any Pin . . . . −0.5 to +7.0 Volts ①

ABSOLUTE MAXIMUM RATINGS*

Note: ① With Respect to Ground.

COMMENT: Stress above those listed under "Absolute Maximum Ratings" may cause permanent
damage to the device. This is a stress rating only and functional operation of the device at these or
any other conditions above those indicated in the operational sections of this specification is not
implied. Exposure to absolute maximum rating conditions for extended periods may affect device
reliability.

*T_a = 25°C

T_a = −10°C to +70°C; V_{CC} = +5 ± 5% unless otherwise noted.

DC CHARACTERISTICS

PARAMETER	SYMBOL	LIMITS MIN	LIMITS TYP ①	LIMITS MAX	UNIT	TEST CONDITIONS
Input Load Current (All Input Pins)	I_{LI}			+10	μA	V_{IN} = V_{CC}
				−10	μA	V_{IN} = 0V
Output Leakage Current	I_{LOH}			+10	μA	Chip Deselected, V_0 = V_{CC}
Output Leakage Current	I_{LOL}			−20	μA	Chip Deselected, V_0 = 0V
Power Supply Current	I_{CC}		70	120	mA	
Input "Low" Voltage	V_{IL}	−0.5		0.8	V	
Input "High" Voltage	V_{IH}	+2.4		V_{CC} + 1.0V	V	
Output "Low" Voltage	V_{OL}			0.4	V	I_{OL} = 2.1 mA
Output "High" Voltage	V_{OH}	+2.4			V	I_{OH} = −400 μA

Note: ① Typical values for T_a = 25°C and nominal supply voltage.

Courtesy NEC Microcomputers, Inc.

DESCRIPTION

The 82S190 and 82S191 are field program-mable, which means that custom patterns are immediately available by following the fusing procedure given in this data sheet. The standard 82S190 and 82S191 are sup-plied with all outputs at a logical low. Out-puts are programmed to a logic high level at any specified address by fusing a Ni-Cr link matrix.

These devices include on-chip decoding and 3 chip enable inputs for ease of memory expansion. They feature either open collec-tor or tri-state outputs for optimization of word expansion in bused organizations.

Both 82S190 and 82S191 devices are avail-able in the commercial and military ranges. For the commercial temperature range (0°C to +75°C) specify N82S190/191, I, and for the military temperature range (-55°C to +125°C) specify S82S190/191, I.

FEATURES
- Address access time:
  N82S190/191: 80ns max
  S82S190/: 100ns max
- Power dissipation : 40μW/bit typ
- Input loading:
  N82S190/191: -100μA max
  S82S190/191: -150μA max
- 3 chip enable inputs
- On-chip address decoding
- Output options:
  82S190: Open collector
  82S191: Tri-state
- No separate fusing pins
- Unprogrammed outputs are low level
- Fully TTL compatible

APPLICATIONS
- Prototyping/volume production
- Sequential controllers
- Microprogramming
- Hardwired algorithms
- Control store
- Random logic
- Code conversion

PIN CONFIGURATION

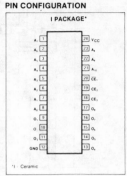

I PACKAGE*

*I - Ceramic

BLOCK DIAGRAM

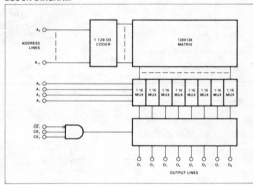

ABSOLUTE MAXIMUM RATINGS

	PARAMETER	RATING	UNIT
V_{CC}	Supply voltage	+7	Vdc
V_{IN}	Input voltage	+5.5	Vdc
	Output voltage		Vdc
V_{OH}	High (82S140)	+5.5	
V_O	Off-state (82S141)	+5.5	
	Temperature range		°C
T_A	Operating		
	N82S190/191	0 to +75	
	S82S190/191	-55 to +125	
T_{STG}	Storage	-65 to +150	

Courtesy Signetics Corp.

82S190-I • 82S191-I

DC ELECTRICAL CHARACTERISTICS
N82S190/191: 0°C ≤ T_A ≤ +75°C, 4.75V ≤ V_{CC} ≤ 5.25V
S82S190/191: -55°C ≤ T_A ≤ +125°C, 4.5V ≤ V_{CC} ≤ 5.5V

PARAMETER		TEST CONDITIONS[1]	N82S190/191			S82S190/191			UNIT
			Min	Typ[2]	Max	Min	Typ[2]	Max	
	Input voltage								V
V_{IL}	Low				.85			.80	
V_{IH}	High		2.0			2.0			
V_{IC}	Clamp	I_{IN} = -18mA		-0.8	-1.2		-0.8	-1.2	
	Output voltage								V
V_{OL}	Low	I_{OUT} = 9.6mA			0.45			0.5	
V_{OH}	High (82S191)	I_{OUT} = -2mA, $\overline{CE}_1$ = Low, CE_2 = High, CE_3 = High, High stored	2.4			2.4			
	Input current								μA
I_{IL}	Low	V_{IN} = 0.45V			-100			-150	
I_{IH}	High	V_{IN} = 5.5V			40			50	
	Output current								
I_{OLK}	Leakage (82S190)	V_{OUT} = 5.5V, $\overline{CE}_1$ = High, CE_2 = Low, CE_3 = Low			40			60	μA
$I_{O(OFF)}$	Hi-Z state (82S191)	V_{OUT} = 0.5V, $\overline{CE}_1$ = High, CE_2 = Low, CE_3 = Low			-40			-60	μA
		V_{OUT} = 5.5V, $\overline{CE}_1$ = High, CE_2 = Low, CE_3 = Low			40			60	
I_{OS}	Short circuit (82S191)	V_{OUT} = 0V	-20		-70	-15		-85	mA
I_{CC}	V_{CC} supply current			130	175		130	185	mA
	Capacitance	V_{CC} = 5.0V							pF
C_{IN}	Input	V_{IN} = 2.0V		5			5		
C_{OUT}	Output	V_{OUT} = 2.0V		8			8		

AC ELECTRICAL CHARACTERISTICS
R_1 = 470Ω, R_2 = 1kΩ, C_L = 30pF
N82S190/191: 0°C ≤ T_A ≤ +75°C, 4.75V ≤ V_{CC} ≤ 5.25V
S82S190/191: -55°C ≤ T_A ≤ +125°C, 4.5V ≤ V_{CC} ≤ 5.5V

PARAMETER		TO	FROM	N82S190/191			S82S190/191			UNIT
				Min	Typ[2]	Max	Min	Typ[2]	Max	
	Access time									ns
T_{AA}[3]		Output	Address		50	80		50	100	
T_{CE}		Output	Chip enable		20	40		20	50	
	Disable time									ns
T_{CD}		Output	Chip disable		20	40		20	50	

NOTES
1. Positive current is defined as into the terminal referenced.
2. Typical values are at V_{CC} = 5.0V, T_A = +25°C.
3. Tested at an address cycle time of 1μsec.

Courtesy Signetics Corp.

329

2332 STATIC READ ONLY MEMORY (4096x8)

DESCRIPTION

The 2332 high performance read only memory is organized 4096 words by 8 bits with access times of less than 450 ns. This ROM is designed to be compatible with all microprocessor and similar applications where high performance, large bit storage and simple interfacing are important design considerations. This device offers TTL input and output levels.

The 2332 operates totally asynchronously. No clock input is required. The two programmable chip select inputs allow four 32K ROMS to be OR-tied without external decoding.

Designed to replace two 2716 16K EPROMS, the 2332 can eliminate the need to redesign printed circuit boards for volume mask programmed ROMS after prototyping with EPROMS.

- 4096 x 8 Bit Organization
- Single +5 Volt Supply
- Three Week Prototype Turnaround
- Access Time - 450 ns (max)
- Completely TTL Compatible
- Totally Static Operation

- Three-State Outputs for Wire-OR Expansion
- Two Programmable Chip Selects
- Pin Compatible with 2716 & 2732 EPROM
- Replacement for two 2716s
- 2708/2716 EPROMS Accepted as Program Data Inputs
- 400mV Noise Immunity on Inputs

ORDERING INFORMATION:

Part Number*	Package Type	Access Time	Temperature Range
MPS2332	Molded	450 ns	0°C to +70°C
MCS2332	Ceramic	450 ns	0°C to +70°C

*Final Part Number will be assigned by manufacturer

PIN CONFIGURATION

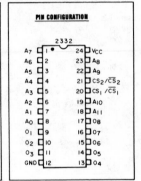

Courtesy MOS Technology, Inc.

Ambient Operating Temperature	0°C to +70°C
Storage Temperature	-65°C to +150°C
Supply Voltage to Ground Potential	-0.5V to +7.0V
Applied Output Voltage	-0.5V to +7.0V
Applied Input Voltage	-0.5V to +7.0V
Power Dissipation	1.0W

Stresses above those listed under "Absolute Maximum Ratings" may cause permanent damage to the device. This is a stress rating only and functional operation of the device at these or any other conditions above those indicated in the operational sections of this specification is not implied.

D. C. CHARACTERISTICS

T_A = 0°C to +70°C, V_{CC} = 5.0V ± 5% (unless otherwise specified)

Symbol	Parameter	Min.	Max.	Units	Test Conditions
I_{CC1}	Power Supply Current		125	mA	V_{IN} = V_{CC}, V_O = Open, T_A = 0°C
I_{CC2}	Power Supply Current		120	mA	V_{IN} = V_{CC}, V_O = Open, T_A = 25°C
I_O	Output Leakage Current		10	µA	Chip Deselected, V_O = 0 to V_{CC}
I_I	Input Load Current		10	µA	V_{CC} = Max. V_{IN} = 0 to V_{CC}
V_{OL}	Output Low Voltage		0.4	Volts	V_{CC} = Min. I_{OL} = 2.1mA
V_{OH}	Output High Voltage	2.4		Volts	V_{CC} = Min. I_{OH} = -400µA
V_{IL}	Input Low Voltage	-0.5	0.8	Volts	See Note 1
V_{IH}	Input High Voltage	2.0	V_{CC}+1	Volts	

A. C. CHARACTERISTICS

T_A = 0°C to +70°C, V_{CC} = 5.0V ± 5% (unless otherwise specfied)

Symbol	Parameter	Min.	Max.	Units	Test Conditions
t_{ACC}	Address Access Time		450	ns	
t_{CO}	Chip Select Delay		200	ns	
t_{DF}	Chip Deselect Delay		175	ns	See Note 2
t_{OH}	Previous Data Valid After Address Change Delay	40		ns	

CAPACITANCE

T_A = 25°C, f = 1.0MHz, See Note 3

Symbol	Parameter	Min.	Max.	Units	Test Conditions
C_{IN}	Input Capacitance		8	pF	All Pins except Pin under Test Tied to AC Ground
C_{OUT}	Output Capacitance		10	pF	

Note 1: Input levels that swing more negative than -0.5V will be clamped and may cause damage to the device.

Note 2: Loading 1 TTL + pF, input transition time: 20 ns.
Timing measurement levels: input 1.5V, output 0.8V and 2.0V

Note 3: This parameter is periodically sampled and is not 100% tested.

Courtesy **MOS Technology**, Inc.

Data Sheets for 2114 R/W Memories

MCM2114
MCM21L14

MOS
(N-CHANNEL, SILICON-GATE)

4096-BIT STATIC RANDOM ACCESS MEMORY

4096-BIT STATIC RANDOM ACCESS MEMORY

The MCM2114 is a 4096-bit random access memory fabricated with high density, high reliability N-channel silicon-gate technology. For ease of use, the device operates from a single power supply, is directly compatible with TTL and DTL, and requires no clocks or refreshing because of fully static operation. Data access is particularly simple, since address setup times are not required. The output data has the same polarity as the input data.

The MCM2114 is designed for memory applications where simple interfacing is the design objective. The MCM2114 is assembled in 18-pin dual-in-line packages with the industry standard pin-out. A separate chip select ($\overline{S}$) lead allows easy selection of an individual package when the three-state outputs are OR-tied.

The MCM2114 series has a maximum current of 100 mA. Low power versions (i.e., MCM21L14 series) are available with a maximum current of only 70 mA.

- 1024 Words by 4-Bit Organization
- Industry Standard 18-Pin Configuration
- Single +5 Volt Supply
- No Clock or Timing Strobe Required
- Fully Static: Cycle Time = Access Time
- Fully TTL/DTL Compatible
- Common Data Input and Output
- Three-State Outputs for OR-Ties
- Low Power Version Available

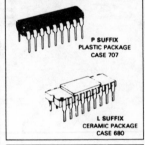

P SUFFIX
PLASTIC PACKAGE
CASE 707

L SUFFIX
CERAMIC PACKAGE
CASE 680

MAXIMUM ACCESS TIME/MINIMUM CYCLE TIME

MCM2114-20 MCM21L14-20	200 ns	MCM2114-30 MCM21L14-30	300 ns
MCM2114-25 MCM21L14-25	250 ns	MCM2114-45 MCM21L14-45	450 ns

PIN ASSIGNMENT

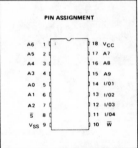

A6	1	18	V_{CC}
A5	2	17	A7
A4	3	16	A8
A3	4	15	A9
A0	5	14	I/O1
A1	6	13	I/O2
A2	7	12	I/O3
$\overline{S}$	8	11	I/O4
V_{SS}	9	10	$\overline{W}$

PIN NAMES

A0 - A9	Address Input
$\overline{W}$	Write Enable
$\overline{S}$	Chip Select
I/O1 - I/O4	Data Input/Output
V_{CC}	Power (+5 V)
V_{SS}	Ground

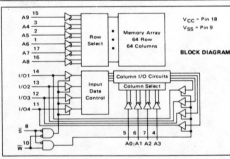

BLOCK DIAGRAM

V_{CC} = Pin 18
V_{SS} = Pin 9

Courtesy Motorola Semiconductor Products, Inc.

ABSOLUTE MAXIMUM RATINGS (See Note 1)

Rating	Value	Unit
Temperature Under Bias	–10 to +80	°C
Voltage on Any Pin With Respect to V_{SS}	–0.5 to +7.0	Vdc
DC Output Current	5.0	mA
Power Dissipation	1.0	Watt
Operating Temperature Range	0 to +70	°C
Storage Temperature Range	–65 to +150	°C

This device contains circuitry to protect the inputs against damage due to high static voltages or electric fields; however, it is advised that normal precautions be taken to avoid application of any voltage higher than maximum rated voltages to this high-impedance circuit.

Note: 1. Permanent device damage may occur if ABSOLUTE MAXIMUM RATINGS are exceeded. Functional operation should be restricted to RECOMMENDED OPERATING CONDITIONS. Exposure to higher than recommended voltages for extended periods of time could affect device reliability.

DC OPERATING CONDITIONS AND CHARACTERISTICS
(T_A = 0° to 70°C, V_{cc} = 5.0V ±5%, unless otherwise noted.)

RECOMMENDED DC OPERATING CONDITIONS

Parameter	Symbol	MCM2114 Min	MCM2114 Nom	MCM2114 Max	MCM21L14 Min	MCM21L14 Nom	MCM21L14 Max	Unit
Input Load Current (All Input Pins, V_{in} = 0 to 5.5 V)	I_{LI}	–	–	10	–	–	10	μA
I/O Leakage Current ($\overline{S}$ = 2.4 V, $V_{I/O}$ = 0.4 V to V_{CC})	I_{LO}	–	–	10	–	–	10	μA
Power Supply Current (V_{in} = 5.5, $I_{I/O}$ = 0 mA, T_A = 25°C)	I_{CC1}	–	80	95	–	–	65	mA
Power Supply Current (V_{in} = 5.5 V, $I_{I/O}$ = 0 mA, T_A = 0°C)	I_{CC2}	–	–	100	–	–	70	mA
Input Low Voltage	V_{IL}	–0.5	–	0.8	–0.5	–	0.8	V
Input High Voltage	V_{IH}	2.0	–	6.0	2.0	–	6.0	V
Output Low Current V_{OL} = 0.4 V	I_{OL}	2.1	6.0	–	2.1	6.0	–	mA
Output High Current V_{OH} = 2.4 V	I_{OH}	–	–1.4	–1.0	–	–1.4	–1.0	mA
Output Short Circuit Current	I_{OS} [2]	–	–	40	–	–	40	mA

Note: 2. Duration not to exceed 30 seconds.

CAPACITANCE
(f = 1.0 MHz, T_A = 25°C, periodically sampled rather than 100% tested.)

Characteristic	Symbol	Max	Unit
Input Capacitance (V_{in} = 0 V)	C_{in}	5.0	pF
Input/Output Capacitance ($V_{I/O}$ = 0 V)	$C_{I/O}$	5.0	pF

AC OPERATING CONDITIONS AND CHARACTERISTICS
(Full operating voltage and temperature unless otherwise noted.)

Input Pulse Levels. . . . . 0.8 Volt to 2.4 Volts

Input Rise and Fall Times . . . . 10 ns

Input and Output Timing Levels . . . . 1.5 Volts

Output Load. . . . . 1 TTL Gate and C_L = 100 pF

MCM2114, MCM21L14

AC OPERATING CONDITIONS AND CHARACTERISTICS
Read (Note 3), Write (Note 4) Cycles

RECOMMENDED AC OPERATING CONDITIONS (T_A = 0 to 70°C, V_{CC} = 5.0 V ± 5%)

Parameter	Symbol	MCM2114-20 MCM21L14-20 Min	Max	MCM2114-25 MCM21L14-25 Min	Max	MCM2114-30 MCM21L14-30 Min	Max	MCM2114-45 MCM21L14-45 Min	Max	Units
Read Cycle Time	t_{RC}	200	–	250	–	300	–	450	–	ns
Access Time	t_A	–	200	–	250	–	300	–	450	ns
Chip Selection to Output Valid	t_{SO}	–	70	–	85	–	100	–	120	ns
Chip Selection to Output Active	t_{SX}	20	–	20	–	20	–	20	–	ns
Output 3-State From Deselection	t_{OTD}	–	60	–	70	–	80	–	100	ns
Output Hold From Address Change	t_{OHA}	50	–	50	–	50	–	50	–	ns
Write Cycle Time	t_{WC}	200	–	250	–	300	–	450	–	ns
Write Time	t_W	120	–	135	–	150	–	200	–	ns
Write Release Time	t_{WR}	0	–	0	–	0	–	0	–	ns
Output 3-State From Write	t_{OTW}	–	60	–	70	–	80	–	100	ns
Data to Write Time Overlap	t_{DW}	120	–	135	–	150	–	200	–	ns
Data Hold From Write Time	t_{DH}	0	–	0	–	0	–	0	–	ns

Notes: 3. A Read occurs during the overlap of a low $\overline{S}$ and a high $\overline{W}$.
4. A Write occurs during the overlap of a low $\overline{S}$ and a low $\overline{W}$.

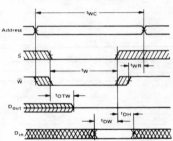

READ CYCLE TIMING (Note 5)

Note: 5. $\overline{W}$ is high for a Read cycle.

WRITE CYCLE TIMING (Notes 6 and 7)

Notes: 6. If the $\overline{S}$ low transition occurs simultaneously with the $\overline{W}$ low transition, the output buffers remain in a high-impedance state.
7. $\overline{W}$ must be high during all address transitions.

WAVEFORMS

Waveform Symbol	Input	Output
——	MUST BE VALID	WILL BE VALID
⟍⟍⟍	CHANGE FROM H TO L	WILL CHANGE FROM H TO L
⟋⟋⟋	CHANGE FROM L TO H	WILL CHANGE FROM L TO H
⨯⨯⨯	DON'T CARE ANY CHANGE PERMITTED	CHANGING STATE UNKNOWN
⟩—		HIGH IMPEDANCE

Courtesy Motorola Semiconductor Products, Inc.

TYPICAL CHARACTERISTICS

SUPPLY CURRENT versus SUPPLY VOLTAGE

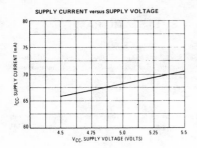

SUPPLY CURRENT versus AMBIENT TEMPERATURE

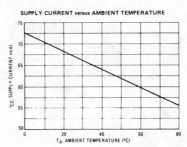

OUTPUT SOURCE CURRENT versus OUTPUT VOLTAGE

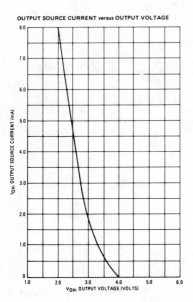

OUTPUT SINK CURRENT versus OUTPUT VOLTAGE

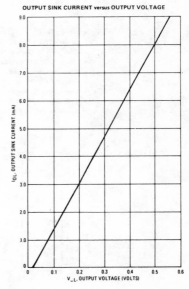

Courtesy Motorola Semiconductor Products, Inc.

4096 BIT (1024 × 4 BITS) STATIC RAM

DESCRIPTION

The NEC μPD2114L is a 4096 bit static Random Access Memory organized as 1024 words by 4 bits using N-channel Silicon-gate MOS technology. It uses fully DC stable (static) circuitry throughout, in both the array and the decoding, and therefore requires no clocks or refreshing to operate and simplify system design. The data is read out nondestructively and has the same polarity as the input data. Common input/output pins are provided.

The μPD2114L is designed for memory applications where high performance, low cost, large bit storage, and simple interfacing are important design objectives. The μPD2114L is placed in an 18-pin package for the highest possible density.

It is directly TTL compatible in all respects: inputs, outputs, and a single +5V supply. A separate Chip Select (CS̄) lead allows easy selection of an individual package when outputs are OR-Tied.

FEATURES

- Access Time: Selection from 150-450 ns
- Single +5 Volt Supply
- Directly TTL Compatible — All Inputs and Outputs
- Completely Static — No Clock or Timing Strobe Required
- Low Operating Power — Typically 0.06 mW/Bit
- Identical Cycle and Access Times
- Common Data Input and Output using Three-State Output
- High Density 18-pin Plastic and Ceramic Packages
- Replacement for 2114L and Equivalent Devices

PIN CONFIGURATION

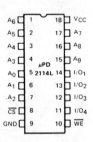

PIN NAMES

A_0-A_9	Address Inputs
W̄Ē	Write Enable
C̄S̄	Chip Select
I/O_1-I/O_4	Data Input/Output
V_{CC}	Power (+5V)
GND	Ground

Courtesy NEC Microcomputers, Inc.

μPD2114L

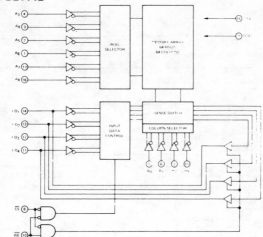

Operating Temperature . . . . -10°C to +80°C
Storage Temperature . . . . -65°C to +150°C
Voltage on any Pin . . . . -0.5 to +7 Volts ①
Power Dissipation . . . . 1 Watt

Note: ① With respect to ground.

COMMENT: Stress above those listed under "Absolute Maximum Ratings" may cause permanent damage to the device. This is a stress rating only and functional operation of the device at these or any other conditions above those indicated in the operational sections of this specification is not implied. Exposure to absolute maximum rating conditions for extended periods may affect device reliability.

*T_a = 25°C

T_a = 25°C; f = 1.0 MHz

PARAMETER	SYMBOL	LIMITS			UNIT	TEST CONDITIONS
		MIN	TYP	MAX		
Input/Output Capacitance	$C_{I/O}$			12	pf	$V_{I/O}$ = 0V
Input Capacitance	C_{IN}			5	pf	V_{IN} = 0V

T_a = 0°C to 70°C; V_{CC} = +5V ± 10% unless otherwise noted.

PARAMETER	SYMBOL	LIMITS			UNIT	TEST CONDITIONS
		MIN	TYP	MAX		
Input Load Current (All Input Pins)	I_{LI}			10	μA	V_{IN} = 0 to 5.5V
I/O Leakage Current	I_{LO}			10	μA	$\overline{CS}$ = 2V, $V_{I/O}$ = 0.4V to V_{CC}
Power Supply Current	I_{CC1}			65	mA	V_{IN} = 5.5V, $I_{I/O}$ = 0 mA, T_a = 25°C
Power Supply Current	I_{CC2}			70	mA	V_{IN} = 5.5V, $I_{I/O}$ = 0 mA, T_a = 0°C
Input Low Voltage	V_{IL}	-0.5		0.8	V	
Input High Voltage	V_{IH}	2.0		6.0	V	
Output Low Current	I_{OL}	3.2			mA	V_{OL} = 0.4V
Output High Current	I_{OH}			-1.0	mA	V_{OH} = 2.4V, V_{CC} = 4.75V
						V_{OH} = 2.2V, V_{CC} = 4.5V

Courtesy NEC Microcomputers, Inc.

AC CHARACTERISTICS Ta = 0°C to +70°C. VCC = +5V ± 10%, unless otherwise noted.

PARAMETER	SYMBOL	2114L		2114L-1		2114L-2		2114L-3		2114L-5		UNIT	TEST CONDITIONS
		MIN	MAX	MIN	MAX	MIN	MAX	MIN	MAX	MIN	MAX		
READ CYCLE													
Read Cycle Time	tRC	450		300		250		200		150		ns	tT = tr = tf = 10 ns
Access Time	tA		450		300		250		200		150	ns	CL = 100 pF
Chip Selection to Output Valid	tCO		120		100		80		70		60	ns	Load = 1 TTL gate
Chip Selection to Output Active	tCX	20		20		20		20		20		ns	Input Levels = 0.8 and 2.0V
Output 3-State from Deselection	tOTD		100		80		70		60		50	ns	Vref = 1.5V
Output Hold from Address Change	tOHA	50		50		50		50		50		ns	
WRITE CYCLE													
Write Cycle Time	tWC	450		300		250		200		150		ns	tT = tr = tf = 10 ns
Write Time	tW	200		150		120		120		80		ns	CL = 100 pF
Write Release Time	tWR	0		0		0		0		0		ns	Load = 1 TTL gate
Output 3-State from Write	tOTW		100		80		70		60		50	ns	Input Levels 0.8 and 2.0V
Data to Write Time Overlap	tDW	200		150		120		120		80		ns	Vref = 1.5V
Data Hold from Write Time	tDH	0		0		0		0		0		ns	
Address to Write Setup Time	tAW	0		0		0		0		0		ns	

TIMING WAVEFORMS

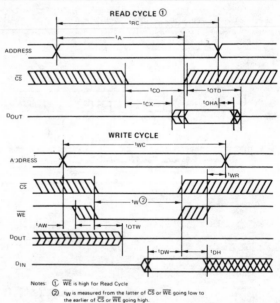

READ CYCLE ①

WRITE CYCLE

Notes: ① WE is high for Read Cycle
② tW is measured from the latter of CS or WE going low to the earlier of CS or WE going high.

Courtesy NEC Microcomputers, Inc.

NORMALIZED ACCESS TIME VS.
SUPPLY VOLTAGE

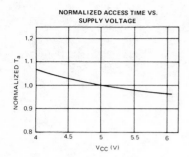

NORMALIZED ACCESS TIME VS.
AMBIENT TEMPERATURE

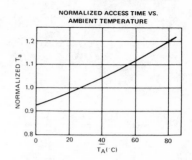

NORMALIZED POWER SUPPLY CURRENT VS.
SUPPLY VOLTAGE

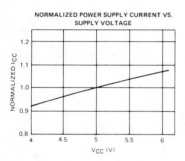

NORMALIZED POWER SUPPLY CURRENT VS.
AMBIENT TEMPERATURE

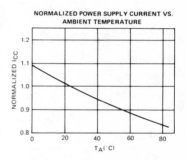

OUTPUT SINK CURRENT VS.
OUTPUT VOLTAGE

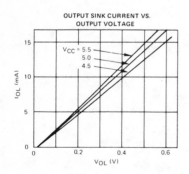

OUTPUT SOURCE CURRENT VS.
OUTPUT VOLTAGE

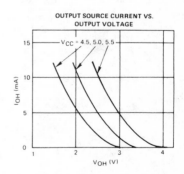

Courtesy NEC Microcomputers, Inc.

Index

READER SERVICE CARD

To better serve you, the reader, please take a moment to fill out this card, or a copy of it, for us. Not only will you be kept up to date on the Blacksburg Series books, but as an extra bonus, **we will randomly select five cards every month, from all of the cards sent to us during the previous month. The names that are drawn will win, absolutely free, a book from the Blacksburg Continuing Education Series.** Therefore, make sure to indicate your choice in the space provided below. For a complete listing of all the books to choose from, refer to the inside front cover of this book. Please, one card per person. Give everyone a chance.

In order to find out who has won a book in your area, call (703) 953-1861 anytime during the night or weekend. When you do call, an answering machine will let you know the monthly winners. Too good to be true? Just give us a call. Good luck.

If I win, please send me a copy of:

_____

I understand that this book will be sent to me absolutely free, if my card is selected.

For our information, how about telling us a little about yourself. We are interested in your occupation, how and where you normally purchase books and the books that you would like to see in the Blacksburg Series. We are also interested in finding authors for the series, so if you have a book idea, write to The Blacksburg Group, Inc., P.O. Box 242, Blacksburg, VA 24060 and ask for an Author Packet. We are also interested in TRS-80, APPLE, OSI and PET BASIC programs.

My occupation is _____

I buy books through/from _____

Would you buy books through the mail? _____

I'd like to see a book about _____

Name _____

Address _____

City _____

State _____ Zip _____

MAIL TO: BOOKS, BOX 715, BLACKSBURG, VA 24060
!!!!!PLEASE PRINT!!!!!